THROUGH SPACE & TIME

LONDON
Cambridge University Press
FETTER LANE

NEW YORK · TORONTO
BOMBAY · CALCUTTA · MADRAS
Macmillan

TOKYO
Maruzen Company Ltd

THROUGH SPACE & TIME

BY

SIR JAMES JEANS

M.A., D.Sc., Sc.D.,
LL.D., F.R.S.

BASED ON THE
ROYAL INSTITUTION LECTURES
CHRISTMAS 1933

NEW YORK: THE MACMILLAN COMPANY
CAMBRIDGE, ENGLAND: AT THE UNIVERSITY PRESS

1935

PRINTED IN THE UNITED STATES OF AMERICA
BY THE POLYGRAPHIC COMPANY OF AMERICA, N.Y.

BINDERY SLIP

JOSEPH RUZICKA

Baltimore, Md.   Greensboro, N. C.

Buckram No.	Rub Enclosed
Pamphlet No.	New Title; Keep Rub
Tp	Do Not Keep Rub
Tpc	Stub For
Index	Use Bench Sewing
Bind Issues in Covers	Refold Plates Before Trimming
Strip Ads in all but First No.	Mount on Guards
Trim	Book Rate
Binding Arranged	Tip In

Special Instructions

18-184

This Volume Lacks:	Letter Spine Exactly as Shown Below
	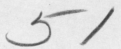

PREFACE

Every year for more than a century, the Royal Institution has invited some man of science to deliver a course of lectures at Christmastide in a style "adapted to a juvenile auditory". In practice, this rather quaint phrase means that the lecturer will be confronted with an eager and critical audience, ranging in respect of age from under eight to over eighty, and in respect of scientific knowledge from the aforesaid child under eight to staid professors of science and venerable Fellows of the Royal Society, each of whom will expect the lecturer to say something that will interest him.

The present book contains the substance of what I said when I was honoured with an invitation of this kind for the Christmas season 1933-4, fortified in places with what I have said on other slightly more serious occasions, both at the Royal Institution and elsewhere.

It is a pleasure to acknowledge many courtesies and return thanks for much valuable help. I am indebted to Sir T. L. Heath for permission to borrow largely from his *Greek Astronomy* and other books; to many Institutions, Publishers and private individuals for the loan of negatives, prints, blocks, etc., and permission to reproduce these in my book—detailed acknowledgment is made in the List of Illustrations. Finally, I have to thank Sir Thomas Heath and my sister, Gertrude Jeans, for help in reading the proofs, and the staff of the Cambridge University Press for their usual careful help in producing the book.

J. H. JEANS

Dorking
August 1934

CONTENTS

LIST OF ILLUSTRATIONS

THROUGH SPACE & TIME

CHAPTER I

THE EARTH

These are restless days in which everyone travels who can. The more fortunate of us may have travelled outside Europe to other continents—perhaps even round the world—and seen strange sights and scenery on our travels. And now we are starting out to take the longest journey in the whole universe. We shall travel—or pretend to travel—so far through space that our earth will look like less than the tiniest of motes in a sunbeam, and so far through time that the whole of human history will shrink to a tick of the clock, and a man's whole life to something less than the twinkling of an eye.

As we travel through space, we shall try to draw a picture of the universe as it now is—vast spaces of unthinkable extent and terrifying desolation, redeemed from utter emptiness only at rare intervals by small particles of cold lifeless matter, and at still rarer intervals by those vivid balls of flaming gas we call stars. Most of these stars are solitary wanderers through space, although here and there we may perhaps find a star giving warmth and light to a family of encircling planets. Yet few of these are at all likely to resemble our own earth; the majority will be so different that we shall hardly be able to describe their scenery, or imagine their physical condition.

As we travel through time, we shall try to extend this momentary picture into a sort of cinematograph film that will shew us not only the present, but also the past and the future, of the universe. We shall see the sky as it was a million years ago, a thousand million, and possibly even a million million years ago; we shall watch vast colonies of stars, each like the sands of the seashore in number, being born, living their lives, and finally dying. As one tiny incident in the great drama, we shall watch one inconspicuous grain of sand—our sun—being broken up in great turmoil and finally producing a family of planets. We shall watch one of the smaller of these planets—our earth—coming into being as a globe of hot gas which gradually cools, and ultimately becomes a suitable abode for life. In due course we shall see life appearing, and finally man arriving, taking possession of his tiny speck of dust in space, surveying with astonishment the strange universe in which his life is cast, and looking wonderingly and perhaps anxiously and fearfully into the future.

Before we start on our long journey, let us pause to examine our own home in space—the earth. We shall learn a lot from it that will be useful in our travels. We know that it is globular in shape; we discover this by travelling over it and mapping it out, by watching ships coming over the horizon, or by examining the shape of its shadow when this passes over the face of the moon at an eclipse. It may sound a simple matter to do all this, but the human race had inhabited the earth for hundreds of thousands of years before doing it. For until the last few hundreds of years most people thought the earth was flat, and a few misguided people still think it is. The ancient Greeks, including Homer, thought the earth was a flat circular disc, with Oceanus, the ocean—which they regarded as a river—flowing all around it. The dome of heaven covered this much as a dish-cover covers a dish. Probably the Greek Pythagoras, who was born about 570 B.C., was the first to maintain that the earth had a globular shape.

We also know that the earth is rotating. Day after day and night after night, we see sun, moon and stars rising in the east, moving in stately procession across the sky, and sinking in the west; and ever since the dawn of human intelligence men must have noticed the same thing. But so long as they thought of the earth as a flat plain, it was easier to picture the dome of heaven as turning over the earth than to imagine that the earth might be turning under the dome of heaven. Even Pythagoras, who believed that the earth was a globe floating in space, did not suspect that it turned round under the stars. He imagined that it stood at rest at the centre of the universe, and that the stars were attached to a sphere which turned around it from east to west. So far as we know, Heraclides of Pontus (about 388–315 B.C.) was the first to state perfectly clearly that it was the earth itself which turned round, and that this was why the heavenly bodies appeared to move across the sky.

It is not difficult to prove for ourselves that it is we who are moving round under the stars, and not the stars that are moving round above our heads. Now that we all drive cars, we are all familiar with the property of matter that we describe as "inertia". About a century after Christ, Plutarch explained it in the words "Everything is carried along by the motion natural to it, if it is not deflected by something else". Fifteen hundred years later, Isaac Newton described the same property of matter by saying that every body perseveres in its state of rest, or of uniform motion in a straight line, unless it is compelled to change by forces impressed on it. When our car is running freely, stopping the engine does not stop the car; the momentum of the car still carries it forward, and to stop it we must either put on the brakes, or wait until friction and air-resistance brake the motion in a more leisurely manner. Not only every object, but every part of an object, seems to want to continue its present motion, and will only make a change if something pulls on it and compels it to do so. If we turn the steering-wheel of our car, we can make the lower part of the car follow the front wheels, but the upper part will seem to want to continue on its old course; if we turn the wheel too abruptly, there is a danger, as we know, that the car will overturn. Or, if the road is icy or muddy, so that the wheels get no grip on the road, the whole back part of the car will tend to follow its old course, so that the car may skid. We shall encounter this property of inertia very often on our journey through time and space.

It is important to us at the moment because it provides us with the simplest and most convincing proof that the earth actually is rotating. If we swing a heavy ball or weight, pendulum-wise, at the end of a string, we shall find that it keeps on swinging in the same direction in space, no matter how much the top of the string is twisted or turned about; we can no more steer the swing of the pendulum in space by turning the top of the string than we can steer a car on ice by turning the steering-wheel.

Now let us set our pendulum swinging in such a direction that it swings towards and away from some clearly defined land-mark, such as a church tower. As we want the motion to con-tinue for a long time, we had better take a really heavy weight and suspend it from a high roof; if we try the experiment on a less massive scale, the pendulum will be stopped too soon by air resistance.

If the earth were standing still in space, our pendulum would naturally continue swinging towards and away from the tower, until the resistance of the air brought it to rest. Instead of this, we shall find the direction of its swing moving gradually farther and farther away from the church tower. The true direction of the swing of the pendulum cannot have changed, so we can only conclude that the church tower must have moved. And this, indeed, is what has happened; the rotation of the earth has carried it round.

Now let us start on our travels by going to the North Pole, and let us take our pendulum with us and perform our experi-ment there. If we disregard the earth, and keep our eyes fixed on the sky, we shall see that the swinging pendulum moves towards and away from the same stars throughout its whole motion; if, for instance, we start it swinging towards Arcturus, it will keep on swinging towards and away from Arcturus. This proves that Arcturus stays always in the same direction in space. If we now look down to the earth, we shall be able to watch the earth's

surface turning round under our non-turning pendulum at the
rate of a revolution once every 24 hours—or, to be more precise,
every 23 hours 56 minutes and 4 1 seconds. In other latitudes
the result of the experiment is less easy both to describe and to
explain.

This experiment is generally known as Foucault's experiment.
The French physicist Foucault performed it in public in 1852,
suspending his pendulum from the dome of the Panthéon in Paris.
Thousands of people watched, and, as they saw the pendulum
change its direction relative to the walls of the Panthéon, many
averred that they could feel the earth turning under their feet.

The same principle of inertia provides a second, but rather less
direct, proof of the earth's rotation. We who live in England are
so accustomed to the incessant and rapid changes in our own
weather that we almost forget that there are large stretches of
the earth over which the weather hardly varies at all. It is always
hot in the vicinity of the equator, and as winds drag air over
these hot regions, the air itself becomes heated and tends to rise
upwards, like the hot air in a stuffy room or the hot gases in a
chimney. In the same way, when the winds drag air across the
Arctic and Antarctic regions, this air becomes cooled and so tends
to fall earthwards.

If the earth were not rotating at all, this local heating and
cooling of air would set the whole atmosphere into a state of
steady circulation in a north-south direction. Air would descend
at both poles; the pressure of other air descending behind it
would then push it along the earth's surface towards the equator,

where it would rise upwards and move back to the poles through the upper reaches of the atmosphere. Such a circulation actually occurs, but is almost concealed by other and more complicated motions produced by the rotation of the earth.

The rotating earth drags the whole circulating system of air round with it, but the latter can never quite keep pace with the solid earth which is forcing its motion. A mountain or other point on the earth's surface in Norway is moving round the axis of the earth at about 500 miles an hour, while one near the equator is moving at about 1000 miles an hour. Now the frictional drag of the earth is never quite forcible enough to speed the air up from 500 to 1000 miles an hour in the course of its southerly journey from Norway to the equator. The earth's mountains and surface are not rough and spiky enough to get a perfectly firm grip on the air, so that this is always slipping backwards a bit—as a motor-car does when the clutch is not holding perfectly. When we feel the air slipping back in this way, we say there is a wind blowing from the east to the west.

This is the origin of the trade-winds which blow steadily westward on both sides of the equator. If the earth were not rotating there would be nothing to cause the trade-winds, so that we can think of these winds as providing a proof of the earth's rotation. It is easier to sail westward than eastward, because in sailing westward the inertia of the air around us keeps us from participating in the full motion of the earth. In sailing eastward, we have the more serious task of overtaking the earth in its motion.

Shortly after Heraclides had explained the rotation of the earth, Eratosthenes of Alexandria measured the earth's size with great skill and surprising success. He believed, with most people of his time, that the sun's distance was enormously great in comparison with the dimensions of the earth. If, then, the earth had been completely flat, the sun would have been directly overhead at all places at the same time. Actually he found that when it was overhead at Syene (the modern Assouan), it was not overhead at Alexandria, which lay 5000 stades to the north. As the sun's rays could not come from different directions at the two places, he argued that the "overhead" directions must be different. Actually he found they were different by a fiftieth of a circle, or $7\frac{1}{5}$ degrees—when the sun was directly overhead at Syene, it was $7\frac{1}{5}$ degrees from the zenith at Alexandria. Hence he concluded that the earth's surface curved through $7\frac{1}{5}$ degrees between the two places, or, as we should say to-day, that the difference of latitude between the two places was $7\frac{1}{5}$ degrees.* An easy calculation shewed that the circumference of the whole circle of the earth must be fifty times 5000 stades, or 250,000 stades. Eratosthenes subsequently amended this to 252,000 stades, which was probably equivalent to about 24,662 of our English miles. As the actual circumference of the earth measured in a north-south direction is 24,819 miles, while that around the equator is 24,902 miles, we see that Eratosthenes' measurement was in error by less than one per cent.

Let us take yet another illustration of the principle of inertia,

* The true difference is about 7° 7′.

which tells us that objects continue moving in a straight line unless something pulls them away from it. We know that if we are swinging a weight round at the end of a string and the string suddenly breaks, the weight will immediately fly off at a tangent into space. Now that the string is broken, the inertia of the

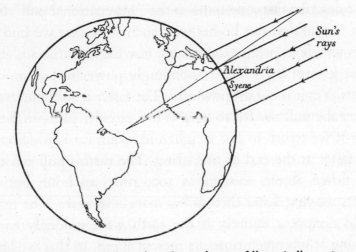

Fig. 1. Eratosthenes found that when the sun's rays fell vertically at Syene, they were a fiftieth of a whole circle away from the vertical at Alexandria. He concluded that the circumference of the earth was fifty times the distance from Alexandria to Syene.

weight carries it on in a straight line; before the string broke something must have been pulling on the weight to keep it moving in a circle; this was of course the pull of the string.

Now objects at the earth's equator are in a similar position to the weight at the end of the string. The earth's rotation carries them round and round in a circle 24,902 miles in circumference once every 24 hours, so that their speed is rather more than

1000 miles an hour. The principle of inertia tells us that they would continue their motion in a straight line, and so fly off at a tangent into space, were it not that something is continually stopping them from doing so—pulling them out of the straight line in which they would otherwise move.

We describe this something as the "gravitational pull" of the earth. It pulls on our bodies with such force that we find ourselves unable to jump more than a few feet into the air, and of course it must exert a correspondingly powerful pull on other objects. Yet it is not all-powerful. The faster a body moves, the greater the pull needed to keep it to a circular path—as we discover if we return to our weight and swing it round faster and ever faster at the end of our string. The earth's pull can easily hold down objects moving at 1000 miles an hour, but with objects moving faster there is less margin to spare. The margin would disappear entirely if the earth were suddenly to start spinning at seventeen times its present speed, so that we had an 85-minute day. We should then see the surprising spectacle of all the objects at and near the earth's equator rising from the ground and flying off at tangents into space, the air and the sea of course accompanying them on their journey. Objects reposing on the earth's surface are rather like drops of rain on the surface of a bicycle wheel: so long as the wheel spins slowly, nothing happens, but when it spins fast they fly off and do not come back.

With things as they are, objects at the equator are very far from being thrown off into space, yet they shew a certain tendency in that direction. For instance, a man at the equator is able to jump to a height of 6 feet with less physical effort than anywhere else on the earth's surface, because his speed of 1000 miles an hour helps him to counteract the earth's gravitational pull. For this reason, athletic records made in different latitudes are not strictly comparable; there ought to be a handicap for nearness to the equator.

We can see further evidence of the same tendency in the fact that the earth itself bulges out at the equator. This is often described by saying that the earth is flattened like an orange, but in actual fact its longest diameter is only 27 miles longer than the shortest—a difference of only about 1 part in 300—and an orange with no more flattening than this would look perfectly round to casual observation. Yet although the earth's flattening is almost inappreciable we shall soon come to planets which are spinning round so fast that their flattening is obvious at the merest glance, while later in our travels we shall come upon bodies of other kinds which are spinning so fast that objects are actually flying off their equators into space.

Our earth is not only like an orange in being flattened, but also in having a rough skin or peel covered with elevations—its mountains and valleys. But again this comparison exaggerates the earth's irregularities. It would only give us a fair picture, properly drawn to scale, if the earth were studded with mountains 50 miles in height; whereas actually the world's highest mountain, Everest, is less than $5\frac{1}{2}$ miles high. On a 12-inch geographical globe even the overlap of the paper represents a precipice about 7 miles high, and so represents greater irregularities than occur on earth. Taking it all in all, the earth comes very near indeed to being a perfect sphere, and certainly resembles a billiard ball much more than an orange.

The comparison with an orange fails in yet a third respect. The earth's mountains do not occur in regular formation, like the excrescences on the peel of an orange, but in irregular ridges and ranges—more like the foldings in the peel of a shrunken apple. And this last happens to be a very good and useful comparison, because the earth's mountain ridges actually are due to shrinkage; they exist for precisely the same reason as the foldings in the apple-peel.

I am afraid we shall not fully understand this, until we have explored quite a bit, both in space and in time—far back into the earth's past history, and far down into its interior.

How are we to explore inside the earth? We might, of course, dig a hole, as the mining engineer does in his search for coal, or bore down, as the oil engineer does in his search for oil; but neither of these methods will take us any appreciable way towards the centre of the earth. Oil-borings only go about 8000 feet down, and coal mines only half as far; the deepest of man-made holes are only the tiniest of pin-pricks in the skin of our apple, and take us nowhere near the central parts.

Because of this, it is surprising but true that until quite recently we knew more about the state of the most distant stars than about the state of the earth a few miles under our feet. But the new science of seismology has shewn us how to probe thousands of times deeper than any hole can take us—and indeed to the very centre of the earth.

There are many indications that the pressure in the earth's interior is for ever varying, and that the earth's structure is for ever gradually shifting and changing as it yields to these ever-varying pressures. Occasionally this gradual yielding gives place to a sudden snap or break which jars the whole earth—an earthquake.

When an earthquake occurs, waves start out from the point of breakage and travel in all directions through the whole earth—just as, when we throw a stone in a pond, waves start out from the point of impact and travel over the whole pond. When these waves finally emerge at the surface of the earth, they bring with them a whole fund of information as to the conditions they have encountered on their long journey through the earth's interior. Consequently, these waves are recorded and studied at hundreds of observatories, which are well sprinkled over the whole surface of the earth. These obtain records of hundreds of earthquakes every year, most of which, happily, are too slight to do any damage to life or property, and would escape observation entirely were it not for the extreme sensitiveness of the instrument known as the seismograph, which is used to detect them.

The essentials of such an instrument are shewn diagrammatically in fig. 3 (facing p. 20). It consists primarily of a long arm or horizontal pendulum, swinging freely on a vertical pivot which is in some way connected with the rock or soil of the solid earth. When the earth is shaken, a wave comes along which gives a jar to the pivot and so causes the boom to start swinging; a pen connected with the end of the boom automatically records the motion on a strip of moving paper. It is necessary to use two such instruments simultaneously, one boom pointing in a north-south direction, and the other east-west. If only one boom were in use, it would give no record of earthquake waves travelling in the direction in which it was pointing.

If the instrument is to serve its purpose, the boom must be suspended very delicately, and then, unfortunately, it cannot be restrained from recording all sorts of jarrings of the earth, whatever their cause. For instance, it faithfully records the passage of every train, omnibus, or motor-lorry, so that unless the observer wishes to be continually distracted by all these, he had better install his seismograph in a quiet place. Even then he will find that the pounding of the sea on our coasts shakes our whole island, and his seismograph with it, so that from observations taken far inland, he can tell whether it is rough or fine out at sea. The records obtained at the Indian Observatory of Colaba are found to vary quite definitely in quality with the conditions in the Bay of Bengal and the Arabian Sea. Storms as much as 1000 miles distant have been detected in this way, and attempts have been made to predict the approach of cyclones or monsoons.

The experienced observer finds no difficulty in distinguishing between local shocks such as these, which affect only a small part of the earth's surface, and true earthquakes, which affect the whole earth. A portion of an actual seismograph record is shewn in fig. 4 (facing p. 20). The big open waves at the right-hand of the second line down are the record of true earthquake waves; all the smaller waves represent minor earth tremors, produced by untraced causes.

When their seismographs record a true earthquake, the various observatories note the times at which the shocks reach them, and from the differences between these, they can deduce the speed with which the waves have travelled through the solid earth.

If the earth's interior were uniform in structure and composition, earthquake waves would always travel at the same uniform speed. Actually, however, it is found that waves which have been deep down into the earth's interior travel at a far higher average speed than those which have stayed near the surface. On the other hand, waves which have been to the same depth always travel at the same average speed. This is true whether their path has been in a north-south, or east-west, or any other direction, also whether they have travelled under a continent or under an ocean, under the old world or under the new. This shews that the earth is everywhere of similar substance and composition at the same depth, although it may be different at different depths.

Thus we may think of the earth's interior as a series of spherical layers surrounding one another like the skins of an onion, or again we may compare it to a globular parcel wrapped up in a great number of wrappings.

When an earthquake occurs, the waves which are most notice-able, and also do most damage, are the "surface" waves which travel along the ground. In addition to these, there are two distinct kinds of waves which travel through the earth's interior —the "primary" waves which consist of longitudinal motions, and the "secondary" waves which consist of transverse motions. Neither a liquid nor a gas can transmit transverse waves, so that the secondary waves can only travel through solid matter. Actually they are found to travel through the whole interior of the earth, except for a region, extending for about 2200 miles in every direction from the centre of the earth, which is known as the "central core" of the earth. It seems safe to conclude that the whole interior of the earth is solid, except for the central core. This may be either liquid or gaseous, unless indeed it consists of matter in some state of which we have no experience. It seems likely that it consists of very heavy liquid, perhaps ten or twelve times as dense as water. This may be mainly molten iron, perhaps mixed with nickel, and possibly, as geologists have thought, similar in its chemical composition to the iron meteorites which often fall on the earth's surface. It is true that these substances are not normally ten or twelve times as dense as water, but we do not normally meet them under high pressures, and the pressure inside the central core must be immense, since it has to support the weight of the greater part of the earth. A rough computation indicates that the pressure at the surface of this core may be about 7500 tons to the square inch, which is a million times the pressure of the atmosphere at the earth's surface. The pressure at the centre of the earth will be even greater, perhaps about 10,000 tons to the square inch.

We may think of the central core as our parcel. Immediately outside it comes the first wrapping—a layer of matter about 1700 miles thick, which is sometimes described as the "barysphere". This transmits both kinds of earthquake waves at speeds which shew that it consists of heavy solid matter, more rigid than steel. Even inside the barysphere the waves do not travel at a uniform speed; as with the earth as a whole, those waves which go deepest travel fastest, shewing that the deeper layers are more rigid than the upper. Inside the barysphere there may perhaps be a gradual transition from such heavy substances as iron and nickel in the lowest layers to those lighter substances of which the earth's surface rocks are formed.

The barysphere extends to within about 50 miles of the earth's surface, so that the remaining wrappings are comparatively thin. These are believed to consist of rocky substances, and are often described collectively as the "lithosphere", or sphere of rocks. Seismologists detect three distinct layers, through which earthquake waves travel in different ways and at different speeds, giving some indication at least as to the structure of the rocky layers. There is no general agreement about the lowest layer of all, but it is thought that the middle layer is probably basaltic, while the uppermost is almost certainly granitic.

Fig. 2 (p. 18) represents the arrangement of the earth's interior as indicated by the evidence of seismology.

The inner core and the various wrappings we have so far described constitute the essential and permanent body of the earth. If we continue to compare the earth to an apple, the central core is its core, the barysphere its flesh, and the lithosphere its skin; such a picture will not be too badly out of drawing in the matter of relative proportions. But outside all these come other layers and wrappings of a more accidental, ephemeral and variable nature, which we may perhaps compare to layers of dust and drops of rain on the skin of our apple.

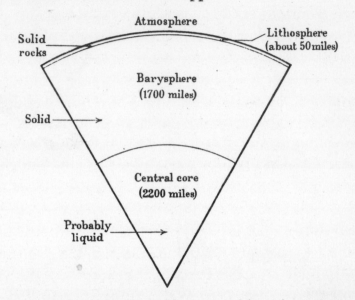

Fig. 2. Diagrammatic representation of the interior of the earth as conjectured from observations on earthquake waves. The height of the highest mountains is only a tenth of the thickness of the lithosphere, and so is less than the thickness of the printed line which represents the surface of the earth.

First of all, like the dust on the apple, come the layers known as "sedimentary", which we shall describe more fully in a moment. There are several such layers, and their total thickness— the thickness of the layer of dust on our apple—varies from many miles to almost nothing, since places can be found (as in fig. 11, p. 30) where the granite rocks of the lithosphere come up almost to the surface.

Next, like drops of rain on the apple, we come to the layer of water which we describe as the ocean; the thickness of this layer varies from 5 miles in the great ocean deeps to nothing at all at places where the dry land emerges from the sea.

Finally, outside all, comes the atmosphere, consisting of two layers called the "troposphere" and the "stratosphere", which we shall discuss in detail in the next chapter.

We see that the earth consists of a great number of distinct shells of matter. In a general way, the inner shells are found to consist of heavier matter than the outer, as though the heavier substances had sunk deep down into the body of the earth, while the lighter had floated to the top. But the separation is far from complete, and some of the heaviest known substances, such as lead, quicksilver and gold, are found in the outermost crust of the earth.

We shall see later how the earth probably started its existence as a hot mass of gas. It was born in a cataclysm which would probably stir up its various constituent substances, and mix them up, even if they were not thoroughly mixed already. Then as peace and calm succeeded to turmoil and confusion, the lighter substances would begin to float upwards, while the heavier would sink towards the centre of the earth.

All this time the earth is cooling; at last it begins to liquefy, and after this to solidify. When a piece of the earth has once solidified, its various constituent substances are no longer able either to sink or rise; they are trapped in the solid mass, and must stay for ever where they were when the process of petrifaction overtook them. The distribution of light and heavy substances in the earth's crust and interior shews that the process of arrangement was well advanced, but not complete, when the earth solidified.

The outermost layers of the earth, having no blankets around them to keep the heat in, would of course cool most rapidly, and so would be the first to solidify. When this had happened, the earth would consist of a solid outer crust enclosing a hotter interior of gas and liquid—rather like a mince-pie, in which we know that a deceptively cool exterior often conceals an interior which is too hot to eat. Just as with a mince-pie left to itself, this would be succeeded by a stage in which the inner layers would also begin to cool, and probably also to shrink, since most substances, and especially gases, shrink as they cool.

The crust of an ordinary mince-pie can easily support its own weight, but the crust of a mince-pie which weighed a million tons would not be able to do so, and it must have been the same with the far more massive crust of the earth. As the inner layers shrank away from under it, and no longer supported its weight, it must gradually have caved in upon these inner layers to find support. In so doing, it was faced with the problem of how suddenly to grow smaller although it had already ceased contracting—a problem which it solved in the only possible way, by crumpling up into wrinkles and folds, just as an apple does when its softer centre shrinks with the onset of old age. Fig. 5 on

PLATE I

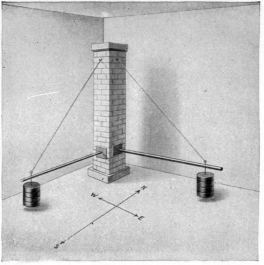

J. J. Shaw

Fig. 3. The essential parts of a seismograph. Any vibration in the earth is transmitted to the brick pile, and sets the two booms swinging through minute angles. These swings are amplified by mechanical levers and recorded as in fig. 4 below.

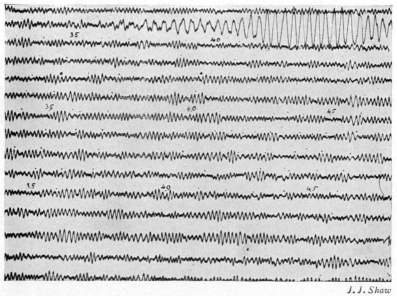

J. J. Shaw

Fig. 4. A portion of a seismograph record. The big waves to the right in the second line down were caused by a true earthquake of considerable violence. All the others represent mere tremors such as might be produced by wind, sea-waves or traffic. The numbers indicate minutes.

PLATE II

Geological Museum

Fig. 5. Layers of black slate and limestone at the south-east end of the island of Kerrera, off Oban, shewing crumpling and folding. The geological hammer on the left shews the scale, but the same thing occurs on a scale 1000 times as big, and also on a scale 1000 times as small.

Geological Museum

Fig. 6. Lava south of Ballantrae on the Ayrshire coast. This flowed down into the sea, perhaps 400 million years ago, and immediately solidified into the shapes it has retained from that day to this.

Plate II shews a nearly vertical section of the earth, exposing the crumpling and folding of layers of slate and limestone; the layers of primitive rock must have crumpled in much the same way.

In some such way as this the earth formed its mountain ridges and valleys. The process is not entirely ended yet; the earth's surface is still moving slightly, falling in here and being pushed up there, so that new elevations and depressions are for ever being formed. Occasionally a sudden slip may result in an earth-quake, such as we have already discussed. At other times the steady pressure of the falling or fallen crust may squeeze the hot material up through cracks and crevices until it emerges on the surface of the earth, as we see in volcanoes, oil wells, and in the spoutings of hot water known as geysers and hot springs; such happenings must have proceeded with incomparably greater vigour in the early days of the earth's history, and have left their marks very unmistakably on its present condition.

For, although there are few active volcanoes on the earth now, the number of mountains which shew evidence of having once been volcanic is enormous. Immense streams of lava and molten rock which they poured out in long-past ages still lie spread over large parts of the surface of the earth, and form the layers of rock which we describe as "igneous"—rocks laid down by fire. Fig. 6 shews a lava flow at Ballantrae, on the Ayrshire coast, which must have flowed directly down into the sea, immediately became petrified into its present "pillow" formation, and has retained its original form, through perhaps 400 million years, to the present day. The basaltic rocks of the well-known "Giant's Causeway" in Antrim form evidence of a similar outpouring of molten rock, which must have crystallised at once into its present hexagonal form. These rocky outpourings from primaeval volcanoes provide us with true samples of the substance of the earth's interior. Water and gases must have been forced up in a similar manner, and would of course make their contribution to the earth's ocean and atmosphere.

When the earth's crust fell in upon the shrinking inner mass, its wrinkles would not form entirely at random. For the crust is not likely to have been absolutely uniform in structure; it probably consisted of lighter and heavier parts. On the whole, the lighter parts would most readily be thrust up to form mountain ranges, while the heavier parts would tend to sink to the bottom of the folds, and form valleys and sea-bottoms. Thus we should naturally expect the mountains to be of lighter substance than the bottom of the sea—of fewer tons to the cubic yard. Recent careful measurements have shewn that this is actually the case.

The scientist does not try to sample his mountains and sea-bottoms by taking out a cubic yard here and there; such a method would be too crude for the mountains, and impossible for the sea-bottoms. In the past he used to take a long pendulum—rather like that from a grandfather clock, but made with the utmost scientific precision—to the top of a mountain, and try to discover the structure of the mountain from the behaviour of the pendulum. In recent years, the pendulum has been replaced

by a more intricate instrument, but the general principle under-
lying its use is much the same.

The top of a mountain is farther than the plain below from
the centre of the earth, with the result that the earth's gravitational pull is less forcible there than down below. Thus, when a
pendulum is pulled aside and set swinging up there, its bob moves
more slowly to its lowest position, and so takes a longer time to
reach this position than it would on the plain below. In other
words, a pendulum which is taken to the top of a mountain will
begin to lose time. We can calculate exactly how much time it
would lose if the mountain were composed of the average stuff of
the earth's crust. Always it loses a little more than this, shewing
that the mountain is of lighter substance than the average. When
the pendulum is taken to the bottom of the sea in a submarine
we have exactly the reverse situation; it gains more than it
would if the sea-bottom were of average substance, shewing
that the sea-bottom is of heavier substance than the average.

Recently, a theory known as isostasy has given greater precision to all of these ideas. It asserts, in brief, that mountains stand
up above the level of the land for just the same reason that ships
stand up above the level of the sea—because they float. It also
supposes that, as with a ship, their total weight determines the
height at which they float. A ship whose total weight—hull,
cargo, crew, captain, and all—is 30,000 tons will float at a height
at which she displaces exactly 30,000 tons of water; in other
words, if she were suddenly lifted out of the water, she would
leave a hole which it would take 30,000 tons of water to fill.

This, of course, is in accordance with the principle that Archimedes discovered 2200 years ago.

The theory of isostasy supposes that the height at which mountains float is determined in precisely the same way. The mountains are not of course supposed to be floating in water, or in any true liquid, but in some inner layer of the earth's substance which is plastic enough to behave like a liquid. Ordinary pitch, as we know, looks like a solid, but will yield to long-continued pressure just as a liquid does to momentary pressure. Pitch is plastic enough to yield in a matter of a few hours or days, ice in months or years (as we see in the flow of glaciers), and glass in years or centuries. The substance we are now considering will serve its purpose if it yields in millions of years. Various calculations suggest that we have to go to a depth of perhaps 20 miles to reach this plastic layer. Now it is a matter of common experience that pitch and other substances become more plastic— i.e. flow more easily—when they are heated; the same is probably true of the substance of the earth's crust, so that the heat at a depth of 20 miles or so may well provide the small degree of plasticity needed. The theory tells us that a mountain which weighs a million million tons will float at just that height at which it displaces a million million tons of this plastic inner layer. The most refined and careful measurements of which science is capable indicate that this theory gives an accurate account of the observed heights of the mountains.

I must here digress to tell you of a more recent theory, put forward by a German scientist, Wegener, which is perhaps even more interesting, although it has not yet gained such widespread acceptance from scientists. According to this theory, the continents and larger islands also are floating, not only like ships, but like independent ships which can approach towards and recede from one another. The old and new worlds are supposed originally to have formed a single big ship, which suffered shipwreck and broke into two, after which the parts drifted away from one another, the one forming Africa and Europe, while the other formed the American continent. It is claimed as evidence that if the New World were towed about 3150 miles to the E.N.E. it would fit very prettily on to the Old World, the point of Brazil on which Pernambuco stands fitting into the Bay of the Cameroons on the African coast, as suggested, although very inadequately by the maps shewn overleaf. We cannot dismiss this close fit as a pure coincidence, for not only are the coastlines similar on the two sides of the Atlantic, but also the mountains, the rocks, and even the fossils. For these reasons geologists have for long suspected that the two continents had once formed a single mass; the new theory provides an explanation of how they became separated. If North America is now towed still farther to the east, it will fit quite well on to Europe, New England fitting on to our Old England. Wegener believes that all the land which stood out above the sea some hundreds of millions of years ago can be fitted together to make one continuous continent, which would then cover about a third of the face of the globe.

Apart from all theories or hypotheses, we know that the

heights of mountains, and even of continents, are not permanent fixed quantities. When we climb a mountain, we expect to see an occasional stone rolling down, but we should be surprised to see one rolling up. Rain, snow, ice and even wind are continually splitting and loosening the rocks high up on the mountain side,

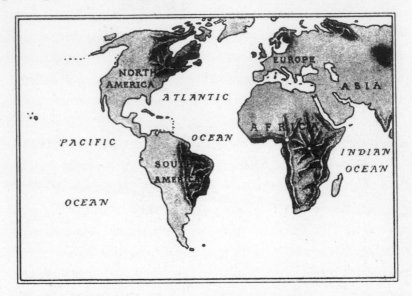

Fig. 7 *a*. The continents in their present positions, with the vast rocky masses that are believed to have existed on them in primitive times.

until finally great pieces break loose and roll down to the bottom, so that huge boulders, piles of scree, and a general rocky detritus form familiar features at the foot of a mountain. Fig. 8 (facing p. 28) shews the accumulation of scree at the feet of the quite small mountains which lie on the east side of Wastwater in Cumberland. On the tops of higher mountains snow falls and turns into glaciers, which slowly flow down into the valleys and bring enormous quantities of large stones and powdered rock with them. On the foothills rain falls, and makes the mountain torrents dirty with particles of earth which have been washed off

Fig. 7 *b*. Wegener's theory supposes that the primitive continents did not occupy their present positions, but were packed together to form continuous land.

the hillside, and are now being carried down to the sea. Everywhere we see the substance of the mountains being transferred to the bottom of the sea, a process which tends to lower the heights of the mountains and raise the level of the sea-bottom.

The theory of isostasy suggests that this general levelling may be compensated, at least in part. For as the substance of the mountain is washed away, the mountain loses weight, and so floats higher, regaining part of the height it had lost. The sea-bottom, on the other hand, oppressed by the extra weight of the silt and sediment which the rivers have carried down to it, sinks deeper and in this way loses part of the additional height which the deposition of silt and sediment would otherwise have given it.

These incessant readjustments of level, and other causes as well, result in all sorts of settlements and upheavals in the surface layers of the earth; a whole continent may be thrust below sea-level, or a new continent may arise from the ocean-bottom and form dry land. As far back as the sixth century before Christ, the Greek Xenophanes recorded that sea-shells had been found far inland, and even high up in mountains, and that imprints—i.e. fossils—of fishes and seaweed had been found in the quarries of Syracuse. We need not travel as far either in space or in time as ancient Greece to find evidence of this process; it surrounds us everywhere, and especially in the chalk hills around London. These are full of fossils and the shells of tiny marine animals, which shew that they once formed the bottom of a fairly deep sea, rather like the middle of the present Atlantic Ocean. We also find submerged forests and even remains of life under the sea round our British coast.

The removal of rock and soil from the mountain tops is described as "denudation", and its deposition in valley bottoms and river beds as "sedimentation". This deposition formed the sedimentary layers that we have already compared to layers of dust outside the main body of an apple. If it were not for re-

PLATE III

Cambridge County Geography

Fig. 8. Scree on the eastern side of Wastwater, Cumberland.

Geological Museum

Fig. 9. Horizontal striations of limestone on Eglwyseg Mountain,
two miles north of Llangollen.

PLATE IV

Harvard University Press

Fig. 10. The north side of the canyon of the Colorado River, shewing layers of early sedimentary rock lying in regular formation one above the other.

peated settlements, upheavals, and general readjustments of level, the different layers of sediment would be deposited perfectly evenly, and would lie horizontally one over the other like the pages of a book on a level desk. Indeed there are large areas of the globe where the different layers lie perfectly regularly over one another in precisely this way—a large part of Eastern Canada, a large part of Eastern Siberia, a large part of the Baltic coast and Western Russia, and the relics of the ancient continent known as Gondwana Land, which included most of eastern South America and South Africa (see fig. 7b, p. 27), Arabia and India. On a far smaller scale, we may often see the different layers of rock or sand lying one above the other in perfectly level layers in a railway or road cutting, or in cliffs on the sea-shore, or on an inland mountain, such as that shewn in fig. 9 on Plate III. The geologist describes these layers as "striations". Fig. 10 on Plate IV shews an immense cutting of this kind—the Colorado Canyon in North America. This cutting is not of the kind which man makes in a few days, but which Nature makes in millions of years. It was made by the Colorado River slowly eating its way down into the earth year after year and century after century, washing away the soft earth as it did so and carrying it down to the sea. We see layer after layer exposed, to a depth of more than 5000 feet; most of the layers look fairly horizontal to the casual glance, but the trained geologist finds evidence in places of elevation, of tilting, and even of subsidence under the sea.

In other places there may be no general subsidence or elevation, but the earth's crust may crack locally, and one side of the fracture may slide past the other, so that the striations no longer run on continuously but form what is known as a "fault" (fig. 13, facing p. 36).

If a river like the Colorado River had cut its way through England, we could have replaced fig. 10 by a view of the different layers of rock under our English soil. We have no river

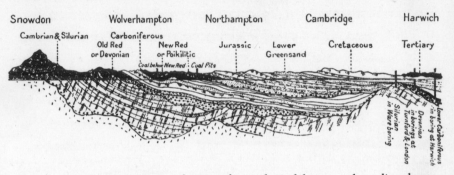

Fig. 11. Diagrammatic section shewing the geological layers under a line drawn across Great Britain from Snowdon to Harwich, a distance of about 200 miles. We see how the underground layers have been folded, and uplifted parts removed.

to provide us with such a view, but a study of the surface formations, supplemented by such knowledge as can be obtained by borings and diggings here and there, enables the geologist to construct a diagrammatic map of the soil under England, which is almost as good and reliable as a real section, such as might be exposed by actual cutting. Fig. 11 shews a map of this kind which exhibits how the strata lie under a line drawn across England and Wales from Snowdon to Harwich;—a line running approximately west to east for over 200 miles.

However things may be in other parts of the world, we see
that in our own country the geological strata no longer lie flat
like the leaves of a book, but have been tilted and crumpled by
rearrangements of level of the kind already described. Clearly
there has been a general tilting movement which has depressed
the east and raised the west, although marked local variations
occur in places. Near the eastern end of our line, for instance,
a subterranean upheaval has brought to within a few feet of the
surface rocks which would otherwise have been many thousands

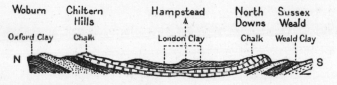

Fig. 12. A section similar to that shewn in fig. 11, but running under London,
approximately north to south, from Woburn to the Weald of Sussex.

of feet down. This tilting of the strata has not brought about any
corresponding slope in the surface of the land, since those parts
which would have stood highest have all been washed away. If
we continue comparing the different strata to the leaves of a
book, we must not only imagine that the whole book has been
very badly twisted and battered, but also that large parts of it
have been rubbed away. There has been so much denudation that
the surface of the land forms an almost horizontal section of the
tilted book, and by merely crossing England from east to west,
we obtain samples of the various pages in turn, all in their
proper order.

In fig. 11 the successive geological layers had to be shewn

on so small a scale that many details were omitted. Fig. 12
shews a more detailed map of a shorter section, about 70 miles
in length, passing under London from north to south. In
this we do not notice any very pronounced tilting either to
the north or to the south; the most conspicuous feature now is
a general bending of the leaves of our book. We see that London
is lying on clay, below which is a crumpled layer of chalk with
a uniform thickness of about 650 feet. We have already seen
how this once formed the bottom of a deep sea, and it is easy to
reconstruct the story of subsequent events. First a subterranean
upheaval so that the level sea-bottom becomes undulating dry
land; then water streaming through this chalky land from still
higher clay land to the west; then a broad river gradually
depositing clay sediment which partially fills up the river bed but
leaves the higher chalky hills unaffected; next a settlement of
primitive men on some convenient land near the banks of the
river; finally the London we know, lying on clay but surrounded
by chalk hills which extend on the south from the white cliffs of
Dover to the hills of Guildford and the Hog's Back beyond,
until they emerge north of the Thames at Henley, and extend
through the Chiltern Hills to the chalk downs of Hertfordshire
and Cambridgeshire.

Even in this map the distortion of geological layers is still on
a fairly extensive scale, but precisely similar distortions can often
be seen in samples of rock only a few inches across, and sometimes even in the minutely thin sections of microscopic slides.

Now the real interest of this book of tilted pages is that it is in effect a history book. No matter how tilted and crumpled its pages may now be, each was originally deposited throughout its whole length and breadth at one definite date, or at least within the limits of one definite epoch, and contains buried within itself a history of that epoch.

To understand this, let us turn our thoughts from the Thames to the Nile. Every year the Nile floods the fields of Lower Egypt, and when it recedes, the level of Egypt has been raised a fraction of an inch by the sediment that the floods have left behind them. If we dig down a foot into this sediment, we shall find objects that had been lost or abandoned on the soil of Egypt 500 years ago; 4 feet down we come upon objects that must have lain there since the birth of Christ. The soil of Egypt forms, in effect, a stratified record of the history of Egypt; to turn over the pages of history, we need only dig down into the soil. Coins and inscriptions tell us the features and achievements of the kings; common implements, weapons, and tools, bring before us the lives of the people.

Other parts of the earth's surface can be treated in the same way, except, of course, that a foot of sediment will not always represent 500 years of history: sediment is deposited in different places at very different rates.. Also, the various pages of history no longer follow one another in regular succession as we dig down; in many places the pages of our book have been crumpled and generally disarranged by faults, settlements, and upheavals of the earth's crust. This is really very fortunate, since if the pages had all lain flat on top of one another, we should have had to dig more than 100 miles down to reach the lowest page. With things as they are, we may often reach the lower pages by boring only a short distance down, and sometimes merely by walking over the earth's surface.

As we review these pages in turn, even if only by walking over the surface of the earth with a discerning eye, we are again in effect turning over the pages of history—no longer of Egypt, but of the earth itself—and passing through the records of its various civilisations. First we read of highly civilised men who left behind them coins and inscriptions; then of earlier men who left implements and weapons of metal and flints, sometimes with the bones of the animals they hunted. Lower down still, we come to the records of ape-like men who had nothing to leave but their own dead bodies, which have since turned into skeletons. Then we come to the world before man was, a world in which we find only the remains of weird animals and ungainly monsters; then only fossils of reptiles, fishes, and plants. Finally a world of lifeless soil, water, and rocks.

It would be thrilling enough to know the sequence of events in the remote past, even if we could not say precisely when they occurred—many of us do not find dates the most exciting part of history. Yet perhaps the reason of their unpopularity at school was that we were expected to remember them with such mathematical precision. It was quite interesting to read how, some seven centuries ago, King John was made to sign Magna Carta when he did not want to, but rather a bore to have to burden our memories with the number 1215.

Now the physicists have recently found a means of dating the pages of the earth's history book, and this in the nicest possible way—with dates that are just exact enough to be interesting, but not exact enough to be tiresome.

We have all seen watches whose hands are visible in the dark because they are painted with radium paint. The hands appear to glow with a steady light, but careful examination with delicate instruments shews that the light is not really as steady as it looks; it results from myriads of separate explosions, each of which is caused by the death of a single atom of radium— perhaps we ought rather to say by the transformation, for the atom of radium does not entirely cease to exist, but leaves an atom of a special kind of lead behind it as a record of its former existence. Now this transformation of radium into lead invariably goes on at an absolutely uniform rate, which can of course be measured in the laboratory. Thus, if we could measure how much radium and how much lead there was in the hands of one of these watches, we could tell how old the watch was.

We can determine the ages of the rocks of the earth's crust in a similar way.

When thin sections of such substances as mica and tourmaline are examined under the microscope, they sometimes shew what is described as a "pleochroic halo"—a display of concentric rings such as is shewn in fig. 14 on Plate V (p. 36). At the centre of the halo there is always a minute speck of radioactive substance which decays in the same uniform unalterable way as radium, only much more slowly; the substance may be uranium or thorium, or perhaps a mixture of both. The rings of the halo have been caused by the disintegration of this radioactive substance. Similar rings can be produced artificially in the laboratory, so that the mode of their formation is well understood. It is found that the colour of the halos deepens with advancing age, and it is often possible to estimate the ages of rocks simply from the general appearance of the halos they contain.

There are, however, a great many kinds of rock which contain uranium or thorium without shewing any halos. In such cases chemical analysis will tell us exactly to what extent these substances have disintegrated, and knowing this we can estimate the ages of the rocks—just as we might do with the hands of the watch. For instance, a large number of samples of the pegmatite rocks of Eastern Canada have been analysed, and all agree in shewing that the rocks solidified about 1230 million years ago. Other rocks shew ages which are even greater, but they are never much greater, and usually cannot be fixed with anything like the same degree of precision.

Thus we may say that the pegmatite rocks are the earliest page of our history book on which a definite and unmistakable date is written. On this page we read that 1230 million years ago the earth had a solid crust over which rivers flowed, washing mud and sand down to the sea. Pages even lower than this, undated, tell of earlier processes of cooling and solidification. We cannot say how long these earlier processes lasted, but they must have lasted through many millions of years, so that it hardly

PLATE V

Geological Museum

Fig. 13. Striations in sandstone at the Clydesdale iron and steel works, Mossend, Lanark, broken by a "fault".

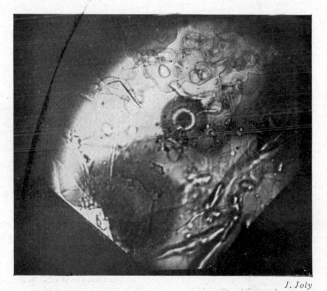

J. Joly

Fig. 14. The halo produced by a minute speck of radioactive substance in mica. A microphotograph with more than 200 magnification.

PLATE VI

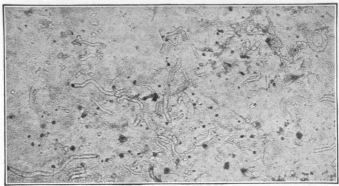

Harvard University Press

Fig. 15. The oldest known fossils—microscopic algae. The photograph shews a slice of rock cut thin enough to be transparent and magnified about 190 times.

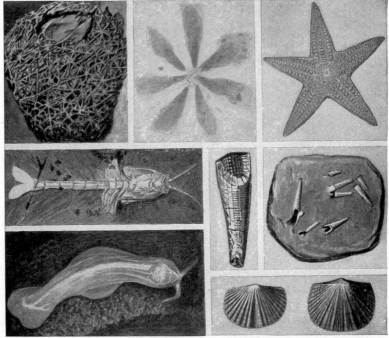

Harmsworth's "Universal History"

Fig. 16. Fossils found in Cambrian rocks. These represent very primitive types of life—sponges, jelly-fish, star-fish, earth-worms and coral—some of which still exist in not greatly altered forms.

seems possible that the earth should be less than 1500 million years old.

The earth cannot be enormously older than this, since, if it were, its radioactive substances would all have disintegrated away by now, and the phenomenon of radioactivity would have been entirely unknown to us, as it probably will be to beings—if any such there be—who will inhabit the future earth of a million million years hence. Unless radioactive substances have a capacity for renewing themselves in some way which is at present unknown to us, a detailed discussion shews that the age of the earth cannot possibly be more than about 3400 million years and is probably considerably less.

Somewhere between these limits—1500 million and 3400 million years—the age of the earth must lie. It is safest to confine ourselves to round numbers, in which case we may think of it as about 2000 million years—more than a hundred thousand times the whole length of recorded human history, and more than a million times the length of the Christian Era. It is not easy to realise what such figures mean. We may perhaps best visualise a million as the number of letters in a fair-sized book—a book, say, of 500 pages, with 330 words on each page, and an average of six letters to a word. If we take such a book to represent the age of the earth, then the whole of recorded human history will be represented by the last word in the book, and the whole Christian Era by less than the last letter. Within the space of this last letter the Roman Empire rose and fell; Christianity has spread over the face of the earth; the countries of Western Europe have changed from the savage countries described by Caesar to what they are to-day; more than sixty generations of men have lived and died. The whole of your life or mine will be represented by less than the final full stop, or the dot on the smallest "i" in the book.

If we want to read further back in time than this last word, our history book must be the earth's crust, with its layers of rock and soil for pages. Many of these have become crumpled in the course of time, but they are still arranged in the right order, and here and there a few of them are dated. Let us imagine that we straighten them out, and then turn them over and read what we can of the history of our earth.

We begin something like 2000 million years ago, and for hundreds of millions of years we watch a lifeless earth cooling and settling down. Page after page tells us only of geological activities, until, somewhere in the region of the "1230 million years ago" page, we begin to read of sediment containing traces of carbon. Some geologists consider that this provides presumptive evidence that some sort of life, possibly of the humblest and lowest description, existed in the sea; life, then, had already arrived on earth. Again we turn over page after page, and read only of geological events—steady sedimentation, varied only by cataclysms and upheavals—until at last, somewhere between 1000 and 500 million years ago, we come upon fossil remains, mere specks embedded in the rocks (fig. 15) which the geologist interprets as definite remains of life, although life of the most primitive kind. Again, long aeons pass before us until,

PLATE VII

"Universal History of the World"

Fig. 17. Fossils of the Silurian period, about 450 million years ago. This is sometimes described as the Age of Sea Lilies, because sea plants such as those shewn grew at the bottom of the sea in such dense masses that their fossil remains now form thick beds of limestone. The "sea lilies" are not true plants, but are more like our star-fish or sea-anemones.

PLATE VIII

W. E. Swinton, "Monsters of Primaeval Days"

Fig. 18. *Dimetrodon Gigas,* a huge and clumsy carnivorous lizard, 9 feet in length, which inhabited North America 250 million years ago.

"Universal History of the World"

Fig. 19. *Cacops Aspidophorus,* one of the reptiles which made its home on dry land in the great drought of about 200 million years ago.

about 500 to 400 million years ago, life becomes both more complex and more abundant. We even find fossils of worms, jelly-fish, and other rudimentary forms of life, which were not enormously different from those existing to-day (fig. 16).

Again, years roll on in their millions, until we open a page of our book on which the pictures—the fossils—look very like the plants of to-day. They look like plants but are not, for they lived at the bottom of the sea; they were more like our sea-anemones, or even star-fish, than plants (fig. 17). Yet shortly after this time life begins slowly to invade the land, and we come upon the first fossils of true grasses and fern-like growths. As the land vegetation multiplies we see the earth gradually assuming something like its present appearance. The roots of the grasses fix the particles of sand and earth to form a solid soil, while animals appear to feed on the vegetation, and others, in due course, to feed on them. This was the beginning of the era when huge reptiles dominated the earth. Typical of the earlier of these was the *Dimetrodon Gigas* (fig. 18), a huge carnivorous lizard, which is believed to have lived in North America about 250 million years ago.

The humbler forms of life, such as the worms, jelly-fish and sponges shewn in fig. 16, have survived, without any very great alteration, from that far-off period until to-day, but the more complicated forms of life were destined to undergo many changes.

For, as we read on in our book, we come to pages on which the geologists have written "Permian Era" and "Triassic Era", and the physicists "about 200 million years ago". On these we read of great mountain upheavals which completely altered the face of the globe. In the northern hemisphere most seas, including the present Atlantic and Indian Oceans, became dry land, and only part of the present Pacific Ocean remained as an ocean. In the southern hemisphere, the great continent which geologists describe as Gondwana Land emerged from the sea, to occupy the whole stretch from eastern South America through Africa to Australia. The geologists shew us small depressions in the rocks, in which the fossils of fish are packed like sardines in a tin, as though they had spent the last moments of their life crowding together where they could take advantage of the last few drops of water before these evaporated. With so little sea to give moisture to the air, the rainfall naturally decreased, and the greater part of the world became a desert. In particular we read of the seas of Northern Europe contracting into salt lakes, which became more and more salty as the drought increased in intensity, until they finally dried up altogether, leaving deposits of solid salt such as we now find in Cheshire and Staffordshire.

Then the drought begins to pass, but many forms of life fail to reappear in the later pages of the great book. They must have perished in the drought, and indeed it is obvious that only those which were able to adapt themselves rapidly to new conditions could hope to survive. An example is shewn in fig. 19 (p. 39) (*Cacops Aspidophorus*, or the Grim-faced Shield-bearer), an enterprising but not beautiful reptile, who somehow managed to find a living on dry land after the seas had dried up.

Next we come to pages marked "Jurassic Era" bearing dates of from 150 to 100 million years ago. These tell us of the seas again flowing over the parched deserts, of moisture returning, and of the earth again becoming hospitable to life. Such reptiles as have survived the drought now distribute themselves again over sea and land, and even invade the air, for we are now coming to those pages of our history book in which the fossils of winged creatures first appear—weird, ungainly birds, some with teeth, some with toothless beaks.

Many of the animals that inhabited the earth at this time were failures and misfits, unsuited to survive in the great struggle for existence, although a number of them contrived to live for a great many years before this fact was relentlessly borne in upon them. Figs. 20, 21, 22 and 23 shew examples of four such creatures, who lived in North America from 80 to 100 million years ago, and have since become extinct.

Fig. 20 portrays the *Triceratops*, who is typical of a whole class of animals who trusted to defensive armour. He had three horns, each many feet long, and when he was attacked, he only needed to stand with his back to the wall and wait until the foe had impaled itself on his horns. He was a huge creature, about 25 feet in length, and standing 9 feet high. He was still a reptile of a sort, and his female laid eggs of vast size.

Fig. 21 shews another creature in much the same class—the *Scolosaurus*, or Thorn-reptile, a member of a family which has been described as consisting of "the most ponderous animated citadels the world has ever seen". His method when attacked was probably to flatten himself on the ground and wag—or perhaps swish—his tail, which, as you see, ended in an immense knob of bone, rather like the spiky maces which the Crusaders used to wield. In those days, the tactics of defence and attack seem to have been equally rudimentary, and did not call for a high level of intelligence; *Triceratops* had a skull 6 feet long, but his brain was the size of a kitten's.

Fig. 22 shews a Pterodactyl—*Pteranodon occidentalis*—a huge bird-like reptile with a wing-spread of about 18 feet. He was one of those unhappy creatures who can do quite a lot of things in a rather futile sort of way, but nothing really well. He had wings which were probably rather too weak to raise his heavy body through the air, so that he could not fly well, and legs which were too weak to carry his great weight on land, so that he could not walk well. Possibly he could not run at all. He could not even sit down very well, since his elbows must always have got in the way, unless he sat perched on the top of a rocky peak. Scientists picture him as spending dreary days trudging laboriously to the top of a hill or cliff, then launching himself into the air currents, floating through these like a glider until he could swoop down upon his prey, and then starting to climb the hill again. I think we may properly feel sorry for him—his life must have been like an endless repetition of learning how to ski without a funicular.

Fig. 23 shews the *Diplodocus*, one of the largest animals that ever lived on earth. He was about 30 feet high, and about 90 feet long, so that a single *Diplodocus* must have weighed as

PLATE IX

W. E. Swinton, "The Dinosaurs"

Fig. 20. *Triceratops Prorsus* lived in North America about 90 million years ago. He lived on vegetation, was 25 feet long, had a skull as large as an elephant's, but a brain inside it no bigger than a kitten's.

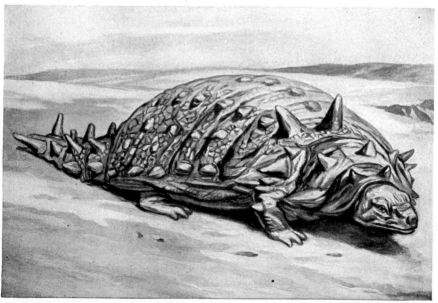

"Universal History of the World"

Fig. 21. *Scolosaurus* lived in Canada about 90 million years ago. His only weapon, either for defence or for attack, appears to have been his knobby tail.

PLATE X

British Museum (Natural History)

Fig. 22. *Pteranodon occidentalis,* a winged reptile, which inhabited North America about 90 million years ago. His wings had a spread of 18 feet, and consisted of thin webs of skin stretched from the fifth fingers of the arms to the hind legs.

W. E. Swinton, "The Dinosaurs"

Fig. 23. *Diplodocus.* This immense reptile lived in North America about 90 million years ago. Most of his great length of 90 feet was taken up by his long neck and very long whip-like tail.

much as a whole family of elephants—father, mother, children, and perhaps several uncles and aunts as well. A good specimen would perhaps have turned the scale at anything from 40 to 50 tons. He was so heavy that his legs could hardly support him on land, and so preferred to live in marshes, where his long neck came in useful at feeding time; indeed, he really needed the buoyancy of water to ease his weight if he was to live in any sort of comfort. Fig. 24 shews another huge, and even more ungainly, reptile—the *Cetiosaurus*, or Whale-reptile. He lived on our own side of the Atlantic, and many skeletons have been, and still are, found in English stone quarries. His length was about 60 feet, and like his American relation, the *Diplodocus*, he found it comfortable to ease the strain on his legs by living in the water. Let us not ridicule the disabilities of these unhappy creatures, for when we reach Jupiter and Saturn we shall find ourselves in an exactly similar predicament, and may have to take similar precautions if we are not to collapse under our own weights.

Just as we shall find that we are unsuited for anything more than a very brief visit to Jupiter or Saturn, so these misfits were unsuited to hold their own for long in the struggle for existence on earth, and were forced in time to yield to their more agile competitors—the smaller mammals, and finally man—who trusted to activity and intelligence rather than to heavy armour or brute size and weight. The big and heavily armoured reptiles gave way for precisely the same reason for which the heavily armoured soldier of the Middle Ages has given way to the unarmoured soldier of to-day, the reason for which fortresses and battleships are yielding place to tanks and torpedo-boats, and the airship to the less unwieldy aeroplane.

After these creatures had become extinct, we come to the age of mammals and of creatures who were in general more like those of to-day. Fig. 25 shews the *Arsinoitherium*, who lived in Egypt some 25 million years ago. He was far smaller than the monsters of the preceding age, and yet was as big as an average rhinoceros, or small elephant. He makes me think of Mr Kipling's "Just-So" story of how the elephant got his trunk. The baby elephant, you remember, was far too inquisitive, or so his family thought, about the facts of natural history; they particularly disapproved of his continually inquiring what the crocodile had for dinner. Finally he asked a crocodile basking in a swamp, who told him to lean down, so that he could whisper the answer in his ear. When he did this, the crocodile very unkindly and treacherously caught on to his nose, saying "Baby elephant to-day", and pulled and pulled until the nose was elongated into the trunk which every elephant now possesses. The *Arsinoitherium* looks rather like baby elephant must have looked half-way through the process, although the protruding part of his face is not really a trunk or nose, but consists of two pointed horns of bone which grew just above his nose. He had also two similar but smaller protrusions over each eye, and must have looked terrifying and fantastic to the last degree.

Fig. 26 shews us a smaller, but much more fearsome, creature —the *Machaerodus*, or Sabre-toothed Tiger, who inhabited Asia

PLATE XI

Fig. 24. *Cetiosaurus*, the Whale-reptile. This is a British relative of the *Diplodocus* shewn in fig. 23. He was about 60 feet in length, and correspondingly heavy.

Fig. 25. *Arsinoitherium* inhabited Egypt about 25 million years ago. In appearance he is somewhat like an elephant, but in many other respects is more like a rhinoceros.

PLATE XII

"Universal History of the World"

Fig. 26. *Machaerodus,* the Sabre-toothed Tiger, was a distant relative of the ordinary cat, but was not a tiger at all.

W. E. Swinton, "Monsters of Primaeval Days"

Fig. 27. *Megatherium,* the Giant Ground-sloth, was a vegetable eater, about 20 feet long, and 12 feet high when he sat up on his hind legs to reach the branches of trees.

and Europe from 1 to 10 million years ago. He was about the size of a large tiger or lion, and his mouth contained two really terrific teeth, immensely long and thin—sharp in front and saw-like behind—which look very formidable, and yet seem to have formed an effective obstacle to his either closing his mouth or eating his food; indeed no one seems quite to understand why he did not die of starvation.

Fig. 27 shews us the *Megatherium*, or Giant Ground-sloth, who lived in South America within the last million years. You can judge of his size from the man who is with him in the picture. This huge creature was quite harmless; he was perhaps hunted by man, and possibly even kept as a domestic animal, for the remains of one were found in the same cave as those of a man.

These huge sloths have been extinct for a long time, but the man is our own ancestor. Somewhere within the last million years ape-like mammals developed—or perhaps suddenly changed—into man, and we are the result. In comparison with a single lifetime, a million years seems almost interminable; in comparison with the total age of the earth, it is merely a small fraction of a fraction. In fig. 28 (p. 46) the principal epochs of the earth's history are drawn to scale. The million years or so of man's abode on the earth are represented by less than half the thickness of the thin line at the top of the diagram.

Yet even through this tiny fraction, man was mainly un-civilised, living little better than the beasts he hunted. We glance over hundreds of thousands of years of human history, and see only savages living in caves like animals, fighting with

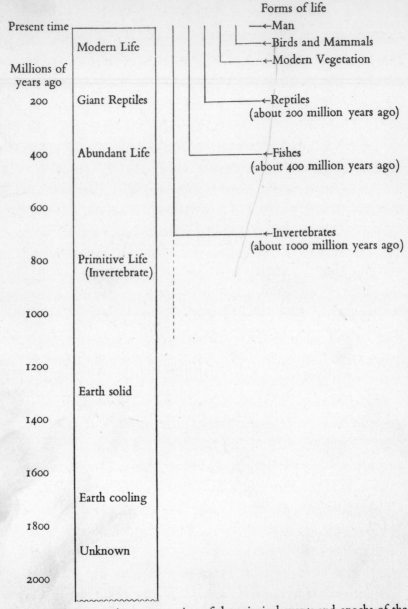

Fig. 28. Diagrammatic representation of the principal events and epochs of the past history of the earth. (The events and dates are highly conjectural.)

animals, and perhaps crying like animals. Then, perhaps 100,000 years ago, he acquires a new capacity for speech; he becomes able not only to plan and devise, but also to exchange his ideas with his fellow-men, and communicate his plans to them. This gives him an almost unchallengeable ascendancy over all other animals, and henceforth his progress is rapid. Perceptible change is no longer a matter of millions of years, thousands suffice, then centuries—now, almost single years. Human life has changed more in the last 50 years than reptile life did in 50 million years in the Jurassic and Permian Eras.

CHAPTER II

THE AIR

Let us leave the earth, in which we have burrowed for long enough, and turn our thoughts, and our eyes, upwards.

We all know what we may expect to see—the sun, the blue sky, and possibly some clouds, by day; stars, with perhaps the moon and one or more planets, by night. We see these objects by light which has travelled to us through the earth's atmosphere, and if we see them clearly, it is because the atmosphere is transparent—it presents no barrier to the passage of rays of light.

Perhaps we are so accustomed to this fact that we merely take it for granted. Or perhaps we think of the atmosphere as something too flimsy and ethereal ever to stop the passage of rays of light. Yet we know exactly how much atmosphere there is, for the ordinary domestic barometer is weighing it for us all the time. When the barometer needle points to 30, there is as much substance in the atmosphere over our heads as there is in a layer of mercury 30 inches thick. This again is the same amount as there would be in a layer of lead about 36 inches thick, for mercury is heavier than an equal volume of lead in the ratio of about six to five. To visualise the weight of the atmosphere above us, we may think of ourselves as covered up with 144 blankets of lead, each a quarter of an inch in thickness. We should hardly expect to see through 144 blankets of lead, so that it begins to look rather surprising, and perhaps something of a lucky accident, that we can see through the equally substantial atmosphere.

If so, it is a piece of luck which many of the planets do not share with us. When we examine the other planets from the earth, we find that most of them are covered in with opaque atmospheres which prevent our seeing their surfaces at all. Thus we may be forewarned that when our travels take us to these planets, we shall not be able to see through their atmospheres to the sky and stars above.

Let us, however, look into this question of opaqueness and transparency to light in some detail. We know that light, like all other forms of radiation, consists of waves, and we know that waves may be either long or short. In the case of sea waves, for example, there are the long breakers, perhaps hundreds of yards long, which rock even the biggest of ships; there are also little ripples only a few inches long, which have no appreciable effect on big ships, but rock row-boats—or perhaps they are too small to affect row-boats, and only disturb still smaller objects, such as pieces of cork or seaweed. It is the same with waves of light; some are long and some are short, and waves of different lengths affect objects in different ways.

Now the radiation which the sun emits contains waves of almost every length all mixed up together, although some lengths of wave occur only in minute quantities. Our eyes are not sensitive to those kinds of waves which the sun sends out only in small amounts, and neither are they sensitive to certain other kinds of waves which are emitted in abundance by the sun, but fail to reach our eyes because our atmosphere refuses them passage. If such waves should suddenly begin to penetrate our atmosphere in abundance they would burn us, and we should turn first brown, then black, and would shortly die, but our eyes would never see the light that was killing us. As a general rule, our eyes are sensitive only to light of those wave-lengths which reach us in abundance—that is, in brief, to waves of the kinds which make up ordinary daylight.

Perhaps this is hardly surprising. We are the offspring of millions of generations of ancestors, whose organs, including their eyes, have been slowly and gradually adapting themselves to their environment for hundreds and millions of years. For this reason, we seldom find either animals or men encumbered with organs that serve no useful purpose. When an organ is no longer needed, so that it falls into disuse and becomes merely a useless burden, it gradually disappears; or if it does not, the animal burdened with it may disappear, as did the heavily armoured reptiles whose acquaintance we made in Chapter 1. Eyes that were sensitive to light such as never reached them from the sun would have been mere encumbrances, both to animals and men, and if the human race had ever had such eyes, they would certainly have disappeared by now.

As our bodies have gradually developed through millions of years, our lungs and blood have adapted themselves to the quality and quantity of the earth's atmosphere and our skins to its climate—black skins for the tropics, white for the temperate zone, and so on. So our eyes have in all probability adapted themselves to daylight, and it is not mere luck that they are mainly sensitive to just those kinds of radiation which reach them in abundance. When we arrive on Jupiter, we shall find that we cannot see through its clouds. If, however, we had lived on Jupiter for thousands of generations, our eyes might have adjusted themselves to some special kinds of waves which pass through the clouds of Jupiter. We might have been saying how fortunate we were to live on Jupiter, with its beautifully transparent atmosphere, and pitying the inhabitants of other planets, such as the earth, who were shut in by opaque clouds.

As our knowledge of everything outside the earth comes to us in the form of radiation, and especially of light, it is very important for us to know the properties of different kinds of light and radiation in some detail. When we look at a rainbow, or a patch of dewy grass in sunlight, we see a profusion of colours. We know that if the sun went out, or even disappeared temporarily behind a cloud, we should no longer see the rainbow or coloured dew. This proves that the light we see started in the first instance from the sun. But it has not come to us by the most direct path—it reaches us from the wrong direction for that. It has been reflected into our eyes by little globules of water—the raindrops of the shower, or the dewdrops on the lawn—and in passing in and out of these tiny drops of water, it has been broken up into the assortment of colours that we see. There are of course more effective ways of breaking up the sun's light; we can break it up by letting it pass through a glass prism, or even a bottle of water, or—most effectively of all—by using the very sensitive instrument known as the spectroscope.

When the sun's light has been broken up by any of these ways, it appears as a band of varied colours, with red at one extremity and violet at the other. This band is called a "spectrum". There are other colours in between, so that the complete succession of colours runs: red, orange, yellow, green, blue, indigo, violet. If we break up any other kind of light, we shall get another spectrum, but whatever kind of light we use the colours invariably follow one another in the order just mentioned. The reason is that the different colours of light are produced by waves of different lengths, and that in every spectrum the different colours of light are arranged in order of their wave-lengths.

We shall obtain a simple proof of this if we break up the light by another instrument—the diffraction grating. This is merely a metal plate on which thousands of parallel lines have been scratched at exactly equal distances from one another with a diamond or other hard point. When light falls on the surface of the metal, this series of scratches picks out the waves of different lengths and reflects them in different directions, thus sorting them out according to their length much as a potato sieve sorts out potatoes by their sizes. The distance between the successive scratches corresponds to the mesh of the sieve, and, when we know this, we can calculate the lengths of any particular waves from the directions in which they are reflected. When light is broken up in this way, the different wave-lengths again form a spectrum, in which the colours appear in precisely the same order as before. But we need no longer grope in the dark as to the meaning of this order; we now see at once that the different colours of light are produced by waves of different lengths and that in the spectrum the colours are arranged in order of wave-length. Actual measurements shew that red light has the longest wave-length, about 33,000 waves going to an inch. As we pass through the other colours—orange, yellow, green, etc.—in order, the wave-length continually decreases, until we come to violet light with 66,000 waves to the inch.

Sound also consists of waves, although of a very different kind; they need air to travel through, and are about a million times as long as light waves. Just as different colours of light are produced by light waves of different lengths, so sounds of different pitch are produced by sound waves of different lengths. For instance, middle C on the piano has a wave-length of 4 feet, while treble C has a wave-length of 2 feet. When one sound has just half the wave-length of another, we say it is an octave higher in pitch. In the same way when one colour of light has just half the wave-length of another, we may say by analogy that it is an octave higher in pitch. Thus, as violet light has just half the wave-length of red light, we may say that violet light is an octave higher in pitch than red light. Indeed, we shall not go far wrong if we think of the seven colours of the spectrum as the seven notes of a scale, red being C, orange D, yellow E, green F, and so on. We have already seen that all the visible spectrum lies within one octave. Our ears can hear eleven octaves of sound, but our eyes can only see one octave of light.

We have also noticed that the sun's radiation consists of far more than the one octave of light our eyes can see. Beyond the deepest violet light that we can see, there is a great deal of light that we cannot see; it consists of waves even shorter than those of violet light, and is spoken of, in a general way, as "ultra-violet radiation", or even as "ultra-violet light". It does not affect our eyes for precisely the same reason for which tiny ripples on the sea do not affect a big ship—its waves are too short. But it does very powerfully affect photographic plates, and if the retinas of our eyes were made of substances similar to the emulsion of photographic plates, we should see ultra-violet radiation.

Out beyond the red end of the spectrum also, there is a great deal of radiation which our eyes cannot see; this consists of waves longer than those of red light, and is commonly described as infra-red radiation. When a solid object is heated up—as for instance a horseshoe at a blacksmith's forge—it glows at first with a dull red light, then, as it gets hotter and hotter, it becomes bright red, orange, and yellow in turn. The act of heating it up causes it to emit radiation, and the hotter it becomes, the shorter the waves it emits. We may say that, as an object gets hotter, its radiation moves along the spectrum in the direction of shorter and shorter waves. We do not begin to see the object by its own light until its radiation has passed into the visible part of the spectrum, but long before this stage is reached it is giving out radiation in the infra-red part of the spectrum. Our skins, but not our eyes, are sensitive to this radiation; if we hold our hand near a hot horseshoe, we shall feel its radiation long before we can see it with our eyes. This shews that the infra-red radiation is of the nature of heat rather than of visible light. Ordinary photographic plates are not affected either by infra-red or by red light; for this reason we can use red light in the dark-room without damaging our sensitised plates. If the retinas of our eyes were made of substances similar to the emulsions used on ordinary photographic plates, we should not see red light at all, and should hardly be able to see yellow or green—only blue, violet, and the ultra-violet which our present eyes cannot see.

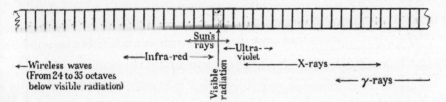

Fig. 29. The central part of the scale of radiation. Each section represents one complete octave of radiation, all being invisible except for the central octave which is shaded dark.

Although we can only see one octave of radiation with our eyes, scientists have found the means of studying as many as sixty-four octaves. Their scale of radiation is like a vast piano with sixty-four octaves, to all of which we are deaf except for the one octave of visible light (cf. fig. 29). Immediately above this one octave, going treblewards, we come to ultra-violet radiation. This makes its presence known by affecting photographic plates, and also by causing a number of chemical substances to "fluoresce", which means that when invisible ultra-violet light falls on them they emit visible light—as though they took the radiant energy and pushed it down several notes in the scale. Then, about ten octaves above the octave of visible light, we come to X-rays. Light substances are more transparent to these than heavy substances, so that when the rays are sent through a mixture of substances, the heavier substances cast deeper shadows than the lighter. Because of this property the surgeon can use these rays to photograph broken bones through the flesh, and they can also be used to examine an old painting even though a modern painting has been superimposed on the same canvas.

Above all these—very high indeed in the treble—come the γ-rays which are emitted by radium; and finally, thirty-two octaves above the octave of visible light, come certain of the constituents of cosmic rays, which can pass through many yards of lead.

In the other direction—down towards the bass—we come first to the infra-red radiation we have already described; the heat radiated from a hot flat-iron is about three octaves down, and that from a kettle of boiling water about four. Special photographic plates are now made which are sensitive to infra-red radiation, so that it is possible to photograph objects by this radiation in what appears to our eyes to be complete darkness. For instance, in fig. 35 (facing p. 76), we see a hot flat-iron photographed in a dark room by its own infra-red radiation.

Far below these—about thirty octaves below visible light—we come to waves which are more than a thousand million times as long as the waves of visible light. These are of special interest and importance, being nothing other than the waves used for radio transmission. Yellow light has a wave-length of only about a forty-thousandth of an inch, but if we want to receive a wireless programme, we tune into such wave-lengths as 1500 metres, 342·1 metres, and so on. Except for everything being magnified a thousand-million fold, these waves have many of the properties of waves of light. For instance, the parallel wires of a beam station treat them almost exactly as the parallel scratches on the surface of a diffraction grating treat the waves of visible light. If we let light of one single colour fall on to a diffraction grating, we find that it is all reflected as a beam in one single direction, the exact direction depending on the wave-length of the light. In the same way, if radio waves of one single wave-length are sent through the aerials of a beam station, they all start off as a beam in one single direction—to India, China, Japan, or anywhere else we wish, according to the length of wave we use.

After this preliminary study of the properties of radiation and light, let us set out to study the atmosphere through which they travel. Perhaps most of us are disposed to think of it as a simple layer of transparent gas stretching up skywards, but scientific study shews it to be a structure of very great complexity. We shall get quite a good general idea of this structure if we think of it, like the earth itself, as a vast number of wrappings or layers, each enclosing the one inside it, until the innermost of all encloses a massive parcel—the solid earth.

The first layer of atmosphere enwrapping the earth is known as the "troposphere"—the sphere of change. Its thickness varies from about 5 to 10 miles at different times and places, being generally about 7 miles. Although this is only a small fraction of the whole thickness of the atmosphere, yet the troposphere contains nearly 90 per cent. of the total substance of the atmosphere. The explanation is of course that the atmosphere is far more dense in its lower layers, where there is a great deal of air above it, and so pressing it down, than higher up where it has but little weight to support. The troposphere is continually being agitated by winds and storms—hence its name—in contrast to the layer above, known as the "stratosphere", which is characterised by almost perfect calm; storms do not reach so high.

The atmosphere consists of a mixture of many kinds of gases, some light and some heavy. If it were left to itself for a sufficient time, the light gases would rise to the top, as the cream does in a basin of milk. Actually it is never left to itself for more than a few days at a time. We have already seen how the earth's rotation causes the trade-winds to blow, and what with this and all sorts of other winds and storms, the troposphere is more like milk in a butter churn than milk standing in a cream basin. This continual churning keeps the gases of the troposphere thoroughly mixed, so that its composition is the same throughout. As we know, it consists of four parts of nitrogen to one of oxygen, with other gases mixed in far smaller quantities.

The principal of these other gases is water vapour, and this has very special properties, since it alone of the constituents of the troposphere can condense into drops of liquid—raindrops—which then tend to fall earthwards in the form of rain or snow. We are all familiar with showers of water, but we have never seen showers of oxygen, nitrogen, or helium. Now water vapour is especially prone to form into these drops when the air is churned up by wind—hence the common belief that rain follows wind. We have said that churning up the air distributes the constituent gases uniformly throughout the atmosphere, but it now appears that we must make an exception in the case of water vapour— churning sends this down to the lowest level of all, the surface of the earth. After a time all the water which has fallen as a shower will evaporate, and in this way be restored to the atmosphere, but before it has ascended very high, another wind is sure to come along and shake it down again. Thus it is not surprising to find that the water vapour is not spread uniformly through the atmosphere, but is confined almost entirely to the lowest levels. Actually about one molecule in eighty is water vapour at sea-level, but at the top of the troposphere the proportion has fallen to 1 in 10,000. This means that practically all the water vapour of the atmosphere lives in the troposphere, which thus becomes the region of rain, snow and fogs. Ordinary rain clouds (fig. 31, p. 68) generally occur at heights which range from a few hundred feet to a mile or more, while the highest clouds of all, the fine-weather clouds known as cirrus and cirrostratus (fig. 30), are at an average height of 5 or 6 miles. Above the top of the troposphere there are no clouds of any kind.

The continual stirring up of the gases of the troposphere has one interesting and important result. When we apply pressure to a gas, it not only contracts in volume, but also rises in temperature—compressing a gas heats it up, as we notice when we pump up a tyre. Conversely, releasing the pressure of a gas lowers its temperature. For this reason, the gas which issues forth from a cylinder of compressed gas always cools as it comes out; it may even freeze and come out in the form of snow—this is how many fire-extinguishers work. Now as air is carried upwards by the winds and storms of the troposphere, the pressure on it is released, so that it cools—just like gas coming out of a gas cylinder. If the same air is dragged down again by more winds and storms, its pressure is increased, and it gets hotter—just like the air in a tyre. For this reason, the upper layers of the troposphere are always colder than the lower. If we climb a mountain, or go up in an aeroplane, we find the air getting colder; if we go down into a mineshaft or valley bottom, we find it getting warmer.

If the atmosphere were a simple mass of churned-up air, we can calculate that its temperature would decrease by 29 degrees Fahrenheit for every mile of height. But many other factors must be taken into consideration, such as the heat of the earth, the sun's radiation, and the irregularities of the earth's surface. Actual observations with balloons shew that the temperature does in fact fall fairly uniformly with the height, but only at the rate of about 17 degrees Fahrenheit per mile. With a temperature of 60 degrees Fahrenheit at sea-level, the temperature 7 miles up will be about 60 degrees below zero. This is approaching the lowest temperature which has ever been recorded on the earth's surface, namely, 94 degrees below zero at Verkhoiansk, Siberia.

Early scientists imagined that anyone who went higher still would find the atmosphere getting colder and colder, until finally it became so tenuous that it could not properly be said to have a temperature at all. Then, in 1898, a series of balloons were sent up near Paris to determine the temperatures at great heights, and this view was found to be fallacious. The temperature was found to remain almost uniform after passing a height of from 7 to 10 miles, and sometimes even shewed a slight increase. The reason, as we now know, was that the balloon had passed out of the turmoil of the troposphere into the calm of the stratosphere; here there were no storms alternately to compress and rarefy the atmosphere and so to cool it up above and warm it down below. For a layer of gas which is repeatedly stirred up like the troposphere will develop a temperature gradient, but one which is left to itself, like the stratosphere, tends to assume a uniform temperature.

When we try to explore the heights of the stratosphere, we encounter much the same difficulties as in trying to explore the depths of the earth. The most obvious way of exploring the earth was to dig a hole, and either go down it ourselves, or send instruments down, to bring up a sample. But this only took us a very short distance down, after which we had to let waves do the exploring for us. In the same way, the most obvious method of exploring the stratosphere is either to go up ourselves in a balloon, or get a sample of air down in a balloon. Both these methods are in common use, but they do not take us very far. Up to the present, human beings have never gone higher than 13·7 miles, the height reached by a balloon sent up from Moscow in January 1934, and then they did not come down alive. The greatest height reached by a balloon without passengers was

23 miles attained by a balloon sent up from Padua. Heights greater than these can at present only be explored by the passage of waves. Only one kind of waves, namely earthquake waves, are available for the study of the earth, but there are three distinct kinds available for the study of the stratosphere—waves of light, waves of sound, and radio waves. Waves of all these three kinds pass through the stratosphere, and can be made to bring a message down with them, almost as a balloon filled with self-registering instruments does.

The waves of light which pass through the stratosphere are of course the radiation of the sun and stars. They bring with them a message that they have been robbed of some of their constituent wave-lengths in their passage through the atmosphere. Many of the missing wave-lengths are in the ultra-violet part of the spectrum, and are found to be precisely those which cannot pass through ozone. Thus it is natural to conclude that ozone is responsible for the robbery. Ozone is a specially heavy variety of oxygen gas, having three atoms to the molecule in place of the usual two. Popular imagination credits it with remarkable powers in the matter of making our seaside resorts bracing, bringing the glow of health to pallid faces, and so forth. Science knows nothing of this, chemical analysis shewing that there is remarkably little ozone either at our seaside resorts or anywhere else on land or sea.

It is found that the amount of ultra-violet radiation which reaches the earth is not uniform, but varies with the position of the sun in the sky. There is a quite definite relation between the two, and this makes it possible to estimate the position of the ozone by which the ultra-violet radiation has been absorbed. Recent investigations by Professor Dobson of Oxford and other scientists shew that most of the ozone lies within 25 miles of the ground, its average height being about 15 miles. The amount of ozone is extraordinarily small, its total weight being only that of a layer of paper about a two-thousandth of an inch in thickness—the thinnest of tissue paper. The sun's light can pass through miles of ordinary air without appreciable absorption, and yet this thin layer of ozone is enough to stop its ultra-violet rays from reaching us. In a sense, then, there may after all be some luck in our atmosphere being transparent to any light at all. For we might have been surrounded by an atmosphere whose different constituents shut off various parts of the sun's light as effectively as the ozone shuts off the ultra-violet rays, so that neither sunlight nor any other light could pass through it at all.

The ozone does not shut off all the ultra-violet radiation, and this is fortunate, since a certain amount of it is beneficial to us. It is said that miners, and other people whose work keeps them much below ground, find that their health is improved if they occasionally expose themselves for short intervals to artificially produced ultra-violet radiation. Children who have to all appearance been starving from want of adequate food, have sometimes been restored to health merely by letting this radiation fall on their skins, thereby producing the vitamin D which is essential to health. On the other hand, too much of the radiation may prove even more disastrous than none at all, and we sometimes hear of people dying from over-exposure to it.

The ozone layer controls the supply of ultra-violet radiation we receive from the sun, and, broadly speaking, gives us just about the amount we need. When we travel on other planets, we may find that their atmospheres let through too much or too little of this radiation to suit us and our health will suffer accordingly. Yet once again the reason that our own atmosphere appears to treat us so well is probably that our bodies have, after millions of generations, learnt how to get on with exactly what is meted out to them. If we had lived for millions of generations on some other planet, we might find the amount of ultra-violet radiation on earth intolerable.

Other lengths of waves are also missing in the radiation we receive from the sun and stars, particularly in the red and infra-red parts of the spectrum. These omissions can, however, be traced to the presence of oxygen, water vapour and carbon dioxide, and so tell us nothing new about the composition of the atmosphere.

So much for what light waves have to tell us; we shall find that we can learn even more from radio waves. Unlike light waves, these do not come into the atmosphere from outside—except perhaps in quite inappreciable amounts—so that we must study the waves emitted by our own wireless stations. We have seen that these are of the same general nature as waves of light, except that they are thousands of millions of times longer. Being of similar nature, they have many properties in common with light waves. Both for instance travel in straight lines, and both are stopped by the solid body of the earth. Just as we can never hope to see round the earth, so it might have been anticipated that we should never be able to pick up a wireless signal emitted by a station at the other side of the earth.

For this reason, the earlier experimenters were greatly mystified when they found that they were picking up wireless stations at the opposite ends of the earth without difficulty; they can now pick up stations near their receiving sets by waves that have travelled twice round the world, and taken nearly half a second on their journey. Not only so, but everyone who has ever played with a wireless set knows that quite distant stations are often received better than near-by stations of equal power.

Gradually the conclusion was reached that radio waves were sent out in all directions, but that as soon as a beam reached a certain height above the surface of the earth, it was in some way bent back and returned to earth. If we found light waves behaving in a similar manner, we should conclude that somewhere up in the sky there was a gigantic mirror which reflected them back to earth. To some extent thick clouds behave just like such a mirror for light waves—for instance, when the sky is covered with clouds, the glare of the lights of London can be seen far out into the country. Yet the mirror which reflects radio waves back to earth must be something quite different from this—it must be completely transparent to ordinary light, because distant stations are often received perfectly well on a clear night.

It is known that an ordinary mirror reflects light because its surface is a conductor of electricity. The surface usually consists of quicksilver or metal, but air and other gases can also be made to conduct electricity under special conditions, so that there is no reason why a mirror should not consist of air or gas. Generally speaking, gases conduct when they are "ionised", which means that electrons have been torn off from their molecules and so are free to move about and transport an electric current—which, incidentally, is exactly the process by which a film of quicksilver or a surface of metal conducts electricity. In 1902 two scientists, Kennelly in the United States and Heaviside in England, independently suggested that there must be a layer of ionised gas high up above the earth which acted as a mirror for radio waves, and turned them earthwards again. Since then, their conjecture has been amply confirmed, and the layer of ionised gas is known as the E, or Kennelly-Heaviside layer. It is usually found at a height of 65 or 70 miles, although it may occasionally be found as much as 20 miles outside these limits—i.e. at heights ranging from 45 to 90 miles.

A second layer of ionised gas has recently been discovered above this, and is called the F, or Appleton layer, after its discoverer. Its height varies from 90 to 250 miles, and so is even more variable than that of the Kennelly-Heaviside layer. Neither of these two layers reflects all the waves that fall on it, and many waves escape through the Kennelly-Heaviside layer only to be caught and reflected back to earth by the Appleton layer. Indeed, if it were not for this, the Appleton layer could never have been discovered.

Other layers have been discovered in the same way, the lowest, known as the D layer, possibly being as little as 25 or 30 miles above the ground. This layer is specially active in the early morning, trapping long waves, and sending them back to earth. Apart from this, the majority of waves pass through it quite easily, although only to be caught and reflected back by one of the upper layers. When next we listen to a foreign wireless station let us pause and think out the route by which the radio waves have brought us the programme. We shall see them leaving the station and mounting upwards, possibly dodging through the D layer, and ascending higher until they reach the upper layers, where they set millions of millions of electrons scurrying about, like so many goal-keepers in front of miniature goals, trying to prevent the waves from getting through, and kicking such as they can back to earth. These fall on our aerials, where again they set electrons scurrying about. If our station is the Daventry National station with a frequency of 200 kc., every goal-keeper up in the skies must run backwards and forwards 200,000 times every second; down on earth the electrons in our aerials run backwards and forwards just as often, and unless we have a bad contact at our intake, they also run into and out of our sets, where they make other electrons jump about inside our valves. And so, as the result of the varied activities of millions of millions of electrons, we finally hear the programme.

It may seem strange that there are so many distinct layers of ionised gas, but we must remember that the atmosphere consists of a mixture of many kinds of gas, and its different constituents may be ionised at different heights. Also, ionisation may be produced by a variety of different agencies, and these may operate at different heights. The principal agency is perhaps ultra-violet light, which is known to be very potent in ionising molecules of gas. Thus it is significant that all the ionised layers are well above the layer of ozone which shuts off the sun's ultra-violet light.

Quite recently other reflecting layers have been discovered so high up that they must be many miles beyond the top of the atmosphere, and so right out in space. We can tell the height of a reflecting layer by noticing how long it takes for an echo to come back to us from the layer. If, for instance, the echo returns after a delay of a thousandth part of a second, then, since radio waves travel at 186,000 miles a second, we know that the up and down journeys together measure 186 miles, and the layer must be 93 miles high. Now experimenters have recently heard echoes coming back from space after intervals which have ranged from 3 to 30 seconds, shewing that there must be reflecting layers at distances up to nearly three million miles from the earth. Like the nearest layers, these very remote layers probably consist of electrified particles, but these particles cannot be suspended in the atmosphere, because there is none where they are. They are more likely to be electrified particles in transit from the sun to the earth.

For when we go to the sun, we shall find that it is continually shooting out electrified particles, some of which impinge on the earth's atmosphere, after travelling through space for 30 hours or so. It is a general law of electricity that a moving electrified particle is pulled out of its course by a magnet, and we of course

PLATE XIII

C. J. P. Cave, "Clouds"

Fig. 30. Cirrus clouds. These, the highest clouds of all, are usually at a height of from 4 to 6 miles, and consist of minute ice crystals. Practically all other clouds consist of minute drops of water.

C. J. P. Cave, "Clouds"

Fig. 31. Clouds and fog in the Rhone Valley. Above the mountains are cumulus and stratus clouds, the latter being sometimes described as fog which is not in contact with the ground. The valley itself is filled with fog, which may equally well be described as cloud which is in contact with the ground.

PLATE XIV

Royal Society

Fig. 32. A very fine "draped" aurora, as seen by Captain Scott's Antarctic Expedition. The "draped" aurorae are usually the richest in colour, the commonest hues being white, yellow and rose-carmine.

Royal Society

Fig. 33. An aurora of different type consisting of a circular arc with vertical streamers, also seen by Captain Scott's Antarctic Expedition.

know that our earth is a huge magnet. The consequence is that, as these particular particles approach the earth, they no longer travel in straight lines, but are drawn towards the north and south magnetic poles of the earth. Professor Stormer has shewn that, at certain places on their paths, they may be forced to take a very circuitous route indeed, and so be delayed for a long time without making any appreciable progress towards the earth. At such places there must be great accumulations of particles, running round and round for a long time, and it may well be that these accumulations constitute the reflecting layers from which the echoes are heard; the same particles, after they have arrived in the earth's atmosphere, may be responsible for the Polar Lights or Aurora Borealis, which often appear so sensationally in the regions surrounding the north and south magnetic poles of the earth (figs. 32 and 33 on Plate XIV).

Let us next consider what we can learn about the atmosphere from the passage of sound waves through it. As with radio waves, there are no sound waves falling on to the earth from outer space; there could not be, since sound waves can only travel through an atmosphere, and there is no atmosphere to transmit them in outer space. Thus our study must depend on the noises we ourselves make on earth.

When an explosion or other big noise occurs, waves of sound spread out from it in all directions, much as radio waves do from a wireless station. Those which start in an upwards direction might meet with many fates—the only one to which they cannot be condemned is that of going on for ever in a straight line, because there would be no air for them to travel through. Actually it is found that after travelling to a certain height, they are turned back to the earth by some reflecting layer, much as radio waves are. Our radio sets will often pick up a station 200 miles away while a station 100 miles away is quite inaudible. In the same way, the sound of heavy firing or a big explosion will frequently be heard clearly 200 miles away, although it is quite inaudible at a distance of only 100 miles.

We are all familiar with the children's method of telling the distance of a lightning flash—count seconds between the flash and the thunder, divide by five, and the quotient will be the distance of the flash in miles. The reason for the rule is of course that sound travels through air at about a mile every 5 seconds. Now when the same rule is used to find the distance to a big explosion, it is often found not to work. The sound seems to take too long on its journey, or at any rate longer than it would if it had travelled straight along the ground. It has, in fact, been up to the reflecting layer and down again, and the amount of time by which it has been delayed tells us the height of the layer. Calculation shews that it must be well up in the stratosphere. And now it is easy to surmise what bent the rays back. For we have already seen how the temperature of the stratosphere begins to increase again after a certain height is passed, and it is well known that when sound waves encounter a layer of warmer air, they will be bent back again into the colder air from which they have come.

We can test this property of sound for ourselves, without going up into the stratosphere. Shortly after sunset on a warm autumn evening, mists often form a few feet above the ground, while the air above remains perfectly clear. This shews that the upper layers of air are warmer than the lower, so that in the matter of temperature the two layers—the clear and the misty—form a sort of miniature model of the stratosphere and the troposphere. Under these conditions we shall find that sound travels very distinctly and for great distances along the ground; the waves cannot spread upwards, because every time they try to do so, the upper layer of warm air turns them back again. Similar conditions may often be found over frozen ground at night, and over the surface of a lake at dusk. In each case sound is reflected back to earth just as, at a much greater height and on a far larger scale, it is reflected back by the warmer layers of the stratosphere.

The fall of meteorites, which we shall discuss below (p. 104), provides further evidence that the temperature goes on increasing as we ascend in the stratosphere, and that after being very unpleasantly cold at heights of from 10 to 20 miles, it may become quite comfortable again at a height of about 100 miles.

Fig. 34 (p. 72) gives a diagrammatical view of the different shells or layers of the earth's atmosphere.

We have been so much concerned with the transparency of the earth's atmosphere, that we have hardly remembered that it is not completely transparent, and is often not transparent at all. Living in England, we know only too well how the blue sky may be replaced by clouds, and sometimes by mist or fog.

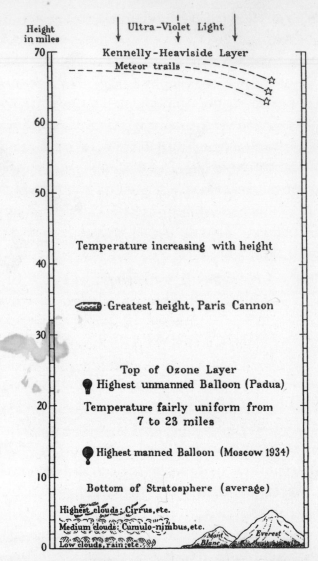

Fig. 34. The results of exploring the atmosphere shewn in diagrammatic form. On the same scale the earth is a sphere 50 feet in diameter.

Moreover, even when clouds, mist and fog are completely absent, there is a sense in which the atmosphere is never entirely transparent. When we arrive on the moon and look upwards, we shall not see a blue sky, but a black one, the reason being that the moon has no atmosphere. In the same way, if the earth's atmosphere were gradually removed, we should see our own sky changing from blue to black. We can see the earlier stages of the process by going up in an aeroplane, thus leaving the greater part of the atmosphere beneath us. Here is the colour of the sky at different heights, as recorded by the observers in the U.S.S.R. balloon "Stratosphere" which went up from Moscow in January 1934:

Height 5·27 miles (8,500 metres)—sky blue.
        6·82 ,, (11,000 ,,)— ,, dark blue.
        8·06 ,, (13,000 ,,)— ,, dark violet.
       13·02 ,, (21,000 ,,)— ,, black-violet.
       13·64 ,, (22,000 ,,)— ,, black-grey.

If we could ever go entirely outside the atmosphere, there is no doubt that the sky would look completely black. When we look upwards, we are in effect looking at crowds of particles of air, dust, water vapour, and so forth, every one of which catches some of the sun's rays and scatters them in all directions. Some of these scattered rays enter our eyes, with the result that the sky looks light and not dark to us.

Actually it looks blue, and we may wonder why blue rather than any other colour—for the sun's rays are not specially blue. The explanation is that the sun's light is a blend of waves of different lengths, as we have already seen, and the particles of air, dust, and water vapour do not treat all these different waves in the same way. The waves of blue light are smaller in size than those of red light, while the particles we are now considering are smaller by far than either. Yet because these particles are nearer in size to the waves of blue light than to those of red, they scatter the former waves more effectively, with the result that when we look up at the sky, the scattered rays which enter our eyes are mainly blue, and we say that the sky looks blue. The smaller the particles, the more they scatter the blue light, so that the sky looks bluest of all after heavy rain, when the big dust particles have been washed out; it also looks very blue over the sea and high up a mountain, because here we get away from the more dusty layers. In all these cases only the minute molecules of air are engaged in scattering the light. When the larger dust particles scatter the light we see the familiar haze of a dusty atmosphere.

When we look directly at the sun, the only rays which enter our eyes are those which have not been broken up and scattered. Since the blue rays have suffered more than the red in this respect, it follows that more rays are left of red or reddish colour than of blue, so that the sun looks redder than it really is. If the layer of air or dust between us and the sun is specially thick, as for instance at sunrise or sunset when the sun's rays travel slantwise through the atmosphere, the sun will look even redder than usual. This was observed in a very striking way in the year 1883, when the volcano Krakatoa erupted, and threw out immense clouds of volcanic dust. This dust first shrouded the earth in complete darkness for a distance of 100 miles away from the eruption, and subsequently encircled the world. For the few months during which the earth's atmosphere was permeated with it, the sunrises and sunsets were of an indescribable magnificence.

Particles of water vapour and fog often have a similar effect, so that the sun may look redder when seen through fog. Street lamps shew the same effect, those which are farthest from us looking reddest. Clouds are usually so thick that they blot out the sun's light altogether except near their edges; here we get the proverbial silver, or perhaps golden, lining in the daytime, and the familiar deep red tints at sunset.

The particles of dust, water vapour and fog scatter all the light which tries to pass through them to a greater or less degree, but the red light is scattered less than the blue because its waves are longer. The still longer waves of infra-red radiation are so long that they are hardly scattered at all, so that if our eyes were sensitive to infra-red radiation we should see distant objects through a thick fog just as clearly as we see them through ordinary air.

The camera comes to the rescue to make good the deficiencies of our eyes. We have already noticed that photographic plates are made which are sensitive to infra-red radiation. Fig. 35 (facing p. 76) provides a demonstration of their effectiveness. The two pictures below this (figs. 36 and 37) shew the same landscape photographed simultaneously in ordinary and infra-red radiation. We notice how very clearly the infra-red picture shews distant objects through the intervening haze. When the air is too thick or foggy for our eyes to see distant objects at all, the special infra-red plates can often see them, and the best way of photographing distant objects, fog or no fog, is by using these red plates. Ships have recently been using infra-red photography in the North Atlantic in the hope that it may give them warning of the proximity of icebergs. Infra-red photography also provides a new and very modern proof of the curvature of the earth, since an aeroplane can take photographs of a very distant horizon from such a height that the curvature of the earth is quite distinctly visible.

PLATE XV

Fig. 35. An electric flat-iron photographed by its own
heat radiation at a temperature of only 400° Centigrade
at which it emits no visible light.

Ilford Co.

Ilford Co.

Fig. 36. Bowen Island, British Columbia, photographed by ordinary light
from a point 12 miles distant on the mainland.

Ilford Co.

Fig. 37. The same scene as the above, photographed
by infra-red radiation.

PLATE XVI

Helwan Observatory

Fig. 38. Brooks' Comet (1911).

E. E. Barnard, Yerkes Observatory

Fig. 39. Comet iii of 1908. The star images are elongated because the telescope was made to follow the motion of the comet, which was moving past the stars.

CHAPTER III

THE SKY

Let us now turn our thoughts beyond the earth and its atmosphere to the phenomena which may properly be described as astronomical. We see a procession of objects moving ceaselessly across the sky—the sun by day, the moon and stars by night. These all appear to cross the sky from east to west, because the rotation of the earth, from which we view the spectacle, causes us to move continually from west to east.

The most conspicuous phenomenon is of course the daily motion of the sun across the heavens, producing the alternations of light and darkness, heat and cold, which we describe as day and night. The rising and setting of the moon and its passage across the sky are only one degree less conspicuous, and must have been not only noticed, but also familiar, since the days when human beings first appeared on the earth.

The sun shews no changes either of shape or brightness, except when our own atmosphere dims its light, but the moon continually varies in both respects. Every month it goes through the complete cycle of changes, which we call its "phases". It begins as a thin crescent of light, which we describe as the new moon. This increases in size until after about a week we have the semicircle of light we call half moon, and then a week later the complete circle we call full moon. After this the moon decreases, until it is again reduced to the thin crescent of the new moon.

When the moon is new, it is always near to the sun in the sky; as its size increases, its distance from the sun also increases, until finally, by the time it is full, it is almost exactly in the direction opposite to that of the sun. Because the full moon is opposite the sun in the sky, it is always in the south at midnight.

Whether the moon is new or full or intermediate, the lighted part of its surface is invariably turned towards the sun, and the dark part away. This suggests that the moon emits no light of itself, and only looks bright where it is lighted up by the sun. On somewhat infrequent occasions, the earth comes exactly between the sun and the moon, and so temporarily prevents the sun's light from falling on the moon. We call such an occurrence an eclipse of the moon, and, when it happens, we can see for ourselves that the moon has no light of its own.

There are other, and even rarer occasions, when the moon comes exactly between the sun and the earth—we call such an event an eclipse of the sun. Again the body of the moon, as it passes across the face of the sun, appears as a completely dark screen, and again we have a direct visual proof that the moon emits no light of its own.

Now that all this has been discovered, it sounds as if it must have been simple to discover it. Actually the discovery took a long time. Early man was easily misled by superficial appearances, and so had the most grotesque ideas as to the sizes, motion and physical structure of the sun, moon and stars. For instance, in the sixth century before Christ, the Greek philosopher Anaximander (about 611–546 B.C.) maintained that the sun, moon and stars were simply holes in the firmament, through which fires shone from above. He thought that the phases of the moon resulted from the gradual opening and closing of the moon-hole, while eclipses, both of the sun and moon, occurred when the corresponding holes were completely stopped up.

A few years later we find Anaximenes (about 585–526 B.C.) maintaining that the sun, moon and stars consisted of fire that had risen aloft from the earth. He imagined the sun to be a sort of flat leaf of fire, which floated in the air because of its breadth— rather like a glider or an aeroplane. The moon was something of the same sort, but the stars were of an entirely different nature, being more like fiery studs nailed into the crystal sphere of heaven. As there was nothing in all this to make eclipses, Anaximenes had to suppose that the sky also contained dark bodies "of an earthy nature". Although he did not say so, these presumably made eclipses by coming between our earth and the bright sun and moon.

Next came Xenophanes (born about 570 B.C.) who thought that sun, moon and stars were a succession of clouds of fire sailing across the sky. He believed—as the Egyptians had believed before him—that there was a new sun every day, the sun of the day before having gone so far west as to be invisible; every now and then one of the clouds of fire burned out, and there was an eclipse.

Heraclitus (born about 544 B.C.) thought that the sun, moon and stars were basins or bowls, which collected fiery exhalations from the earth and produced flames from them. The moon-bowl

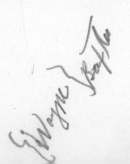

gradually turned round, and this caused the moon to wax and wane and go through its well-known cycle of phases. If the bowls of either the sun or the moon happened to be turned right away from us there would be an eclipse.

So far no one had got very near to the truth, when suddenly Anaxagoras (born about 500 B.C.) gave the true explanation of all the phenomena in one single flash of insight. He said that the moon was "of an earthy nature, having plains and ravines on it", and that it derived its light from the sun. He explained how its phases were the natural consequence of its following the course of the sun, by which it was illuminated. He also stated clearly that eclipses of the moon were caused by its passing within the shadow of the earth when this came directly between the sun and the moon, and so always occurred at full moon; while eclipses of the sun were due to the interposition of the moon between the sun and the earth, and so always occurred at new moon.

As was not unnatural, the early vague ideas as to the physical nature of the sun and moon were accompanied by equally vague ideas as to their sizes and distances. As the sun and moon always look about the same size in the sky, it is clear that they must always stay at about the same distances from the earth, but there was endless difference of opinion as to what these distances were. Anaximander had maintained that the sun was as big as the earth; a few years later Heraclitus maintained that it was only a foot in diameter, while Anaxagoras took an intermediate view, and held that it was larger than the Peloponnese. The first serious effort to discover the true facts was made by Aristarchus of Samos (about 310–230 B.C.); he proceeded in the only possible way— by calculations based on actual measurements.

At the moment of half moon we see exactly half the moon's face lighted up by the sun, so that the angle of *EMS* in fig. 40 must be a right angle. If the angle *MES* between the moon and the sun is now measured, all the angles of the triangle *EMS* are

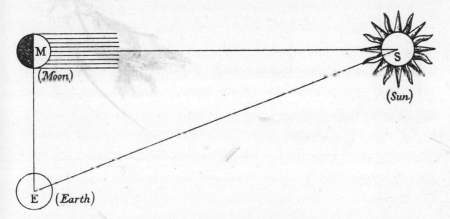

Fig. 40. Diagrammatic representation of the geometrical method by which Aristarchus of Samos tried to measure the distances of the sun and moon.

known, and it is easy to deduce the relative lengths of the sides of this triangle. Aristarchus estimated that the angle *MES* fell short of a right angle by 3 degrees, and deduced that the sun was between eighteen and twenty times as distant as the moon. This was not a good estimate, for, in actual fact, the angle differs from a right angle by less than a twentieth of 3 degrees, and the sun is at about 400 times the distance of the moon.

Aristarchus also had an ingenious means of measuring the distances themselves. At an eclipse of the moon, we see part of the earth's shadow projected onto the face of the moon; it is never more than part, since the whole shadow is far larger than the moon, actually having about four times the diameter of the moon. Aristarchus estimated, however, that the whole shadow was only double the size of the moon, and concluded that the earth itself was double the size of the moon. Having calculated the size of the moon in this way, it was easy to deduce its distance from the angle it subtended in the sky. The moon looks the same size in the sky as a halfpenny held 9 feet away, and for a body 2000 miles in diameter to look as small as this, it must be about 240,000 miles away.

This is a modern calculation; unhappily the measurements of Aristarchus were so faulty throughout that he did not get anywhere near to the true values of the quantities he was trying to evaluate. As we have already seen, he measured the angle *MES* incorrectly, and also took the earth's shadow on the moon to have only double, instead of four times, the diameter of the moon itself. Besides this, he over-estimated the apparent size of the moon in the sky no less than four times, and did not know the dimensions of the earth with any accuracy; some years were yet to pass before Eratosthenes made the surprisingly accurate estimate we have already discussed (see p. 8).

We have seen how the earth is rotating in space, while the so-called "fixed stars" such as Arcturus and Sirius always remain in the same direction in space, and so form a fixed background. The sun and moon appear to move in front of this background, as also do the other objects known as "planets"—from the Greek word πλάνητες, which means wanderers. The five most conspicuous of these—Venus (the morning and evening star), Jupiter, Mars, Saturn, and Mercury—were known before the dawn of recorded astronomy, although it was not always clearly understood that Venus was a single star which appeared alternatively in the morning and evening, or that the same was true of Mercury. The Babylonians, however, appear to have known this, and we find Pythagoras and Parmenides explaining it to the Greeks in the sixth century before Christ. Then, in quite modern times, three more planets were discovered—Uranus in 1781, Neptune in 1846, and Pluto in 1930. Besides these large planets, there are thousands of planets of minute size known as "minor planets" or "asteroids" (p. 143).

To superficial observation the planets appear to wander in very erratic ways. Other astronomical objects move across the sky from east to west with a stately and steady motion, but the planets often fall behind in the procession, and can sometimes be observed moving among the stars from west to east, in what is described as "retrograde" motion. At regular intervals their retrograde motion carries Venus and Mercury backwards across the face of the sun, after which they make a spurt and get in front again; thus the motion of these two planets consists of continual oscillations to and fro about the sun, the westerly swing always being performed much more rapidly than the easterly.

The motions of the planets form so striking a contrast to the orderly motion of the "fixed" stars, that they puzzled the ancients more than a little. The Pythagorean school insisted that the apparent irregularities must be illusory, and that the real motions of the planets must in some way be perfectly even and regular. Geminus wrote that "they could not brook the idea of such disorder in things divine and eternal as that they should move at one time more swiftly, at another time more slowly, and at another time stand still. No one would credit such irregularity even in the case of a steady and orderly man on a journey", while Plato is said to have commended to all earnest students the problem of finding what "uniform and ordered movements" would account for the motions of the planets.

It is a matter of common experience that when an object is performing two distinct motions at once, its actual path in space may be quite complicated, even though each of the two motions is exceedingly simple. If I ride my bicycle along a straight road, the motion of my foot round and round at the end of the pedal-crank is very simple, and so is the motion of the bicycle along the road, and yet my foot moves through space in a very complicated path. The early astronomers tried time after time to explain the complicated paths of the planets across the sky in a similar way.

The first attempt was made in the fourth century before Christ, by Eudoxus of Cnidos (408–355 B.C.). He tried to explain the planetary motions by systems of wheels within wheels—or rather spheres within spheres. These spheres all had the same centre, the earth, but each was pivoted inside the one next outside it, and the spheres all turned in different directions. Each moving object had its own system of spheres, and was supposed to be itself attached to the outermost sphere of the system. Eudoxus found he needed three spheres each for the sun and moon, and four for each of the five planets—twenty-six spheres in all. At a later date Callippus (about 370–300 B.C.) found that even this elaborate system failed to explain the phenomena completely, and added seven more spheres, making thirty-three in all.

The scheme was getting very complicated, but a return to simplicity—and a great step towards the truth—was made almost at the same time by Heraclides of Pontus, whom we have already mentioned as having discovered the rotation of the earth (p. 3). He saw that no complicated systems of wheels or spheres were needed to explain the motions of Venus and Mercury; it was only necessary to suppose that these planets did not revolve around the earth at all, but around the sun like satellites. Then Aristarchus of Samos made an immense step forward by proposing that the earth also revolved around the sun. To quote the description of Archimedes (287–212 B.C.): "Aristarchus of Samos brought out a book consisting of certain hypotheses, in which the premises lead to the conclusion that the universe is many times greater than that now so called. His hypotheses are that the fixed stars and the sun remain motionless, that the earth revolves about the sun in the circumference of a circle, the sun lying in the middle of the orbit, and that the sphere of the fixed stars, situated about the same centre as the sun, is so great that the circle in which he supposes the earth to revolve bears the same proportion to the distance of the fixed stars as the centre of the sphere bears to its surface"

Such views as these were not popular in the days of ancient Greece—or in any other days. Man has never liked being told that his home in space is not the hub of the universe, as he has so often fondly imagined, but a mere speck circling round another speck, on so minute a scale that the whole is only like a point in the vast sphere of the universe. And so we read in Plutarch how Cleanthes thought that Aristarchus ought to be indicted for the impiety of putting into motion the Hearth of the Universe—i.e. the earth. Aristarchus had told men a truth which they found unpalatable, but they easily found other astronomers who were only too ready to tell them everything that they wanted.

Throughout nearly two thousand years after Aristarchus, the most favoured explanation of the motion of the planets was one of cycles and epicycles—not the wheels within wheels of Eudoxus, but rather wheels upon wheels. Heraclides had supposed that Mercury and Venus wheeled round the sun while the sun itself wheeled round the earth. It was soon found that an extension of this scheme would explain the motion of all the astronomical bodies. Thus the earth was still made the centre of the universe in spite of Aristarchus; A wheeled round the earth, B wheeled round A, and C around B, and so on—like the house that Jack built—until a point on the rim of the last wheel was found to reproduce exactly the observed motion of a planet.

About A.D. 150 Ptolemy of Alexandria put this theory of cycles and epicycles in a form which held almost unchallenged sway throughout the intellectual darkness of the Middle Ages. Here and there a doubter may have been found to express his doubts, but no serious challenge occurred until A.D. 1543, when the Polish monk Copernicus proposed replacing the whole system of Ptolemy by one very like that which Aristarchus of Samos had propounded eighteen hundred years earlier. In brief, he supposed that the sun stood still, while the earth and the other five planets all revolved around it. Two-thirds of a century later, the telescope of Galileo established the truth of his views.

Such views proved to be no more popular in mediaeval Europe than they had been in ancient Greece, and Copernicus had, with great worldly prudence, withheld the publication of his book until he lay on his death-bed; Galileo, less endowed with prudence of this particular kind, boldly proclaimed what he believed to be the truth and found himself in frequent trouble with the ecclesiastical authorities throughout the rest of his life.

As Aristarchus and Copernicus had in effect proclaimed, the planets only appear to move irregularly because we on earth view the scene from a non-central position; we are like the spectators at a theatre who cannot see the play in its proper setting because they are too far to the right or left of the stage. The sun provides the proper central position from which to view the planetary motions, and an observer who established himself on the sun would see each planet repeating the same almost circular path over and over again with the utmost regularity. He would also see that the paths of the planets were all very nearly in the same plane, a plane which is inclined at a small angle of about 7 degrees to the sun's equator.

Just as such an observer, from his position on the sun, would see our home, the earth, moving round him in a circular path across the sky, so from our position on earth we see his home, the sun, moving in a circular path across the sky. This apparent path of the sun across the sky is called the "ecliptic", and, as all the other planets move nearly in the same plane as the earth, we see these also moving across the sky in almost the same path as the sun. The three nearest planets—Venus, Mars and Mercury—may at times be as much as 9, 7 and 5 degrees respectively away from it, but none of the other five planets ever go as much as 3 degrees away. Thus the paths of the sun and planets all lie within a quite narrow track across the sky. This narrow track was known to the ancient Egyptians and Babylonians, and also, probably through the Babylonians, to the ancient Greeks. It is called the "Zodiac".

These early races of course regarded the stars merely as points of light, but they could hardly help noticing that these points of light fell rather naturally into the groups which we call "constellations". They named these after animals, heroes of legend, or familiar objects—sometimes from a supposed resemblance which was often rather fanciful, but more often for no apparent reason at all. The Babylonians divided the Zodiac into twelve equal parts, and placed one constellation in each. All of these were originally named after animals, and all but one still are. The word Zodiac means "animal circle", and the twelve constellations were originally supposed to be the houses of animals which the sun visited in turn, one each month, as it moved across the sky. For astronomical reasons, it is usual to start the list with the month of April, or, more precisely, with the spring equinox. We can remember the twelve constellations in their proper order by a jingle written by Dr Watts, the hymn writer:

> The Ram, the Bull, the Heavenly Twins,
> And next the Crab, the Lion shines,
>   The Virgin and the Scales,
> The Scorpion, Archer, and He-Goat,
> The Man that holds the watering-pot,
>   The Fish, with shining tails.

The Greeks and Egyptians had very similar names for many of the constellations of the Zodiac, but the Chinese Zodiac is named after twelve quite different animals. In place of our Ram, Bull, Twins and Crab, they have Dog, Cock, Ape, Ram, and so on.

The remainder of the sky has also been divided into constellations, some of which are mentioned by very ancient writers. Orion and the Great Bear are mentioned both in Homer and in the Book of Job, while the Little Bear was described by Thales in the seventh century before Christ. Many of the constellations also are common to many languages and peoples. The Orion constellation, for instance, is often associated with a hunter or hero, and the Taurus constellation with a fierce animal.

All the constellations which could be seen from ancient Greece were drawn on a globe by the astronomer Eudoxus, a pupil of Plato, in the fourth century before Christ, and subsequently described in verse by Aratus. Most of them are associated in some way or other with the legends or fairy tales of long ago—either of ancient Greece or of some still earlier civilisation. Thus we read of Helice and Cynosura, the Great Bear and the Little Bear, the latter being a hunter who was changed into a bear so that he should not kill his mother, whom Juno had already changed into a bear out of jealousy; or again of Hercules (whom Aratus describes merely as "The kneeling man") and the dragon; or—best story of all, a real thriller—of Perseus arriving in the nick of time to rescue Andromeda who was chained to a rock in the sea while Cetus, the sea-monster, was coming to devour her. He made Cetus look at the Medusa's head, which turned everyone to stone who saw it, but escaped this fate himself by looking at it in a mirror. I have heard it suggested that our more modern nursery rhyme, which describes the cow jumping over the moon, was inspired by the sight of the moon moving through, or perhaps under, the constellation Taurus. The little dog who laughed to see such fun would no doubt be Canis Minor, the next constellation. There is also a dish (Crater) in the sky to run away with the spoon.

The Greeks were not great travellers, so that there were parts of the sky south of the equator which they did not see at all, and so could not divide into constellations. It was a pity, for the moderns who named the constellations in this part of the sky did not always maintain the dignity and simplicity of the older names. We find such constellations appearing as the Printer's Workshop, the Painter's Easel, the Engraver's Pen, the Chemical Furnace, and, even more ridiculous, the Honours of Frederick, the Harp of the Georges, the Oak-tree of Charles I. Even more recently a French astronomer, Lalande, tried to insert a cat into heaven. He wrote: "I love cats; I adore cats; I may be pardoned for placing one in the sky after sixty years of arduous labours" But it has since disappeared, perhaps because it did not enjoy the society of its neighbours, Canis Major, Canis Minor, and Canes Venatici.

As Greece lies about 40 degrees north of the equator, the parts of the sky which the ancient Greeks could not see would be those which lay within 40 degrees of the South Pole. We might then reasonably expect that all the constellations with modern names would lie inside a circle 40 degrees in radius, having the South Pole as centre.

Broadly speaking, we find that they all lie within a circle of 40 degrees radius, but its centre is not the South Pole. The reason for this is both interesting and informative.

The earth spins in space like a spinning top, but its axis does not always point in the same direction. The bulge round the earth's equator is continually being pulled by the sun's gravitational pull, and as this pull twists the earth's axis round in space, the earth top wobbles, rather as the ordinary schoolboy's top does when it is "dying".

It is found that the earth's axis wobbles round in a complete small circle once every 26,000 years. At the present moment the axis points to the tip of the tail of the Little Bear, but 4000 years ago it pointed to the Bear's left ear, and 5000 years ago to the tip of its nose. And 13,000 years ago the whole Little

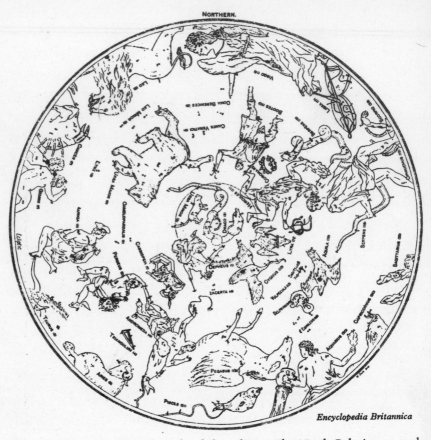

Encyclopedia Britannica

Fig. 41 *a*. The constellations north of the ecliptic. The North Pole is not at the centre of the figure, but is approximately where the small (dotted) circle cuts across the tail of the Little Bear. As the earth wobbles about in space, the north pole of the earth's axis moves round and round this small circle, at the rate of one revolution every 26,000 years.

Fig. 41 *b*. The constellations south of the ecliptic. The constellations of the Zodiac
(see p. 89) lie along the circumference of either this or of fig. 41 *a*, opposite.

Bear was well down in the northern sky, while the earth's axis pointed near Vega, which is now well down in the sky. Because the spinning top on which we live is rolling about in space, the inhabitants of Greece must have seen different parts of the sky at different epochs—just as, when we live on a rolling ship, we see different sights through the porthole of our cabin. This goes some way towards explaining why many southern constellations, such as the Centaur, have Greek names; those parts of the sky are not visible from Greece now, but they were 4000 years ago, when people believed in Centaurs.

The constellations which Aratus mentioned in his poem are not even those which the Greeks were able to see at the time of Aratus; they are, broadly speaking, those which had been visible from the latitude of Greece about 2500 years earlier, or about 2800 years before Christ. Thus it seems likely that Aratus merely described constellations which had been named in the first instance by people who resided in the same latitude as Greece, at the period of about 2800 B.C. This points very strongly to the Babylonians, especially as there is other evidence that some at least of the principal constellations had been known to the Babylonians at an even earlier date.

The constellations owe their familiar outlines, and sometimes their names as well, to the brightest of their stars, but they also contain a great number of fainter stars, many of which we can only just see with our unaided eyes, and a still greater number which cannot be seen at all without a telescope.

With average eyesight and good conditions, the human eye

can just see the light of a single candle at about 6 miles distance. If we dim the light, or move to a greater distance than 6 miles from it, we shall not see a fainter light, but no light at all. Thus the light we receive from a single candle 6 miles away forms what we may call the "threshold of vision".

Let us take the amount of light we receive from a single candle 6 miles away as our unit of brightness, so that the faintest stars we can see with our unaided eyes have a brightness of exactly one unit. On this scale the star which looks brightest of all, Sirius, is found to have a brightness of 1080 units—in other words, it looks as bright as a 1080 candle-power lamp would at a distance of 6 miles—while the second brightest, Canopus, far down in the southern sky, has only 550 units. These two stars are quite out-standing; their nearest competitors are a succession of stars with about 200 units of brightness each—Vega with 220, Capella with 205, Arcturus with 200, α Centauri and Procyon with 180 each, and so on. There are only about twenty stars in the whole sky which shine with 100 units of brightness or more. After these come about 200 more which shine with between 100 and 10 units of brightness, and then about 4500 more shining with between 10 and 1 units. This completes the list of stars that we can see with average unaided eyesight—the stars that have more than one unit of brightness. We see that there are only about 4720 in the whole sky—not only in the part we can see, but in the part below the horizon as well. Not more than about half of this number will be above the horizon at any one moment, and even of these a fair proportion are likely to be hidden by the mist or clouds near the horizon. On the whole, we shall be lucky if we see as many as 2000 at any one moment with average eyesight, although naturally people with specially good eyesight may expect to see more.

Most people find it hard to believe that the number is so small; if they are asked to guess how many stars they can see, they usually put the number far too high—except, of course, those who have read books on astronomy, and so know the answer already.

There is another guessing game in which the victim is invited to guess the greatest number of threepenny pieces that can be laid flat on a half-crown without overlapping. The answer is one, but most people are sure they can put two on—until they have tried. Here is a similar question: How many visible stars does the full moon conceal? In other words, if the moon suddenly became transparent, so that we could see through it, how many stars should we be likely to see lying behind it with our unaided eyes? The answer is none at all, which again most people find hard to believe.

The sun and moon are so bright that most people over-estimate their sizes enormously. Each of them takes a whole day to move round the sky, and we can easily verify that each takes only about 2 minutes to cross the length of its own diameter—in other words, the whole sun or moon moves past any fixed point in 2 minutes. This shews that it would take 720 suns or moons placed in contact side by side to make a circle round the sky. From this we can calculate that if we had to wallpaper the whole

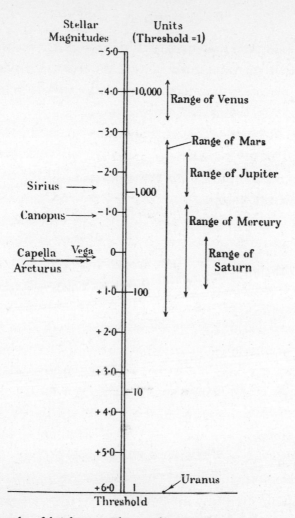

Fig. 42. The scale of brightness. The numbers on the right represent multiples of our unit of brightness, the threshold of vision being unity. The numbers on the left represent "stellar magnitudes", by which the astronomer measures brightness in a more technical manner. The relation between the two measures is obtained by comparing numbers on the two sides of the central line.

The brightnesses of a few stars are shewn on the left-hand side of the diagram, and those of the planets on the right.

sky with suns and moons, we should need about 200,000 of either.
This is rather more than forty-two for each visible star, so that
there is a chance of less than one in forty of there being a visible
star behind the moon.

As soon as we bring telescopic power to our aid, the number of
stars we can see naturally increases by leaps and bounds. The
primary function of a telescope is to collect the waves of light
which fall on a large area—the object glass or mirror of the
telescope. It then throws these waves into our eyes much as an
ear trumpet collects sound waves and throws them into our
ears. The diameter of the human eye is only a fifth of an inch, so
that a telescope of 1 inch diameter will collect twenty-five times
as much light as an unaided eye, and enables us to see stars whose
brightness is anything above a twenty-fifth of a unit. There are
about 225,000 such stars, so that even a 1-inch telescope will shew
us 220,000 stars more than we can see without it—nearly fifty
new stars for every old one. The great 100-inch telescope at
Mount Wilson will shew us stars of only about a three-millionth
part of a unit, the total number of these being perhaps 1500
million. Yet even this vast number, as we shall see later, is only
about one per cent. of the total number of stars.

In spite of the immense number of stars, their total light, as
we know, is not overpowering. Indeed the total light we receive
from all the stars in the sky other than the sun is only about
100,000 units—rather less than a hundred-millionth part of the
light of the sun. It is equal to the light of a single candle 100
feet away.

The stars shine by their own light, but the planets only because they are lighted up by the sun. Naturally, then, a planet sends out enormously less light than a star, but its nearness may often make up for the feebleness of its light. Indeed it occasionally more than makes up, so that a planet may often appear the brightest object in the whole sky.

The inexperienced observer will not always be able to distinguish planets from stars by a mere superficial glance at the sky, although it may help him to remember that a planet can never wander by more than a very short distance from the ecliptic, the central line of the Zodiac. The brightest planets, Venus, Mars and Jupiter, can frequently be identified from their mere brightness (see fig. 42, p. 97). Venus, when it can be seen at all, is always the brightest object in the sky, but Mars and Jupiter may be either brighter or fainter than the brightest star, Sirius.

Most of the stars shine with a steady light, and as they stay at the same distance from us, their brightness does not vary. The brightness of the planets, on the other hand, varies for two reasons. As they move round the sun, their distance from us continually varies, as does also the fraction of their surface which we see illuminated. These changes are most marked in the case of our nearest neighbour Venus, its illuminated surface and apparent diameter varying in the way shewn in fig. 43 (p. 100). It is clear that Venus cannot look brightest when it is nearest to us, because then we only see a thin crescent of it illuminated—like the new moon; neither does it appear brightest when its full

surface is illuminated, because it is then so far away from us that
its surface looks very small. It is brightest when it is in an intermediate position in which its appearance is as shewn in fig. 43 (*c*).
It then shines with 13,000 units of brightness, and so looks twelve
times as bright as Sirius. When Mars and Jupiter are at their

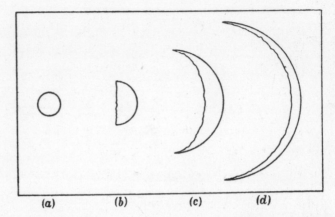

(a)   (b)   (c)   (d)

Fig. 43. *The phases of Venus:* (*a*) when at its greatest distance from the earth—
a circle 9½ seconds in diameter; (*b*) when farthest from the sun in the sky—a semicircle 18 seconds in diameter; (*c*) when its brilliancy is greatest—a crescent 40 seconds
in diameter; (*d*) when of the largest diameter at which it can be seen—a crescent
62 seconds in diameter.

As the planet passes even nearer to the sun, its diameter further increases to 63 or
64 seconds, but it is then so much immersed in the sun's glare as to be invisible.

brightest, they shine with 3300 and 2500 units respectively,
so that they can both be considerably brighter than Sirius, but
the other planets cannot rival the brightest stars, Mercury having
only 760 units at its best, and Saturn only 360 units.

The full moon has a brightness of 26 million units, and so is
two thousand times as bright as Venus at its best, while the sun,

in the full light of day, shines with 12,300,000,000,000 units, and so is nearly half a million times as bright as the full moon.

It may seem surprising that such lights as these do not blind us, when our eyes are so sensitive that they can see as little as a single unit of light. Actually our salvation lies in the fact that the effect on our eyes does not depend so much on the number of units of brightness, as on the number of digits in this number—or, more strictly, on what the mathematician calls the logarithm of the number. The effect on our eyes is not given by

Sun 12,300,000,000,000; Venus 13,000; Sirius 1080; Faintest star 1;

but rather by

Sun 14; Venus 5; Sirius 4; Faintest star 1;

and now the sun does not look so overpowering.

Although the positions and brightnesses of the planets are continually changing, the sky looks much alike night after night, so that its changes usually cause no surprise. Yet occasionally far more exciting apparitions are seen than the orderly procession of sun, moon, planets and stars. Foremost among these less usual sights are comets and shooting-stars. To the untutored savage comets must look like stars which have gone crazy, and rush about the heavens with their hair streaming out behind; indeed, early writers used to refer to all comets indiscriminately as "the hairy star", as though there could be but one such remarkable object in the sky. Shooting-stars look—not only to the savage but to everyone else as well—very like stars which have lost their foothold in heaven and have fallen to earth. We shall discuss the physical constitution of these objects later; at present we are only concerned with their appearance and movements in the sky.

Comets move round the sun like the planets, but in very different paths. A planet moves nearly in a circle, and so stays always at about the same distance from the sun, but a comet usually moves in a very elongated orbit, and its striking appearance is usually restricted to the few weeks or months in which it is nearest to the sun. During this time the radiation of the sun causes the comet to eject a long tail, which invariably points away from the sun. Typical examples of comets are shewn in figs. 38 and 39 (facing p. 77).

Before their true nature was understood, comets were regarded as portents of evil, and, oddly enough, many of the most conspicuous appearances of comets seem to have coincided with, or perhaps just anticipated, important events in history. Homer (*Iliad*, 19) writes of:

> The red star, that from his flaming hair,
> Shakes down diseases, pestilence, and war.

It was not until Newton had explained the motions of comets, shewing that they obeyed the same laws of motion, and were guided by the same gravitational pull, as the planets, that they ceased to be regarded in this sinister light.

Shooting-stars may make even more sensational displays in the sky. These often come singly, but often also in showers. Occasionally on looking up on a clear night we may see dozens of these, sometimes myriads, darting through the sky like huge

PLATE XVII

W. T. Gordon

Fig. 44. The huge Hoba meteorite, estimated to weigh 60 tons.

W. T. Gordon

Fig. 45. A pile of iron meteorites collected in the
Gibeon district of south-west Africa.

PLATE XVIII

Royal Geographical Society

Fig. 46. Meteor Crater near Cañon Diablo, Arizona. The view is an air photograph, taken from the north-west, and looking almost exactly along the direction in which the meteor is believed to have been moving when it struck the earth.

Royal Geographical Society

Fig. 47. The aerial photograph shewn in fig. 46 does not convey an adequate idea of the immense size of the Meteor Crater. Fig. 47 shews the highest point on its rim, Barringer Point, with a man on horseback at the summit to give an indication of the scale.

fireflies. The early Chinese and Japanese seem to have been greatly affected by shooting-stars and kept careful records in which they are described as falling like snow, or heavy rain, or leaves from the trees in autumn. Here is a description of a Korean meteor shower in A.D. 1519, which has been unearthed by Y. Iba of the Kobe Observatory:

Some shooting through the sky like arrows gone astray, some rampantly ascending like red dragons, some bursting like fire-balls, some curling like bended bows, while others looked like bifurcated bodkins, and transformed themselves into many motley shapes and appearances.

Actually these objects have no right to be described as stars at all. They are not immense bodies, millions of miles away in space, but tiny fragments of hard rocky or metallic substance, most of them so small that we could hold hundreds, perhaps even thousands, in one hand. And they are quite near home—in our own atmosphere, in fact.

Tiny pellets of hard material are continually travelling through outer space; millions of them strike the earth's atmosphere every day, travelling at hundreds of times the speed of a rifle bullet. When they first enter the atmosphere, the friction of the air causes them to become first hot, then very hot, then red hot, and finally white hot; it is at this stage that they look like stars. They become so hot that, after a brief life of only a few seconds' duration, they disintegrate into gas and dust and disappear from sight.

It may seem surprising that so small an object as a shooting-star can look as bright as a real star such as Sirius or Arcturus, but we must remember two things. First, the shooting-star is much nearer—it is playing to a much smaller audience, only a few miles of earth instead of millions of millions of miles in space. Second, it shines for a far smaller time—only a few seconds, whereas the real stars shine for thousands of millions of years at least.

Of the same nature as these small bodies are the larger bodies called meteors. When these dash through the air, they often appear far brighter than any star, and may light up the whole landscape; we then describe them as fire-balls. Sometimes their outer surfaces become so hot that they crack and burst—just as a cold glass may burst if hot water is suddenly poured over its surface—and they often make loud, and even terrifying, reports as they do so. For instance, a Japanese record of date A.D. 1533 tells us that "stars dazzlingly scintillated all over the sky, and shot down to the land and sea, breaking into pieces like stones and giving out tremendous clangours, so that there were fears lest the earth might be knocked about, and the Kingdom decay, and the whole populace lamented awfully in dismay".

Such displays were frequently regarded as evidence of the displeasure of the gods, and often resulted in kings and nations altering their ways of living. Livy tells how a fall of meteors in 650 B.C. led to a nine days' solemn festival in the hope of propitiating the angry gods, and the Japanese records tell of many occasions on which the whole nation set about mending its ways after the supposed admonition by a fall of meteors. The diary of Columbus tells us how, even after his sailors had seen tropical birds, and so must have known they were near the long looked-for land, "they saw a meteor fall from heaven, which made them very sad".

The little shooting-stars invariably dissolve into vapour before they reach the earth, but generally speaking the larger meteors do not; they usually fall to earth, and are then described as meteorites. The smaller may lie about in deserts or in farmlands until they are discovered and removed to museums or to laboratories for analysis. The majority prove to be mere stones or masses of crystalline rock, but a few consist of iron, sometimes mixed with rock or stone and sometimes with nickel and cobalt. Figs. 44 and 45 on Plate XVII (facing p. 102) shew the largest of known meteorites and a pile of smaller iron meteorites.

Even larger meteorites may bury themselves in the earth, and often make great holes or craters where they fall. Plate XVIII (facing p. 103) shews two views of a large hole in the earth in Arizona, which is known as the "Meteor Crater"; it is oval in shape, with a circumference of 3 miles, and a depth of 570 feet. It is conjectured that this must have been formed by the fall of a huge meteor about 500 feet across, and weighing perhaps 14,000,000 tons. Plate XIX (facing p. 106) shews views of a group of similar but smaller craters, known as the Henbury Craters, in Central Australia; the largest has dimensions of about 220 yards by 120 yards, and is about 50 feet deep. We can hardly doubt that these craters were formed by the fall of meteors, since masses of meteoric iron have been found in all of them.

These craters were made by meteors which fell in pre-historic times, so that we know nothing of the circumstances of their falling. But one which fell in Siberia in 1908 shewed how much havoc a meteor can make when it buries itself in the earth, and then explodes. Trees were singed and blown down for distances of more than 30 miles from the centre—thousands of square miles devastated by the fall of a single meteor. It is difficult even to imagine what the surrounding country must have looked like after the fall of far greater meteors in Arizona and Central Australia.

PLATE XIX

A. R. Alderman

Fig. 48. The Henbury Craters, Central Australia. General
view of the main crater, taken from the air.

A. R. Alderman

Fig. 49. Another view shewing the interior of the same crater.

PLATE XX

NORTH

SOUTH   *Puiseux, Paris Observatory*

Fig. 50. The moon 12½ days old, photographed with a 24-inch telescope. Parts of the moon's surface are shewn in greater detail on Plates XXI–XXIV below.

CHAPTER IV

THE MOON

We know that the moon always looks about the same size in the sky and from this we can conclude that it is always at about the same distance from the earth. And we can measure the distance in the same way as we measure the distance of an inaccessible mountain peak, or the height of an aeroplane.

When an aeroplane is up in the air, people who are standing at different points must look in different directions to see it. If it is directly overhead for one man, it will not be directly overhead for another man a mile away, and its height can be calculated simply by noticing how far its position appears to be out of the vertical for the second man. Using this method, astronomers find that the distance of the moon varies between the limits of 221,462 miles and 252,710 miles, the average distance being 238,857 miles. Thus, in round numbers, we may think of the moon as being a quarter of a million miles away.

At such a distance, we can hardly expect to see much detail with our unaided eyes. Indeed, as we watch the moon sailing through the night sky, we can detect nothing on its surface beyond a variety of light and dark patches, which, with a bit of imagination, we can make into the man in the moon with his bundle of sticks, or an old woman reading a book, or—as the Chinese prefer to think—a jumping hare. Naturally no sane people have ever thought these creatures actually resided in the moon, but in past ages many people thought that the moon was a huge mirror which merely reflected the features of the earth, so that what appeared to be light and dark patches on its surface were simply the reflections of our own lands and seas; others thought that the dark patches were objects suspended in space between ourselves and the moon. We have seen how Anaxagoras, who first explained the phases and eclipses of the moon (p. 80), declared that "the moon is of an earthy nature, having plains and ravines on it".

As soon as we look at the moon through a telescope, or even through a pair of field-glasses, the mystery of its structure is solved, as Galileo found when he turned his newly-made telescope onto it in 1609. He announced at once that the moon was a world like our own, having its own seas and mountains. For a long time the dark patches were believed to be seas of real water, and they were named accordingly. For instance, the three largest "seas" in the upper half of Plate XX (facing p. 107) are named in succession, running from left to right:

"Mare Imbrium"—The Sea of Showers.
"Mare Serenitatis"—The Sea of Serenity.
"Mare Tranquillitatis"—The Sea of Tranquillity.

Yet we know now that these cannot be seas of real water, since we never see the glitter of sunshine reflected from them as we so often do from a distant lake in a landscape on earth. As the moon moves and turns about in space, the sun's rays fall on it from all directions in succession, but a shining reflection of the sun has never yet been seen, and we now believe that the so-called seas are really dry deserts. We can understand why Tranquillity and Serenity were chosen as appropriate names for the supposed lunar oceans—nothing was ever seen to happen there. The Sea of Showers was a less appropriate choice—in fact a mere effort of imagination; perhaps the early astronomers felt the need for variety.

Not only is there no water on the moon, but there is also no air or atmosphere of any kind, unless in quite inappreciable amount. This is shewn very clearly when the moon eclipses the sun by passing in front of it. Just at the end of the eclipse a moment comes, the last moment of darkness, when the vividly bright sun is just about to emerge from behind the dark moon—the sun is, so to speak, about to rise from behind the lunar mountains. Now if the moon possessed any atmosphere at all, the sun's coming would be heralded by tints of dawn, just as it is when the sun rises behind mountains on earth. But in the actual occurrence nothing is seen until the sun bursts forth in full brilliance.

A large modern telescope enables us to see a great deal of detail in the scenery of the moon, and to photograph even more. For it can readily be transformed into a huge camera, and the driving clock of the telescope will turn this to follow any part of the moon, or any other object in the sky we please, so that a photographic plate can be exposed for any length of time without fear of blurring.

Plate XX (facing p. 107) shews the moon, when nearly full, photographed through the 24-inch telescope of the Paris Observatory. To make this look the same size as the actual moon in the sky, we must set the picture up at a distance of 50 feet from where we stand. If we now illuminate the picture, we shall be able to pick out the man in the moon, the old woman, the hare, and so forth. Then if we walk towards the picture, we shall see all these imaginary inhabitants gradually dissolving into plains and mountain ranges.

The four photographs shewn in Plates XXI–XXIV were taken with a still larger telescope—the great 100-inch telescope at Mount Wilson—and shew various details of lunar scenery.

We know how objects on earth cast very long shadows at sunrise and sunset, but shorter shadows when the sun is high up in the sky. It is the same, of course, on the moon, and the heights of the lunar mountains can be estimated from the lengths of the shadows they cast at various times of the lunar day. Although the moon has only a quarter of the diameter of the earth, its mountains are found to be rather higher on the average than those of the earth, a great number being more than 15,000 feet in height, while many are far more precipitous.

So far we have merely been looking at the moon from a distance. Let us now charter a rocket to take us there, so that we can actually walk on its surface.

Our rocket must be shot off at a high speed—6·93 miles a second at least—for if it starts at any lesser speed it will merely fall back to earth, like the shot from an ordinary gun. If it starts with a speed of exactly 6·93 miles a second, it will just get clear of the earth's gravitational pull, but after it has got clear, it will have no appreciable speed left to carry us on our

PLATE XXI

Mt Wilson Observatory

Fig. 51. A part of the northern half of the moon, which can easily be identified on Plate XX. The big "sea" which occupies the centre of the plate is the Mare Imbrium; the range of mountains which bounds it to the south-east is the Apennines. At the southern extremity of this is the big and deep crater named Eratosthenes, while still lower down and to the left is the even larger crater Copernicus which is shewn on a larger scale on Plate XXIV (facing p. 113).

PLATE XXII

Mt Wilson Observatory

Fig. 52. A part of the southern half of the moon. The "sea" which is about half an inch from the left-hand edge will readily be identified with the most southerly sea on Plate XX; it is the Mare Humorum. To the right of it lies the larger Mare Nubium.

journey. Let us start it with a speed of 7 miles a second, then it will still have a speed of 1 mile a second left after it has got clear of the earth's pull, and we shall reach the moon in a little over 2 days.

We only take a few seconds to pass through the earth's atmosphere, which is relatively hardly thicker than the thin skin of a plum or a peach. As we pass through this, we gradually leave beneath us all the particles of air, dust, water vapour and so on, which scatter the sun's light and make the sky look blue. As the number of these particles decreases, we see the sky assuming in turn the colours already described (p. 73)—blue, dark blue, dark violet and black-grey. Finally we leave the earth's atmosphere beneath us and see the sky become jet black, except for the sun, moon and stars. These look brighter than they did from the earth, and also bluer because none of the blue light has been subtracted from them to make a blue sky. And the stars no longer twinkle at us as they did on earth because there is no atmosphere to disturb the even flow of their light. They seem now to stab our eyes with sharp steely needles of light. If we look back at our earth, we shall see about half of its surface shrouded in mists, clouds and showers. But in front, the whole surface of the moon shines out perfectly clear; it has no atmosphere to scatter the sun's light, and no fogs and rains to obscure the illumination of its surface.

Naturally this clearness persists after we have arrived on the moon's surface, and far exceeds anything we have ever experienced on earth. We have seen how our atmosphere is the

cause of the soft tones that add so much to a terrestrial landscape—
the oranges and reds of sunrise and sunset, the purples and greens
of twilight, the blue sky of full day, the purple haze of the distance. Here on the moon there is no atmosphere to break up
the sun's rays into their different colours and distribute them—
the blue to the sky, the red to the dawn, and so on. There are only
two colours—sunshine and shadow, white and black; everything
in the sunshine is white, everything else black. We feel as though
we were in a cinema studio lighted only by one terribly powerful
light—the sun. A valley stays utterly dark until the moment
when the sun rises over the surrounding mountains; then full
day comes, with all the suddenness of turning on an electric
light.

It is clear that if we want to step out of our rocket and walk
about on the moon, we must bring our own air with us; we shall
need an oxygen apparatus, such as the climbers on Mount
Everest had. We may perhaps think that the weight of this will
make walking or climbing very arduous, but as soon as we set
foot on the soil of the moon, we shall find that the contrary is the
case. The moon contains less than an eightieth part of the substance of the earth, and so exerts a gravitational pull which is
much smaller than the earth's—in fact it is only about a sixth as
great. For this reason, we find we can carry extraordinary
weights without fatigue, and as our bodies seem to weigh almost
nothing, we can jump to great heights. We feel so athletic that
we may even try to break our own jumping records. It ought
not to be difficult to break both our own and everybody else's;

PLATE XXIII

Mt Wilson Observatory

Fig. 53. This is part of the edge of the moon which will readily be identified rather more than half-way down on Plate XX. The "sea" at the left-hand edge of the plate is the Mare Nectaris; to the right of this is the Mare Foecunditatis, and above it a deep bay of the Mare Tranquillitatis.

PLATE XXIV

Mt Wilson Observatory

Fig. 54. Detail of the crater Copernicus which is 46 miles in diameter. It is easily found at the bottom edge of Plate XXI. Fig. 58 (facing p. 116) may help us visualise how the crater would appear to a traveller on the moon.

a good high jumper ought to jump about 36 feet, and the long jump of a fair athlete ought to be at least 120 feet. If we feel inspired to play cricket, the ball will simply soar off our bat, so that if it is not to be entirely a batsman's game, the pitch and field must each be six times the size they are on earth. Unfortunately, all this will make the game six times as slow as on earth, and perhaps cricket, played six times as slowly as on earth, would not be much of a game after all.

If we fire a gun, our shot will travel a terrific distance before falling back to earth—or rather to moon. We remember the big guns which fired shells nearly eighty miles in the Great War; if similar guns were mounted on the moon, their projectiles would go right off into space and never return. We shall not want to start setting big guns up on the moon, but we can produce the same effect with something much simpler—a breath of air from our breathing apparatus.

For we know that ordinary air consists of tiny particles, called molecules, which are incessantly jumping about—some quite slowly, the majority at about the speed of a rifle bullet, and a few at far higher speeds. Some move faster than any projectile which has ever been fired from a gun.

We had to start our rocket from earth with a speed of about 7 miles a second, in order that it might overcome the earth's gravitational pull; with any lower speed it would have merely fallen back to earth like a cricket ball. And a projectile of any other kind needs precisely the same speed if it is to get clear of the earth. Now it is only at very rare intervals that molecules of air attain a speed of 7 miles a second, so that they seldom jump right off the earth into space—this is why the earth retains its atmosphere. On the other hand, a projectile only needs a speed of 1½ miles a second to jump entirely clear of the moon, and molecules of ordinary air frequently attain speeds as high as this. We see at once that an atmosphere of air could not survive on the moon for long, since each molecule would jump off into space the moment it attained this critical speed of 1½ miles a second.

Just because there is no atmosphere on the moon there can be no seas, rivers or water of any kind. We are accustomed to think of water as a liquid which does not boil away until it reaches a temperature of 212 degrees, but if ever we picnic high up on a mountain, we find out our mistake; we soon discover that water boils more easily and at a lower temperature there than on the plain below. The reason is that there is less weight of air to keep the molecules of the liquid pressed down, and so prevent them flying off by evaporation. If there were no air-pressure at all, the water would evaporate no matter how low its temperature, and this is precisely what would happen on the moon. Clearly then we shall find no water on the moon; we must take drinking water with us, and it will not be well to pour it out and leave it standing; if we do it will have disappeared by the time we want to drink it—its molecules will have danced off, one by one, into space.

Knowing that there is neither air nor water on the moon, we shall hardly expect to find men or animals, trees or flowers. And

PLATE XXV

James Nasmyth

Fig. 55. Slanting across the lower half of the plate are the Lunar Apennines; above them is the large crater Archimedes. This scene is easily recognised on the right of the photograph shewn in Plate XXI.

PLATE XXVI

J. Nasmyth

Fig. 56. The large crater to the left is Plato, while the furrow to the right and slightly lower down is known as the "Valley of the Alps". Both are easily recognised in the upper right-hand part of the photograph shewn in Plate XXI.

J. Nasmyth

Fig. 57. The isolated mountain which can be seen to the south of the crater Plato, either in fig. 56 above or on Plate XXI, is known as Pico. It rises directly from the plain to a height of 8000 feet, and would probably look somewhat like this to a pedestrian walking on the moon.

in actual fact, the moon has been observed night after night and year after year for centuries, and no one has ever found any trace of forests, vegetation or life of any kind. No changes are detected beyond the alternations of light and of dark, of heat and or cold, as the sun rises and sets over the arid landscapes. The moon is a dead world—just a vast reflector poised in space, like a great mirror reflecting the sun's beams down onto us.

Let us now step out of our rocket, and survey the lunar scenery. I cannot shew you detailed pictures of what we shall see, but I can do the next best thing. About 50 years ago, the engineer James Nasmyth made calculations of the heights of a great number of the mountains in the moon, both large and small, and constructed a model to shew the results he had obtained. Fig. 55 on Plate XXV (facing p. 114) illustrates a small part of the model, which is easily recognised again in Plate XXI. Fig. 56 shews another region which also appears in Plate XXI. The small isolated mountain to the right is named Pico, and Nasmyth's drawing of this is reproduced in fig. 57. Figs. 58 and 59 on Plate XXVII (facing p. 116) are imaginative drawings of scenery of yet other kinds.

It is natural to wonder why the scenery of the moon is so different from that of the earth. Is the moon formed of different stuff from our earth, or was it formed out of similar stuff but in a different way, or can the whole difference be traced to a difference of physical conditions?

We have already seen how our terrestrial mountains, volcanoes, craters, etc., were formed. In brief, the earth started life as a ball of very hot gas, which shrank and cooled and then liquefied, so that it finally became rather like a sponge filled with drops of liquid and bubbles of gas. Then the sponge shrank still further, and the bubbles were squeezed out to form oceans and atmosphere. A solid crust formed, and as this too shrank, it wrinkled up to form mountain-ranges, such as our Himalayas and Alps. These may originally have been five or ten times as high as at present, but have been flattened and smoothed out by rain, snow and frost.

Now it seems probable that the lunar mountains also were formed in the first instance as wrinkles on the cooling moon. But the gases and water vapour which were expelled from the interior could not stay encircling the moon in the form of atmosphere and seas; their molecules would simply soar off into space. Thus the factors which have smoothed the outlines of our terrestrial mountains have been lacking on the moon from the very outset, and the lunar mountains have remained perfectly clear-cut in shape.

Yet something must have happened on the moon to give the mountains those sharply-cut outlines; they are broken rocks, and something must have broken them. Indeed, observers have occasionally seen what they have believed to be clouds of dust such as might result from falls of rock. As there is neither rain nor ice on the moon to break up its rocks, there must be something else at work. If we take a walk on the moon, we may soon find out what this is.

We have seen how hard fragments of rocky or metallic sub-

PLATE XXVII

Nasmyth and Carpenter, "The Moon"

Fig. 58. This does not attempt to represent any particular crater on the moon, but is typical of the kind of scenery which occurs in regions where the whole lunar surface is mottled with craters of all sizes.

Nasmyth and Carpenter, "The Moon"

Fig. 59. A typical landscape in a mountainous part of the moon, at a moment when the sun is just being eclipsed by the earth. The bright ring round the earth is produced by the earth's atmosphere; the band of light is the zodiacal light.

stance are continually bombarding the earth's atmosphere from outer space. The smaller fragments live a brief, but very vivid and brilliant, life as shooting-stars, and evaporate harmlessly into dust before they reach the surface of the earth, but we have seen that the larger fragments may do a great deal of damage.

Similar bodies must of course be continually bombarding the moon, but here they find no atmosphere to check their fall and to dissipate the majority into dust before they can do any harm. Big and little meteors alike strike the surface of the moon with exactly the motion with which they have previously been moving through space—like a rain of small bullets and big cannon-balls. I have read a great many stories of travels on the surface of the moon, but their writers all forgot that the explorers would be under a continuous hail of fire from these objects. The experience might not be altogether amusing. At a moderate computation, more than a million shooting-stars and meteors must strike the surface of the moon every day, their speeds averaging perhaps 30 miles a second, which is about 100 times the speed of a rifle bullet. And such a speed as this makes them formidable, even though their size may not. At a speed of 30 miles a second, a tiny pellet of matter has as much energy—and also as much capacity for doing damage—as a motor-car moving at 30 miles an hour, while a half-pound meteor has the same energy as the Royal Scot rushing along at 70 miles an hour; there would not be much left of a house if such a meteor fell on it. Clearly we terrestrials owe a good deal to our atmosphere for saving us from this sort of adventure. And we can see that the impact of meteors provides a quite sufficient explanation of any clouds of dust or falls of rock that may have been observed on the moon.

It has sometimes been conjectured that falls of meteors may also have produced the ring-shaped formations which form so conspicuous a feature of a lunar landscape. Such falls may have produced some of the smaller craters, but cannot have produced them all. For if they had all been produced in this way, we should expect them all to look rather like the meteor craters we find on earth. Actually they differ in many respects. The largest of the ring-formations on the moon are far larger than any meteor craters known on earth, and are also far more regular in shape. Meteor craters, being produced by the impact of meteors at all sorts of oblique angles, may shew any degree of elongation or irregularity, but nearly all the lunar craters are circular in shape, and this seems to shew that they were produced by something acting inside the moon rather than by something coming from outside. A great number have central elevations like the vent holes of terrestrial craters, and this suggests that we must attribute them to the same kind of volcanic action—in brief they seem to be the craters of extinct volcanoes.

This and other evidence makes it likely that the surface of the moon consists in the main of a mass of volcanoes and their out-pourings of lava and volcanic ash. On the earth, the combined influences of air, rain and frost disintegrate volcanic outpourings and transform them into soil, which ultimately sustains vegetation and life, but on the moon there is nothing to act on the products of volcanic eruption, and change their quality, so that these are likely to stand for ever as lava and ash.

It is possible to test this conjecture scientifically. In fig. 59 (facing p. 116) the artist has depicted an eclipse of the sun. Let us imagine such an event occurring during our visit to the moon. What shall we find?

We must expect our foremost sensation to be one of extreme cold. Those of us who have been present at an eclipse of the sun on earth know that it can get fairly cold when the sun's light is suddenly shut off, but the earth has warmth stored in its atmosphere and soil which saves us from being completely frozen. Here on the moon there is no atmosphere to store up warmth, and we cannot expect much from the soil, since volcanic ash is an exceedingly poor conductor of heat, being just about as poor as the asbestos which the plumber packs round hot-water pipes to prevent the heat escaping. Even if the moon's interior stays reasonably warm, its warmth will do us little good, since we shall be on the wrong side of a thick asbestos-like screen. Thus, when the sun's light and heat are shut off, we must expect the more than tropical heat of the full sun to give place to a cold more intense than anything known on earth.

And this is what happens. In a factory we may occasionally see a workman pointing an instrument, known as a pyrometer, towards some point of an oven or fire to discover its temperature. In precisely the same way, in an observatory an astronomer may occasionally point a telescope furnished with a thermocouple towards a star or a point on the moon's surface to discover its temperature. In this way the changes of temperature on the moon's surface can be followed through the various stages of an eclipse. The changes are found to be quite sensational, both in amount and rapidity. As the earth's shadow passes across the face of the moon, and covers any particular spot in darkness, the temperature at that spot may be observed to fall from about 200 degrees Fahrenheit to about 150 degrees below zero within a few minutes.

Such a rapid fall of temperature suggests at once that but little of the heat stored in the moon's interior comes up to its surface, which of course means that the moon's surface layers must be bad conductors of heat. Actual calculations shew that they must have just about the same feeble conducting capacity as volcanic ash.

Equally violent changes of temperature occur at the ordinary rising and setting of the sun, although of course not with the same startling rapidity. The temperature may be as low as 250 degrees below zero Fahrenheit before sunrise and may have risen to more than 200 degrees Fahrenheit, or about the ordinary temperature of boiling water, by the time the sun is directly overhead. Through all these changes, the blanket of volcanic ash keeps the interior of the moon at a fairly uniform temperature; if we dig only about an inch down we shall come to a steady temperature somewhere near to that of melting ice.

There are still other ways of discovering what the moon is made of. Judging by its appearance, people have guessed that it is made of all kinds of substances—ice, snow, rocks, silver and even green cheese. We cannot, however, tell what an object is made of by merely looking at it; a great many substances look alike that are really very different in structure, as, for example, diamonds and paste, or real pearls and false. We may do better if we look at our object in a number of different coloured lights in succession, for substances that look alike in one light will often look very different in another.

Now the spectroscope enables us to do just this; it sorts out the different colours of light and lets us use them separately. We can, so to speak, let each colour of light tell its own story—by itself and undisturbed by the others. In a police court, the magistrate insists on the witnesses speaking separately; the policeman describes the accident, and tells how he arrested the man who is charged with furious driving, the people who saw the accident say in turn what they saw, the owner of the car tells his story, and so on. It would be hard to arrive at the truth if they all shouted at once. Now each different colour of light that we receive from objects out in space has got its own story to tell of the nature of the objects from which it comes, and the spectroscope enables us to hear the different stories one at a time.

Although two different substances may conceivably look similar in a few isolated colours of light, they are sure to give different records for some colour or other. Thus, if two substances behave in the same way for all colours, and so give identical records throughout the whole range of the spectrum, we may be reasonably sure that they are of identical material.

In Plate XV (p. 76), we have already seen a landscape photographed in infra-red and in ordinary light. We notice at once that different kinds of objects give very different records, and this shews that they are made of different substances. When, however, the moon is photographed in the same way, all its various parts are found to give similar records, not merely in these two colours of light, but in all other colours of light as well. We conclude that all parts of the moon's surface are made of much the same substance. Further, if we can find any substance in the laboratory which again gives the same record in all colours of light, we shall suspect that it is of similar structure to the moon's surface.

There is a further and more technical method of study which leads to even more definite results. Light can not only be broken up into waves of different lengths (i.e. into different colours), but also into waves which vibrate in different directions. When we play on a violin string with a bow, the string vibrates in more or less the direction in which it is dragged by the bow, and this is parallel to the body of the instrument. But if we pluck the string by hand, it vibrates in the direction in which we pluck it, and this may be perpendicular to the former direction. The string gives out the same note as before, but its vibrations take place in a different direction.

Now when light is reflected by any substance, the direction of its vibrations is turned round in space, and the extent to which it is turned depends very largely on the nature of the substance. Thus we can to some extent identify substances by the extent to which they turn the plane of vibration of light.

Before we finally conclude that the moon is made of any particular substance, it is important to test whether the substance in question turns the plane of vibration about in the right way. The test is a very stringent one, for we can test not only for each colour of light, but also for each colour reflected at every possible angle.

Now volcanic dust or ash passes this test quite triumphantly, and indeed reproduces the actual record of the moon's surface in every respect, except for one small spot close to the crater Aristarchus. This looks black in ultra-violet light, but hardly shews in ordinary light. Its record can be matched by volcanic rock stained by a thin deposit of sulphur spread lightly over it —and sulphur is a common ingredient in the outpourings of volcanoes on earth.

Thus, taking all the evidence together, it seems very probable that the moon's surface consists of volcanic ash; it looks like volcanic ash not only in light of one colour but in lights of all colours; it rotates the plane of vibration of light in the same way as volcanic ash, not only for one colour but for all; it behaves like volcanic ash in its very low capacity for conducting heat; and, finally, it lies at the feet of what are almost certainly volcanoes.

CHAPTER V

THE PLANETS

There are nine planets circling round the sun, of which of course the earth is one. Of the other eight, five have been known from pre-historic times, while the remaining three—the three farthest from the sun—are comparatively recent discoveries.

The row of models exhibited in fig. 60 shew how greatly these nine planets differ in size. Those which are nearest to, and farthest away from, the sun are the smallest, while the middle members, Jupiter and Saturn, are the largest. Jupiter, the central member, is largest of all, with a diameter of nearly 90,000 miles, and a volume 1300 times that of the earth. Jupiter stands in the same proportion to the earth as a football to a marble, while on the same scale Mars would be hardly larger than a pea.

If we wish to complete our model by placing the objects shewn in fig. 60 at their proper distances, the nearest planet, Mercury, must describe an orbit which is not quite circular, but is such that, even at its nearest approach to the sun, the planet would be 20 feet away. The earth must keep at a distance of 50 feet from the sun, while Pluto, the farthest planet of all, must describe an orbit nearly half a mile in radius.

We see that the solar system consists mainly of empty space, and yet the emptiness of the solar system is as nothing compared to the emptiness of space itself. For if we wish to continue constructing our model on the same scale, we must place the

Carnegie Institution

Fig. 60. The relative sizes of the sun (above) and the planets (below) of the solar system. The planets are arranged from left to right in order of their distance from the sun: Mercury, Venus, Earth (with moon), Mars, Jupiter, Saturn (with rings), Uranus, Neptune, Pluto.

 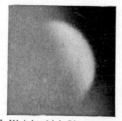

W. H. Wright, Lick Observatory

Fig. 61. Venus in ultra-violet light (left) and in infra-red light (right).

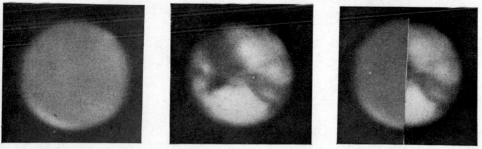

W. H. Wright, Lick Observatory

Fig. 62. Mars in ultra-violet light (left) and in infra-red light (centre). The composite picture on the right shews that the ultra-violet image is larger than the infra-red, the difference in size resulting from the thickness of the Martian atmosphere.

nearest fixed star nearly three thousand miles away—somewhere near New York. We see that space is very empty.

The nine planets all move round the sun in the same direction, and as we have seen, very nearly in the same plane, thus making a sort of regular "one-way" traffic. All except Mercury, Venus and Pluto—the planets nearest to and farthest from the sun— have one or more satellites, the giant central planets Jupiter and Saturn being exceptionally rich with at least nine each, and probably more, for Dr Jeffers of Lick Observatory has recently discovered a tiny object which moves with Jupiter and is believed to be a minute tenth satellite of Jupiter only a few miles in diameter.

With unimportant exceptions, all the satellites move round their planets in the same direction in which the planets themselves move round the sun, and approximately in the same plane.

Besides the planets and their satellites, there are thousands of bodies known as minor planets or asteroids, which again move round the sun in this same direction; 1264 such bodies were known at the end of 1933. There are also a large number of comets, again moving round the sun in this same direction. The "rule of the road" is the same throughout the solar system. How is this rule enforced, and how is the traffic regulated and kept going?

If the planets were left entirely to themselves, each would move steadily onward in a straight line, and soon lose itself in the depths of space. We, on earth, should find ourselves running off at a rate of 19 miles a second into the petrifying cold of outer space.

Yet the history book we explored in the first chapter tells us that the earth has been at much the same distance from the sun for many millions of years past. We can only conclude that something is holding the earth in, and preventing it running off into space, just as when we see a horse running round and round a groom in a field, we conclude that something is holding the horse in.

√ This "something" is of course the sun, and its hold is what we describe as the force of gravitation. You probably all remember how—at least according to the story—Isaac Newton watched an apple fall to the ground, and reflected that if the earth attracted to itself objects which were near its surface, such as apples, it must also attract to itself bodies far out in space, such as the moon. He did not expect that the earth would pull on a distant object as strongly as on a near one, but thought the pull would probably weaken according to the inverse square of the distance—the law according to which apparent brightness of an object, as well as many other quantities in nature, are observed to fall off.

If so, it would of course be possible to calculate the earth's pull on the moon. The moon is sixty times as far from the centre of the earth as we are, so that the earth's pull ought to be 3600 times as strong here as out where the moon is. Here it causes objects to fall 16 feet in a second towards the earth. There—if Newton were right—it would cause objects, including the moon itself, to fall only 1/3600th part of this—rather more than a twentieth of an inch—in a second towards the earth. Small though this is, it is exactly the fall needed to keep the moon in its orbit, and prevent it flying off into space. Although the moon travels at a speed of nearly 2300 miles an hour—forty times the speed of an express train—yet the continual repetition, second after second, of this small fall earthwards, results in its being no farther from the earth now than it was a thousand years ago.

Just as the earth's pull keeps the moon moving in an approximately circular path round the earth, so the sun's pull keeps the earth and the other planets moving in circular, or nearly circular, paths round the sun. Each planet may be compared to a weight whirled round our hand at the end of a string. Our hand is the sun, and the pull in the string is the sun's gravitational pull. The faster we whirl a weight round, the greater the pull in the string by which we hold it. Now observation shews that the nearest planets are being whirled round the sun far more rapidly than the outermost, so that the sun's pull on the nearer planets must be far more intense than on the outer. This fits in with Newton's law that the intensity of the force of gravitation falls off according to the law of the inverse square of the distance. Indeed it is this law that determines the speeds and distances at which the planets move; they adjust their speeds and distances so that the force of gravitation on each planet is of exactly the intensity needed to keep the planet moving round and round in its orbit.

Naturally, then, Mercury completes its journey round the sun in far less time than Pluto; actually it moves completely round the sun in about 3 months, and so alternates between being a morning and an evening star about eight times every year, while Pluto, which takes a thousand times as long—250 years—to travel round the sun, stays in the same part of the sky for year after year. The other planets naturally move round the sun in times which are intermediate between these extremes—Venus in a little over 7 months, the earth as we know in a year, Mars in rather less than 2 years, Jupiter in nearly 12 years, Saturn in 29½ years, and so on.

The sun pours out heat and light in all directions like a fire; the planets are like a number of sentries walking round and round the fire. The nearest man may be uncomfortably hot, while the farthest may be very cold, unless he has private supplies of heat to keep him warm independently of the warmth he receives from the fire.

If a planet has no supplies of heat stored up in its interior, it will radiate out into space precisely the amount of heat that it receives from the sun. This amount is easily calculated, but the amount that the planet radiates out into space depends on the temperature of its surface—the hotter the surface, the greater the amount of radiation. A planet with no internal supplies of heat will assume the temperature at which there is an exact balance between its receipts and expenditure of radiation. If it were spinning very rapidly round its axis, its whole surface would stay uniformly at this temperature—just like a leg of mutton which is being turned round and round in front of a fire. Actually most of the planets rotate rather slowly on their axes, and that side of a planet which has been facing the sun for a long time must obviously be a good deal hotter than the opposite side which has been kept in the dark. The consequence is that the night temperatures of the planets are generally well below the day temperatures, and the temperature at any point on a planet's surface is not steady, but continually fluctuates about an average.

The amount of heat that the earth receives from the sun is easily calculated, and to radiate this amount of heat away into space the earth would have to be at an average temperature of about 40 degrees Fahrenheit, which is only just above the freezing-point of water—such at least would be the case if the earth were a hard black sphere without any atmosphere. Small adjustments must be made on account of the earth's atmosphere and the quality of its surface, and after all this has been allowed for, we find that the calculated average temperature of the earth is somewhat lower than the mean temperature actually observed, which is about 57 degrees Fahrenheit. This shews that the earth does not obtain all its heat from the sun, but must have slight internal supplies of heat—probably the radioactive substances in its crust, of which we made the acquaintance in our first chapter.

We can calculate in the same way the average temperatures which the other planets would assume if they were warmed solely by the heat of the sun; these range from about 343 degrees Fahrenheit for Mercury to about 380 degrees below zero Fahrenheit for Pluto. On the whole these calculated temperatures are fairly close to the temperatures actually measured with a thermocouple, shewing that all the planets, like the earth, have but little internal heat of their own, and derive their warmth almost entirely from the sun's radiation.

The temperature of Mercury, the planet nearest to the sun, is of special interest. Calculation shews that, if Mercury rotated rapidly, its surface would be at a uniform temperature of 343 degrees Fahrenheit. The more slowly it rotated, the more of course its temperature would fluctuate about the average. In the extreme case in which it always turned the same face to the sun— as the moon does to the earth—one face would be permanently far above 343 degrees, and the other permanently far below; calculation shews that a point which was at the centre of the hot face, and so for ever directly under the sun, would be at a temperature of about 675 degrees. Now the observed temperature of a point directly under the sun is very near indeed to this, and this proves that the planet always turns the same face to the sun— in other words, Mercury has one face on which it is always day and another on which it is always night. The day face, with its perpetual temperature of about 675 degrees, is far too hot for water to exist on it in liquid form. It is also too hot for any atmosphere to be retained. For Mercury only contains about a twenty-fifth part as much substance as the earth, and its gravitational pull is so much less than that of the earth, that a molecule or any other projectile would fly right off into space, as soon as its speed reached about $2\frac{1}{4}$ miles a second. Molecules would frequently attain these speeds in the grilling heat of the hot face, so that if Mercury ever had an atmosphere, this must long ago have flown off into space. We obtain a direct visual proof of this when Mercury crosses in front of the sun. It looks like a perfectly sharp black disc, and, just as with the moon, this shews that Mercury possesses either no atmosphere at all, or so little as not appreciably to refract the sun's rays.

The planet is usually so near the sun as to be completely lost in its glare, and even at the best of times it is exceedingly difficult to see anything of its surface. Yet certain permanent markings can be discerned on it, rather like those that we see, with incomparably greater clearness, on the face of the moon. A study of the light reflected from the planet suggests that its surface may be very similar to that of the moon, possibly a rough surface of volcanic ash or dust.

Venus comes next after Mercury in order of nearness to the sun, and has the special interest of being the planet which is most like our earth. In many respects it is a sort of twin sister to the earth. It has almost the same radius—3870 miles as against the earth's 3960—but its substance is rather less closely packed, with an average density only 4·86 times that of water, as against 5·52 times for the earth. As a consequence of this, Venus has 19 per cent. less total substance than the earth, and the pull of gravity at its surface is 15 per cent. less than that at the surface of the earth. A molecule or other projectile will leave the surface of Venus and fly off into space as soon as its speed reaches 6·3 miles a second, as against the 6·93 miles a second needed on earth.

So far the two planets are clearly very similar; what differences there are result mainly from Venus being much nearer to the sun than the earth is. Calculation shews that Venus ought to have an average temperature about 90 degrees Fahrenheit higher than that of the earth. Even with such a temperature, however, water could still exist in liquid form, and the planet could retain an atmosphere, so that we should expect to find seas and rivers, atmosphere and clouds, storms and rain on Venus, much as on earth.

Certainly our expectations with respect to atmosphere and clouds are fully confirmed. On the very rare 'occasions when Venus passes in front of the sun, it presents a very different appearance from those of Mercury and the moon, which have no atmosphere. At the moments when Venus encroaches upon and leaves the bright face of the sun, we do not see it as a sharply defined and clearly outlined black disc, but as a dark disc rimmed with pearly light, the light being produced by the refraction of the sun's rays as they pass through the atmosphere of the planet. A general study shews that the planet is completely encased in clouds—clouds which are so thick and ever-present that it is impossible to see through them, even though we take advantage of the cloud-penetrating properties of infra-red light.

Fig. 61 (facing p. 124) shews pictures of Venus taken in infra-red and ultra-violet light, and there is clearly no essential difference in quality between the two. A few dark markings can be seen in the ultra-violet picture, but these are not permanent, and are probably only specially dark patches of cloud or fog. If they were features of the solid surface of the planet they would be most conspicuous in the infra-red picture. Thus we must regretfully abandon all hope of ever seeing any sort of solid surface beyond the clouds.

It is not difficult to understand why Venus should be encased in clouds and fog in this way, since its higher temperature must obviously result in more water being kept in a state of evaporation than on earth. But, whatever the reason may be, the clouds are there, and in such profusion as to make all study of the lower reaches of the planet's atmosphere impossible; we can, so to speak, only study the stratosphere of Venus, the region above the clouds and fogs.

We studied the composition of the earth's stratosphere by examining sunlight which had travelled through it. We found that this light had been robbed of certain of its constituent wave-lengths, and deduced the presence of ozone in the stratosphere.

We can use a similar method for Venus. We see its clouds by light which has passed through the stratosphere of Venus twice on its journey from the sun to us—once in passing down to the clouds, and a second time in coming back again, after reflection, from the clouds to our eyes. Again, when this light is compared with light which has come directly from the sun to us, certain wave-lengths are found to be missing. As the loss can only have occurred in the stratosphere of Venus, we can deduce the composition of this stratosphere.

It is at once found to be different in composition from the stratosphere of the earth. It contains no appreciable amount of water vapour, but perhaps this is hardly surprising, as there is not much in the stratosphere of the earth. There is a more marked difference in the fact that Venus hardly contains any appreciable amount of oxygen in its stratosphere. To assess the importance of this, we must remember that most chemical substances shew a great hunger to combine with oxygen, as we see in the familiar processes of rusting, corrosion and combustion. Indeed this oxygen hunger is so intense that it is perhaps rather surprising that any oxygen at all is left in the atmosphere of the earth. That there is any left is probably due to the circumstance that the earth's oxygen is continually being replenished by the vegetation which so profusely covers the surface of the earth. This acts as a vast oxygen factory, and the fact that no oxygen can be found on Venus may very possibly mean that there is no vegetation on Venus to supply it.

To imagine the physical conditions prevailing on the surface of Venus, we must take a very long step away from those we left behind us on the moon and on Mercury, in the direction of conditions now prevailing on our own earth. On the surfaces of the moon and Mercury we should probably find arid and rocky deserts, which are roasted in the presence of the sun or frozen in its absence, and are uniformly undisturbed by either wind or rain. There may also be rocky deserts on Venus, but they cannot be arid, and some changes at least must occur. If Venus turned on its axis as rapidly as our earth, we might confidently expect to find such familiar and home-like phenomena as trade-winds, dry and rainy seasons, and so forth. We have, however, already seen that Mercury always turns the same face to the sun, and it seems highly probable that Venus either does the same or else alternates its faces with extreme slowness. In other words, Venus may have a day face and a night face like Mercury, or may have days and nights which are like our own except for being of extreme length. In either case there may be very little either of wind or rain, merely a perpetually damp and hot climate.

The surface of Venus may well be like that of the earth was in those far-distant days before life had appeared to change the appearance of its surface and the composition of its atmosphere. As we travel backwards in time, we must come to an epoch when the earth was substantially hotter than now, either because it still had appreciable stores of internal heat, or because the sun was itself hotter than now, and so provided a more abundant supply of radiation. It may be that the Venus of to-day provides a picture of the earth of those days, and that the Venus of the future is destined to repeat in some measure the history of our own earth. Even if vegetation is still lacking on Venus, it may appear in due course, and by supplying the atmosphere with oxygen, may open the road to higher and higher forms of life. Yet we know so little of the nature and meaning of life that all such thoughts are at best the wildest of guesses. For aught we know life may be destined to take very different forms on Venus, or may never appear at all. We simply do not know and have no right to guess.

Still travelling out into space and increasing our distance from the sun, we pass by our own earth, which we have already studied sufficiently, and come next to Mars. If Venus is a twin sister of the earth, Mars is the earth's little brother. If Venus is a warmer edition of the earth, Mars is a much colder edition. If Venus suggests a picture of what the earth may have been in the remote past, Mars suggests what the earth may possibly be in the remote future.

Mars cannot compare with Venus or the earth in bulk and substance, having only a little more than half the diameter, and only a little more than a tenth of the substance, of the earth. Also its substance is less densely packed than that of either the earth or Venus, so that its gravitational pull is quite small. With the same effort we shall be able to jump three times as far, or three times as high, as on earth—as against six times on the moon. A molecule or other projectile only needs a speed of 3·1 miles a second to jump off into space, as against the 6·9 needed on earth. If Mars were as near to the sun as Mercury is, the molecules of its atmosphere would attain this speed quite frequently, so that most, or all, of them would probably have disappeared by now. But the greater distance of Mars from the sun has saved it from this fate, and a considerable thickness of atmosphere is still left. Fig. 62 (facing p. 124) shews two photographs of Mars, taken at Lick Observatory in ultra-violet and infra-red light respectively. When the halves of the two photographs are joined together we obtain the third picture on the extreme right of fig. 62, and see at once that the ultra-violet picture is distinctly larger than the infra-red. The difference of course represents the thickness of the Martian atmosphere.

As with Venus, the light by which we see the surface of Mars has passed twice through the whole thickness of the Martian atmosphere, so that again we might expect that certain wavelengths would be missing from the light, and that from the

missing wave-lengths we could deduce the constitution of the
Martian atmosphere. But when the light is analysed it is hard
to find that anything is missing. The Mount Wilson astronomers
have a very powerful equipment at their disposal, and have
specially searched for evidence of either oxygen or water vapour
in the atmosphere of Mars. They can find no evidence of oxygen,
and consider that there cannot, at the most, be as much as a
thousandth part as much oxygen per square mile of surface as
there is in the atmosphere of the earth.

They find no direct evidence of water vapour in the atmosphere
either, although it has often been thought that there is a certain
amount of circumstantial evidence that water vapour is present.
Mars has its alternation of hot and cold seasons as we have,
and it is noticed that certain features of its surface change regularly with the seasons. White caps, for instance, appear round the
poles in the cold season and disappear in the warm season. It has
often been conjectured that these may be ice or snow—perhaps
clouds of icy particles in the air, or perhaps fields of snow on the
ground—although it is of course also possible that the snow may
be merely carbon dioxide or some substance quite other than
frozen water vapour.

It is also noticed that dark patches appear regularly in the
Martian spring, and fade away again in the autumn—mainly in
the tropical regions and southern hemisphere. It was at first
thought that these were real seas of water, but this is now considered improbable. For one thing, they vary too much and too
rapidly in colour; one, for instance, was observed to change from

blue-green to chocolate-brown and back again within a very few months. They also resemble the supposed seas on the moon in never reflecting the sunlight, as sheets of real water would do. At one time astronomers thought they might be forests, or masses of vegetation. Since then the surface of Mars has been examined in the same way as the surface of the moon, and appears to be of somewhat similar composition—possibly volcanic lava or some such substance. Thus the dark patches may be produced by showers of rain wetting a dead dry surface like that of the moon.

If we are planning to take our rocket to Mars, it is clear that we must again take air and water with us. We must also be prepared for an exceedingly inhospitable climate, and we may as well know the worst before we start.

Mars has days and seasons very like our own. It takes 24 hours and 37 minutes to turn on its axis, so that its day is slightly longer than ours. And as this axis is tilted at an angle of 25° 10', as against the earth's angle of 23° 27', we must expect to find the Martian seasons rather more pronounced than ours on earth; there will be a greater difference between summer and winter. On top of this, however, there is a further cause of variation in the climate on Mars.

The earth's path round the sun is very nearly circular—not quite, since the earth's distance from the sun is 3 per cent. less in December than in June. We inhabitants of the northern hemisphere are closest to the sun at our mid-winter, while people in the southern hemisphere are closest at their mid-summer. Thus the small variations in our distance from the sun go to lessen the difference between summer and winter in the northern hemisphere, but accentuate it in the southern hemisphere. As a consequence, we must go to the South Pole rather than to the North for extremes of climate.

Nevertheless, the earth's distance from the sun does not vary enough to produce any great effect on our climate. It is different with Mars, whose path is nothing like so circular as that of the earth. Our distance from the sun varies by less than 3 million miles, but that of Mars varies by more than 26 million miles. Thus, when Mars approaches the sun, the climate of the whole planet becomes appreciably warmer; as it recedes, the whole planet gets colder. These alternations of general coldness and general warmth are of course superposed on top of the ordinary Martian seasons. The maximum of general warmth, the time when Mars is nearest the sun, occurs shortly before mid-summer in the southern hemisphere, so that on Mars, as on earth, we must go to the southern hemisphere for extremes of climate. Furthermore, the extremes will be far more marked than with us.

Now if we are planning to land our rocket on Mars, we may as well take advantage of what warmth there is—even so, we shall soon find there is little enough. Let us then arrange to arrive when Mars is nearest the sun—i.e. at the middle of the period of general warmth—and to land slightly south of the equator at mid-day. Here we may find a temperature as high as 60 degrees Fahrenheit. But if we cherish any hopes that we have come to a fine, warm climate, they will be dispelled as evening closes in. For there are neither clouds nor atmosphere enough to retain the planet's warmth, so that it will get cold with great rapidity as soon as the direct radiation of the sun diminishes—just as on a terrestrial desert, only far more so. It is likely to freeze before sunset, and may well fall to 40 degrees below zero before the sun reappears on the scene.

This is the very best climate Mars can offer. If we travel to the poles we must expect to encounter temperatures of more than 100 degrees Fahrenheit below zero, while if we wait until the planet is at its farthest from the sun, the temperature will be still further reduced all over the planet, and we may be unable to find any spot on the planet's surface at which the temperature is above the freezing-point.

We have already seen that the surface of Mars is probably rather like that of the moon, so that when we step out of our rocket we must expect the general nature of the scenery to be rather like what we found on the moon. We can hardly expect to find any vegetation, at any rate of the kind we know on earth, since it would need more moisture to feed on, and would give out more oxygen, than we find on Mars.

Are we likely to encounter Martians? It is a thrilling question, although now that we know more about Mars it is less thrilling than it was a few years ago.

In 1877, the Italian astronomer Schiaparelli studied Mars very intensively through a low-powered telescope, and announced that in addition to the large markings that looked like seas there were finer markings, which, writing in Italian, he described as "canali". He used this Italian word merely to indicate channels of water, like the Grand Canal and the other canals in Venice, and did not mean to suggest that there were canals in the English sense, either straight lanes of water or the work of intelligent beings. Yet, as his description of them was translated into English by the word "canals", people began to argue that if there were canals, there must be intelligent beings to make the canals, and have so argued ever since.

Of late, however, doubts have been expressed as to the very existence of these channels or canals. There seems to be little doubt that astronomers see two different kinds of markings on Mars, which may properly be described as "subjective" and "objective". When the human eye is straining to its utmost to see things by inadequate light, there is an unmistakable tendency for it to see imaginary straight lines connecting up dark patches. An astronomer of my acquaintance illustrated this by putting an illuminated picture of a planet at the end of his garden, and asking his friends to observe it through a small telescope. A number were convinced they saw distinct black lines, like the Martian canals, although in actual fact there were no such lines to see; the simple explanation was that on the feebly lighted picture detail could only be seen with an effort, and the effort resulted in the seeing of non-existent lines. Another astronomer rubbed the canals off a drawing of Mars, and asked a class of schoolboys to draw what they saw. The boys at the back of the room put numerous canals into their drawings, and these were rather like the canals which had previously been drawn in by astronomers (Plate XXIX, p. 144). As the lines which the boys saw were imaginary, it is reasonable to suppose that those which the astronomers had seen were also imaginary.

Astronomers who claim to see canals on Mars usually draw these as straight lines on their maps, yet it is obvious that whether they really were straight on Mars or not, they could not look straight in all positions of the planet; a canal which looked straight when Mars was in one position would look curved, as a result of the curvature of the surface of Mars, when the planet had rotated to a new position (see fig. 65, facing p. 145). This again seems to indicate that the canals are mainly subjective illusions. The same conclusion is suggested by the fact that canals similar to those of Mars have been seen on surfaces where it is improbable that canals could exist, as, for example, on Venus, which is now believed to be covered in with thick clouds, on Mercury where water would boil (fig. 65, facing p. 145), and on satellites of Jupiter where it would freeze.

The camera is usually supposed to provide the final test of reality, and, although photographs of Mars shew quite definite markings, these do not resemble the supposed systems of canals. Perhaps this is not conclusive evidence, because photography is, for technical reasons, unsuited to the recording of very fine markings, and it is quite possible, as the canal observers claim, that these are best seen by the eye.

Taking it all together, the general accumulation of evidence and the general opinion of astronomers are equally against the supposed canals having any real existence. This does not of course prove there is no life on Mars, but it removes the main cause which has led a great many people to think there may be.

Thus, if we decide to take our rocket to Mars, I do not think we need trouble much about the prospect of meeting Martians. We are more likely to find an uninhabited and inhospitable desert, which may not shew quite the same extremes of climate as the moon, but may be even worse in some ways, since what warmth there is will never last for more than a few hours at a time.

If we leave Mars and continue our journey outwards into space, we shall find that we have to travel a very long way to pass from Mars to the next planet, Jupiter. Our journey may not be devoid of incident, since it will take us through the shoals of minor planets or asteroids, which have already been mentioned. The largest of these, Ceres, has a diameter of only 480 miles, which is less than a quarter of the diameter of the moon, and the only known limit to the size of the smallest asteroids is that set by the power of the observer's telescope. Smaller than the smallest asteroid we can see, there must be thousands that we do not see from the earth because they are too small to be seen. We may be able to see a number of them from our rocket, as this traverses the long distance between Mars and Jupiter.

Many of the asteroids are turning round in space, a complete rotation frequently occupying from 8 to 10 hours, and a number vary in brightness as they rotate. The reason for this variation is probably that the asteroids in question are irregular in shape, so that, as they rotate, the amount of surface they expose to our view continually varies. The huge gravitational pull of a big object such as the earth results in the object becoming very nearly spherical in shape, but a small body is not affected in the same way, and many of the asteroids are so small that gravitation can have done but little to mould them to a spherical shape. On many of them the pull of gravitation is so feeble that a good cricketer would be in danger of bowling all his balls off into space, and the batsman of making every ball a lost ball—lost for ever and ever, as the ball would itself become a new planet circling round the sun. Needless to say these asteroids are far too small to retain atmospheres.

At last we find ourselves clear of this swarm of asteroids, and are approaching Jupiter. Even from afar we see that it is far from spherical in shape; it is about twenty times as much flattened as the earth, so that at last we have found a planet of which we can truly say that it is flattened like an orange (fig. 66, facing p. 145).

The planet could not have been flattened like this if it had been standing at rest, for then its huge gravitational pull would have made it almost perfectly spherical. Thus it is not surprising to find that it is in rapid rotation, a complete rotation occupying a few minutes less than 10 hours. The flattening is quite adequately explained as the result of this rapid rotation, a point on the equator of the planet moving round the axis at a speed of about 28,000 miles an hour—as against 1040 miles an hour for a point on the equator of the earth.

We found Mars cold enough, but we shall find Jupiter incomparably colder. It is at more than five times the earth's

PLATE XXIX

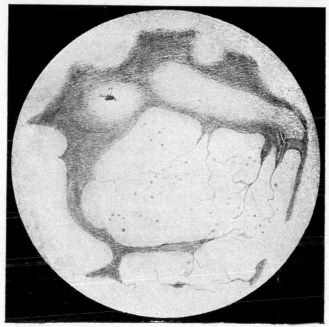

Royal Astronomical Society

Fig. 63. An attempt to examine the reality of the canals which some astronomers believe they can see on Mars. The above drawing of Mars, which contains no canals, was put before a class of schoolboys who were asked to draw the picture as it appeared to them.

Royal Astronomical Society

Fig. 64. Many of the boys put canal-like lines in their drawings, although no such lines appeared in the drawing from which they copied. Here are two such drawings.

PLATE XXX

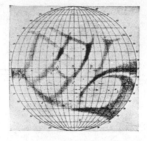

Fig. 65. The surface detail of Mercury after a
drawing by Schiaparelli.

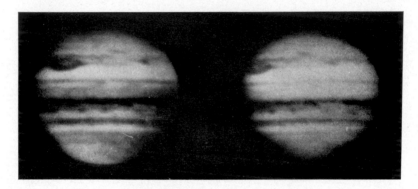

Fig. 66. Jupiter photographed in ultra-violet (left) and in blue light (right).

Fig. 67. Saturn with its system of rings.

distance from the sun, so that 25 acres of its surface receive less of the sun's radiation than a single acre on earth. We can get a vague idea of the physical state of Jupiter by imagining the earth's supply of radiation suddenly reduced to a twenty-fifth or less. Its whole surface would very soon be frozen solid, and all activity would cease. We might naturally expect to find Jupiter in an equally dormant state, but it is not. Like Venus, it is completely covered in with clouds which are so dense that even infra-red light cannot penetrate them to any appreciable extent. These clouds shew remarkable and continuous changes. The best-known example is provided by the feature known as the great red spot. This was first noticed in 1878, and gradually increased until it attained a length of about 30,000 miles and a width of about 7000 miles—an area about equal to the total surface of the earth. It then became gradually more circular in shape and diminished in size, until it has almost disappeared by now. It is conceivable that this particular spot may have been produced by some special cataclysm, but other minor changes which are in progress all the time make it clear that Jupiter is no dead frozen mass. This is also shewn by the circumstance that belts of clouds in different latitudes rotate at different rates, those which are nearest to the equator rotating fastest.

All this activity was at one time regarded as evidence that Jupiter had a fairly high temperature, and so added substantially from some internal supplies of its own to the meagre supplies of heat it received from the very distant sun. We know now that this is not the case. Direct measurements shew that the temperature of Jupiter is at least 180 degrees below zero Fahrenheit, which is about what we should expect if it were warmed mainly by the sun's radiation, and had very little heat of its own.

With the temperature of Jupiter as low as this, it is clear that its clouds cannot be ordinary water vapour; they must consist of substances which remain in the vapour state at temperatures at which water vapour has long been frozen. As with the other planets, the composition of the atmosphere of Jupiter is studied by examining what wave-lengths are missing from sunlight which has passed into the atmosphere and out again. The observations are not easy to interpret, but they provide distinct evidence of two gases being present in the atmosphere of Jupiter, namely, ammonia and methane.

We all know ammonia as the stuff that draws tears to our eyes when we smell it, or when we unhappily break the bottle in which it is kept. Often also we can recognise its presence in smelling salts; it is the more efficacious but less agreeable ingredient, which the manufacturer tries to disguise by mixing with something more pleasant to the smell. We also find it useful to put on bee stings and mosquito bites, since, being very alkaline, it neutralises the acid of the sting, and so relieves our discomfort.

Methane is better known under its popular name of marsh gas. When vegetable matter decomposes under water this gas rises to the surface, where it may become luminous and appear as the "will o' the wisp" which is supposed to lure men on to destruction. It is also an ingredient of the fire-damp which is liable to explode in coal-mines, and also of the gases emitted at volcanic eruptions.

Neither of these gases is very attractive, and on the whole, the atmosphere of Jupiter appears to be what Hamlet would describe as "No other thing than a foul and pestilential congregation of vapours". We had better not take our rocket there; we should spend our time coughing, sneezing and crying. Moreover, as Jupiter contains 317 times as much substance as our earth, its gravitational pull is something to be treated with respect. We should not repeat the joyous experience we had on the moon of breaking our own and everyone else's athletic records without appreciable effort; on the contrary we should be very much concerned with the problem of how to support our own weight. The legs of a 12-stone man would have to stand as much strain as those of a 32-stone man on earth, and we might collapse under our own weight unless we did as the *Cetiosaurus* used to do on earth, and immersed ourselves in liquid to reduce the strain. If we are to travel round the universe without misadventure, we must not be above taking hints even from an extinct reptile (fig. 24, facing p. 44).

It is difficult to imagine that any planet could be less inviting than Jupiter, but Saturn appears able to fill the bill, and the planets still farther out—Uranus, Neptune and Pluto—are probably even less attractive than Saturn. We really know very little about any of these distant planets. Saturn appears to have rather less ammonia in its atmosphere than Jupiter, but makes up by having more marsh gas. It is even colder than Jupiter. On the other hand, its gravitational pull is more like what we are accustomed to, being only a sixth more than the earth's. It is the most distinguished in appearance of all the planets, being surrounded by a system of rings which look highly picturesque in a telescope, and yet would bring disadvantages of their own if we took our rocket to Saturn. For these rings consist of myriads of little moons, each of which circles round Saturn in a very nearly circular orbit (fig. 67, facing p. 145). Yet, as these little moons are continually pulling on one another gravitationally, their orbits cannot be perfectly circular, so that the tiny moons must occasionally crash into one another. When this happens, broken fragments of moon must be expected to fall onto Saturn itself, with results which might be disastrous to a visiting rocket.

Before we leave these melancholy scenes, let us take a glance at Pluto, the most recently-discovered, the remotest, and also the chilliest, of all the planets. We know far less about it than about any of the others, but it may perhaps be a sort of twin brother to Mars, about equal in size and mass, but existing under very different physical conditions. Each square yard of its surface receives only a 1600th part of the radiation that a square yard of the earth receives, so that its physical state is impossible to imagine. Its gravitational pull is so feeble that it can hardly have much of an atmosphere, but it may have more than Mars, since its temperature is so far below that of Mars.

Surveying the whole scene, it seems likely that we may travel through the whole solar system without meeting men like ourselves, or even animals or vegetation of the kinds we know on earth. Yet on our own planet, the only part of the system with which we are familiar, life is so all-pervading that we can hardly believe that there are any physical conditions under which it is impossible for life to exist in some form or other. We find it in the coldest climates of our earth as well as in the hottest, in the depths of the sea, in the solid soil, and even in the streams of oil under the earth. In these various places it has assumed very different forms, each suited to its particular environment. This being so, we can hardly deny that it may have assumed still other forms on other planets, suited to the very different environments there. We have no right to say we shall find no life elsewhere than on earth, but it seems safe to suppose that if we do, it will be very different from any life we know—perhaps very different from any we can imagine.

The planets have proved so interesting that we have hardly left time to do more than glance at their satellites or moons. The earth has only its one solitary moon, but many of the planets are far richer—Jupiter, for instance, has ten, while Saturn has nine of respectable size, as well as the millions which form the rings. Uranus has four, Mars two, Neptune one, while Mercury and Venus, the two planets nearest the sun, have none, and the same is probably true of Pluto, the planet farthest from the sun.

Apart from the tiny moons in Saturn's rings, the nine planets have twenty-seven moons between them—an average of three moons apiece—so that the earth, with only one, may seem to have fewer than its fair share. This is true so long as we merely judge by numbers. On the other hand, if we judge by weight, our earth has more than its fair share; it has more moon substance in proportion to its weight than any other planet.

We are all familiar with the tides which the moon raises in our oceans. As the moon's distance is approximately thirty diameters of the earth, its gravitational pull is a thirtieth part more at that point of the earth's surface which is just under it than at the centre of the earth. In the same way, it is a thirtieth part less at the antipodes of this point. In fig. 68, we can represent the

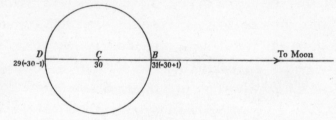

Fig. 68. Diagrammatic representation of the tidal force exerted by the moon on the earth.

moon's pull at *B, C, D*, by the numbers 31, 30 and 29 respectively. If we break up 31 into 30 + 1, and 29 into 30 − 1, we may suppose that there is a uniform pull 30 all over the earth, with a pull + 1 towards the moon at *B*, and a pull − 1 towards the earth at *D*. This latter is of course the same thing as a push + 1 away from the moon. The uniform pull 30 is exactly used up in keeping the earth and moon in their proper orbits, so that we need not trouble any more about it. On top of this uniform pull, however, are the pulls + 1 and − 1 acting at opposite sides of the earth. These opposing pulls stretch the earth much as we might stretch a piece of india-rubber by pulling in opposite directions with our two hands, and in this way cause tides. We have already seen that the earth is more rigid than steel, so that it yields less to the pull than the fluid ocean above. As a consequence, we are hardly conscious of any tides except those in this fluid ocean, yet the tides we see are really the difference between the tides in the ocean and those in the solid earth, the latter being quite small in comparison with the former.

If the little moon can stretch the big earth in this way, it stands to reason that the big earth must stretch the moon even more, and the same must be true of all the planets and their moons. We can never see our moon being stretched, because we can never see it broadside on, but we can see the process very clearly in the case of one of Jupiter's moons. A telescope shews that the moon which is nearest to the giant planet is so stretched out that it looks more like an egg than our idea of what a moon should be. In course of time this little moon will move in even closer to Jupiter. The nearer it goes, the greater Jupiter's pull will be, and the more stretched and egg-shaped the little moon will become—Jupiter is stretching it out more and more just as though it were a piece of rubber or elastic.

Yet we know that no piece of elastic can stand being stretched out indefinitely. It must snap in time—and so must the little moon. Calculation shews that the moon will at first snap into two distinct pieces, and Jupiter will have one more moon than now. But as these two new little moons will still be just about as near to Jupiter as the old moon was, they too will be strained and egg-shaped. In time they too must break up, and, as the process continually repeats itself, the number of Jupiter's moons will increase indefinitely.

We can say that Jupiter is surrounded by a sort of danger zone. When a moon or other body approaches this danger zone, it becomes egg-shaped; when it finally enters the danger zone, it is broken up—and if it stays within the danger zone for long enough it will be broken up into a vast number of tiny moons.

This is not mere guess-work, but the result of precise mathematical calculation. As soon as we know the gravitational pull either of a planet or of any other object, we can map out its danger zone. There are naturally different danger zones for different substances; a cloud of tenuous gas is in danger in regions where a rigid steely solid can venture in perfect safety. Now such calculations shew that the little egg-shaped moon of Jupiter is very near indeed to its danger zone. One of the little moons of Mars is also near—although not so near—to the danger zone of Mars, and one of Saturn's moons to the danger zone of Saturn.

This latter danger zone is of very special interest, because the millions of little moons which surround Saturn and form its rings are already inside it. It looks as if at some time in the past an ordinary moon had wandered inside the danger zone of Saturn and had been broken up into the millions of tiny moons which now form the rings. These rings are a standing proof that the danger zones have a real existence, and caution other bodies as to the fate awaiting them if they get caught by the gravitational pull of bigger masses. I have already reminded you of

Mr Kipling's story of how the elephant got his trunk. I have now tried to tell you the story of "How Saturn got its Rings"—perhaps not with Mr Kipling's grace and charm, but at least I believe that my story is a "really-truly" story, and not merely a "Just-So" story.

Our own earth, too, has its danger zone. So far the moon has kept well outside it, but in time the earth and moon must draw nearer together, and as they do so the moon will become more and more egg-shaped, until it finally crosses the danger line and begins to break up. It is only a matter of time until we have a fringe of rings like Saturn. In those far off days we shall have lost our moon, but not our moonlight, for the myriads of tiny moons will still reflect the sun's light down to us at night; indeed, there will be even more moonlight than now, for a moon, like everything else, increases its total surface when it breaks up into fragments. There will also be moonlight all through the night. Still, life on earth will not be very comfortable, for every now and then two of the tiny moons will collide with one another, and their broken fragments will fall to earth like immense meteors, precisely as they must even now be falling on Saturn.

The solar system provides other evidence that these danger zones exist. We have already seen that comets do not move round the sun in circular paths like the planets, but in elongated oval curves which we call "ellipses". Usually a comet does not begin to be interesting until it has approached quite near to the sun. Then the sun's radiation beating down on it causes it to throw out a huge "tail", which may often be millions of miles long. The comet then becomes an interesting, beautiful, and even terrifying object.

Sometimes a comet will pass inside a danger zone, perhaps of the sun, or perhaps only of Jupiter or Saturn, and break up in consequence. Quite a number have been observed to break up into two pieces, while one has been observed to break into four. The most interesting story is that of Biela's comet, which broke in two while under observation in 1846. Six years later, when the comet's orbit again brought it near to the sun, the two pieces were observed to be 1½ million miles apart. Since then, neither of them has been seen in cometary form, but the place where they ought to be is occupied by a swarm of millions of meteors, known as the Andromedid meteors. Occasionally these meet the earth in its orbit, and make a grand meteoric display—usually on or about November 27. It seems quite clear that since the comet first broke into two, both its pieces must have again traversed some other danger zone, and have been broken into innumerable small pieces in consequence. There are many other instances of comets disappearing as such, and being replaced by swarms of meteors.

Not only the sun, but of course every other star as well, exerts a gravitational pull, and so has a danger zone surrounding it. As the stars move onwards through space, it must occasionally happen that one wanders into the danger zone of another and more massive star. Events like those we have just been considering must then occur, but on a far grander scale. Just as the crocodile pulled the trunk out of the baby elephant, so the bigger star will pull a sort of trunk out of the smaller—a long nose or filament of gas, which will gradually break up into little pieces. It seems likely that sometime in the past the sun met with a misadventure of this kind, and that the pieces are our planets. So we can add another incident to our story—"How the Sun got its Planets".

The planets may also have met with misadventures of the same kind, wandering into the danger zone of the sun, and themselves getting broken up in turn. If so, we can write a further chapter—"How the Planets got their Moons". The saddest part of this chapter will be the story of one particular planet which seems to have met with a specially hard fate. It moved originally, we think, between Mars and Jupiter, but its motion took it into some danger zone, probably that of Jupiter. It began by breaking up, as though to make a few moons for itself, and ended up by being nothing but moons. At any rate nothing seems to have been left of it but tiny fragments, which are, as we believe, the asteroids or minor planets that we have already described. That one, Eros, which comes nearest the earth, is found to be shaped like an egg or a pear or a dumb-bell; perhaps it was about to break up still further, and just got away in time.

CHAPTER VI

THE SUN

So far we have been concerned only with the smaller of the objects in space. Smallest of all were the pellets of matter which we describe as shooting-stars when they fall into the earth's atmosphere; these are so small that we could hold thousands of them in each hand. The largest object we have discussed so far has been the giant planet Jupiter, with about eleven times the diameter of the earth. A box big enough to hold Jupiter would hold $11 \times 11 \times 11$ or 1331 earths—eleven each way. Yet even Jupiter is quite small in comparison with the sun, which we shall examine in the present chapter, and the sun is smaller still in comparison with the larger stars and other objects that we shall examine subsequently. Broadly speaking, the sun is as much bigger than Jupiter as Jupiter is bigger than the earth—Jupiter could contain more than a thousand earths, but the sun could contain more than a thousand Jupiters. To carry on the sequence, each of the blue stars we shall consider later could contain more than a thousand suns, while each of the "giant red" stars could contain more than a thousand blue stars. And each of certain nebulae which we shall discuss in our last chapter of all not only could contain, but actually does contain, thousands of millions of stars.

We can put this sequence in tabular form as follows, all the numbers of course being only very rough approximations:

PLATE XXXI

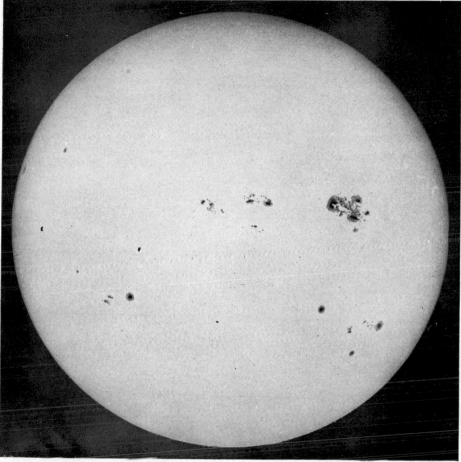

Greenwich Observatory

Fig. 69. The sun photographed on August 12, 1917, when it exhibited very complicated and numerous sunspots whose total area was the greatest observed at any time since 1870.

PLATE XXXII

A. E. Douglass

Fig. 70. The cross-section of a beam of Douglas fir, shewing the variations of climate from A.D. 1073, when the tree started to grow, until A.D. 1260, when it was felled. Subsequently to A.D. 1260, the log was used as a beam in a dwelling, which subsequently fell into ruins. The beam was unearthed and studied in 1933, and is of value as filling in the weather record of the two centuries of its growth.

Fig. 71. The cross-section of a Scotch Pine felled at Eberswalde, Germany. The rings indicated by black spots were the growths of the years in which sunspots were most frequent from 1830 to 1906.

Earth	1
Jupiter	1,000
Sun	1,000,000
Blue stars	1,000,000,000
Red stars	1,000,000,000,000
Nebulae	1,000,000,000,000,000

Let us imagine we take our rocket up once again, and examine the sun's surface from close quarters. Fig. 69 (p. 156) shews it as it might appear when we were well on our way. Perhaps the most noticeable feature is the darkening at the edge, or "limb" as the astronomers call it; at a casual glance it looks as though the edge of the sun were far less bright than the central parts of its surface. We can see the same darkening, even more clearly, on Plate XXXIV (facing p. 161). Now if the sun were solid or liquid, its surface would appear equally bright all over, as of course does the surface of a plain luminous globe. The apparent darkening of the limb provides a proof that the surface of the sun is gaseous.

We can see no other detail in our picture except groups of sunspots. These are rather unusual both in size and complexity; there are half a dozen at least which could swallow the earth quite easily, since, on the scale of the photograph, the earth would be only a grain of sand a twenty-fifth of an inch in diameter. Yet even these immense spots are nothing phenomenal in size, and occasionally sunspots appear which are large enough to swallow all the planets at one gulp.

We cannot see such sunspots as these every day, or even every year, but we can quite often see some spots. They do not come in a steady stream, but rather in gusts or waves, their numbers fluctuating up and down every 11 years or so. Sunspots were especially numerous in 1906, 1917 and 1928, and will be so again in 1939.

When we search the face of the sun for sunspots, we must be careful to look through dark glass, or at least through a piece of heavily smoked glass, or else we may find our eyes damaged beyond repair. Galileo, who was the first to study the spots on the sun, became blind in his old age, and attributed his misfortune to his gazing with unprotected eyes at the brightness of the sun.

People often discuss whether astronomical events, such as the coming of new or full moon, have any effect on the weather. Generally speaking, scientists are not able to trace any connection between the weather and any astronomical phenomena whatever, with the single exception of sunspots. There is, however, some evidence that the weather passes through a regular cycle having the same 11-year period as the frequency of sunspots. With the waxing and waning of the number of sunspots, the summers gradually change from being hot and dry to being cold and wet and then back again, the complete cycle taking about 11 years. Two instances will illustrate the nature of the evidence.

When a tree is cut down, we see a succession of concentric rings in the cross-section of its trunk, and each ring is known to be the growth of a single summer. We can tell how many years old the tree is by counting these rings. Yet, although the years must all have been of equal length, the rings are not of equal thickness. Some were formed in moist summers, when the tree grew luxuri-

antly and added profusely to its girth, others in dry summers which
added but little to the size of the tree. By identifying the various
rings with the successive years of the life of the tree, Professor
Douglass claims that he can discover whether any particular
year was dry or wet; the tree is, so to speak, a standing record of
the weather it experienced throughout its life. Fig. 70 (facing
p. 157) shews an interesting example. Now a careful study of

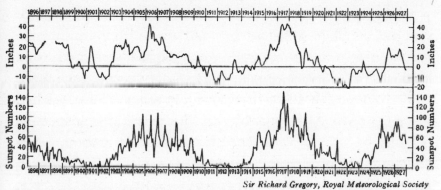

Sir Richard Gregory, Royal Meteorological Society

Fig. 72. The upper curve shews the height of water in Victoria Nyanza, while
the lower shews the frequency of sunspots at the same time. We see that the curves
keep almost perfectly in step with one another, demonstrating that sunspots have an
influence on terrestrial weather.

such cross-sections of trees frequently shews that the rings change
gradually in thickness in a cycle of 11 years, which coincides
exactly with the sunspot period (see fig. 71, facing p. 157). The
thickest rings were formed in those years when sunspots were
most plentiful, and we see at once that abundance of sunspots goes
with abundance of tree growth and so with moist summers.

Fig. 72 contains an alternative proof of the same thing. The
lower curve shews the numbers of sunspots in the different years

from 1896 to 1927, each up-and-down wave of this curve of course representing a single 11-year cycle of sunspots. The curve above this represents the height of water in Victoria Nyanza, the big fresh-water lake in equatorial Africa. We notice at once that the height of water in the lake keeps in almost perfect step with the frequency of sunspots, and so exhibits an 11-year cycle, just as the sunspots do. The water is of course highest after a wet year, providing proof that the weather is wettest when sunspots are frequent, and *vice versa*.

Although the frequency of sunspots changes slowly and gradually, so that the complete cycle is a matter of years, individual sunspots seldom last more than a few days. Plate XXXIII shews how much a big sunspot may change even within a single day. Plate XXXIV shews the gradual development of a very complicated group of spots, five of the six pictures having been taken on successive days. The spots move steadily to the right, not because they are moving across the face of the sun, but because the sun is rotating, and carrying them round with it. After the sixth day it is impossible to see the spots any longer, because the sun's rotation has taken them away from our sight.

An exceptionally big spot may occasionally disappear in this way, and subsequently come back, about a fortnight later, round the other edge of the sun. It was by measuring this motion of sunspots that Galileo first proved that the sun is rotating, and shewed that its time of rotation is about 26 days.

Passing over one of these spots in our rocket will be like passing over the funnel of a steamer in an aeroplane. We shall

PLATE XXXIII

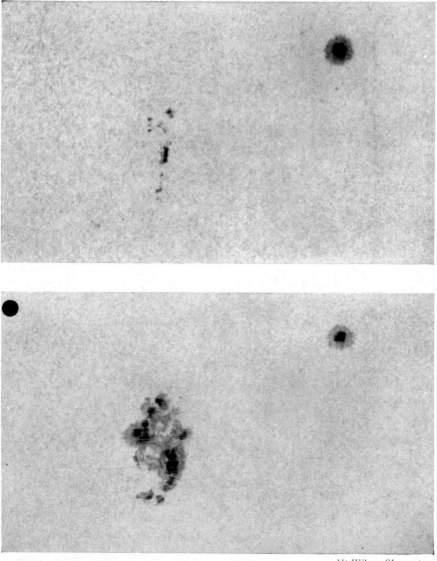

Mt Wilson Observatory

Fig. 73. The development of a group of sunspots within an interval of 24 hours. The black circle on the lower plate represents the size of the earth.

PLATE XXXIV

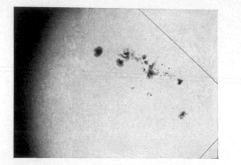

March 19

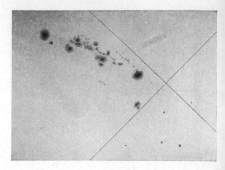

March 20

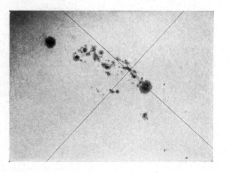

March 21

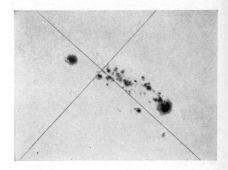

March 22

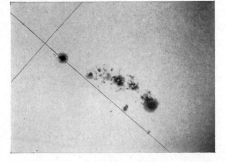

March 23

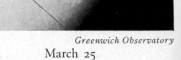

Greenwich Observatory

March 25

Fig. 74. A complicated group of sunspots, shewing motion, development and passage across the sun's disc in a period of 6 days (March 19–25, 1920).

notice a tremendous uprush of heated gas, and shall discover that sunspots are of the nature of vent holes from which masses of hot gas are shot out at terrific speeds. The fierce heat of the sun's interior keeps the sun's outer layers in a state of continual agitation; they may be compared to water which is made to boil furiously by a hot fire underneath. We are all familiar with the large bubbles of air and steam which force their way upwards through boiling water. When they finally reach the surface, the pressure which has so far compressed them is released, and they expand and mix with the outer air. The material which comes up in sunspots behaves in a similar way; as soon as it reaches the sun's surface, the pressure on it is lessened, and it expands. As a consequence of this expansion it becomes cooler for the reason already explained (p. 60).

It is because the sunspots consist of cooler matter than the rest of the sun's surface that they look black. Actually they are of a blinding brightness, and look black only by contrast—because they are less vivid than the hotter gases which surround them. The matter which they eject is probably a mixture of complete atoms and fragments of atoms, which may include electrified particles of various kinds. These are shot out and travel in all directions; after a day or two of journeying through space, some of them will reach the earth, and, penetrating its atmosphere, may produce a display of the Aurora Borealis. Later they may ionise the air and so form the layers which reflect our wireless waves back earthward and enable us to hear distant wireless stations. We have already (p. 68) discussed what happens when these electrified particles arrive on earth; we are now seeing them at the beginning of their journey; we are present at the first of a long series of events, the last of which influences our lives on earth.

The column of gas which is ejected from a sunspot often rises to a great height above the surface of the sun, and is then described as a prominence. The matter which is hurled upwards from a big explosion or a volcanic eruption on earth may travel at a speed of hundreds of miles an hour, but the matter in these prominences is frequently hurled upwards at hundreds of thousands of miles an hour. Plate XXXV shews six successive photographs of such a prominence taken at intervals of only a few minutes. The last picture was taken within 2 hours of the first appearance of the prominence, and yet the ejected matter had already risen to a height of 567,000 miles above the surface of the sun; it must have travelled at an average speed of about 300,000 miles an hour.

Few prominences are as simple as the foregoing; usually their shapes are far more complicated, and change continually. The next series of pictures (Plate XXXVI) shews a prominence of a far more complex type, and its changes within the space of four successive days. As the sun turns round, we gradually discover that what at first appeared like a puff of smoke is an eruption of gas issuing from a sort of long crack in the sun's surface. This eruption was clearly a less explosive and altogether more leisurely affair than shewn in Plate XXXV.

The prominences are of very tenuous substance, being little

PLATE XXXV

7 h. 52 min.

8 h. 35 min.

8 h. 45 min.

8 h. 52 min.

8 h. 58 min.

Kodaikanal Observatory

9 h. 3 min.

Fig. 75. A remarkable eruptive prominence seen on November 19, 1928. The prominence attained a height of 567,000 miles in less than 2 hours.

PLATE XXXVI

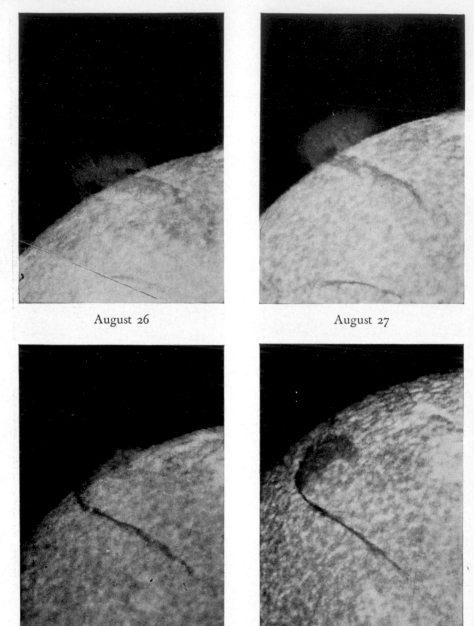

August 26   August 27

August 28   August 29

Meudon Observatory

Fig. 76. The development, and passage onto the sun's disc, of a solar prominence. The photographs were taken in calcium light (K 3) on four successive
days in 1929.

more than wisps of heated gas. They are also much cooler than the main body of the sun. For both of these reasons they look nothing like as bright as the proper surface of the sun, and so are usually lost from sight in the sun's glare, and cannot be seen under ordinary conditions. But when the moon passes in front of the sun and produces a total eclipse, the main body of the sun's light is completely shut off, the stars come out as at night, while the terrestrial landscape gets darker and darker, and finally assumes an ashy or slaty-purple appearance. Now is the time to see all the fainter lights surrounding the sun. The moment the last bit of sun is covered by the moon, the faint pearly light known as the corona flashes into view. The sun is surrounded, to a distance of hundreds of thousands of miles, by a tenuous atmosphere of molecules, atoms, and electrified particles, and the corona is simply this atmosphere seen by the light of the hidden sun. The light of the corona is less bright even than that of the prominences, so that prominences may frequently be seen shining through it. Figs. 77 and 78 (facing pp. 164 and 165) shew two photographs taken with different lengths of exposure at the eclipse of 1919.

Astronomers have devised means for seeing and studying all this, and much else, without waiting for an eclipse. We have seen how the surfaces and atmospheres of the planets can be studied in detail by the device of examining them in different colours of light—encouraging each colour of light to tell its own story. The surface of the sun can be treated by a similar method, not only with much greater ease, but also with far more profit. We no longer have to deal with a meagre quantity of reflected light, for the sun is itself pouring out a mixture of lights of all colours in such overwhelming profusion that it is easy to arrange for it to photograph itself in any colour of light we select. We need only break up the sun's light in a spectroscope, and then allow just that light which is of the precise colour we want, and no other, to pass out of the spectroscope into our camera. Yet there are very essential differences, which we must now consider, between this and the method used for the study of the planets.

Light and sound both consist of waves, and for this reason are similar in many respects. All the great noises of nature, such as the sound of a waterfall, a forest fire, a storm at sea, consist of mixtures of sound waves of all possible lengths. Of a different quality altogether from these confused torrents of noise, are the simpler and gentler noises we describe as musical sounds—cow bells on the mountains, church bells, the notes of a piano or violin. The confused torrent of sound contains waves of all lengths, but the musical sound contains waves of only a few lengths; that is why we find them pleasing to our ears.

It is the same with light. Sunlight, like the sound of a fire or a waterfall, contains waves of all lengths mixed, but there are other kinds of light which contain waves of only a few lengths—like a musical chord. If a beam of such light is passed through a spectroscope, we do not get a band of all colours, as with sunlight. We find that most colours are entirely absent, so that the "spectrum", instead of being a continuous band of colour ranging from red to violet, consists only of a few thin bright lines of colour here and there—we call it a line spectrum.

PLATE XXXVII

A. C. de la C. Crommelin

Fig. 77. The solar corona, as photographed at the eclipse of May 29, 1919. A solar prominence can be dimly seen through the coronal light at the top left-hand edge (cf. fig. 78, overleaf).

PLATE XXXVIII

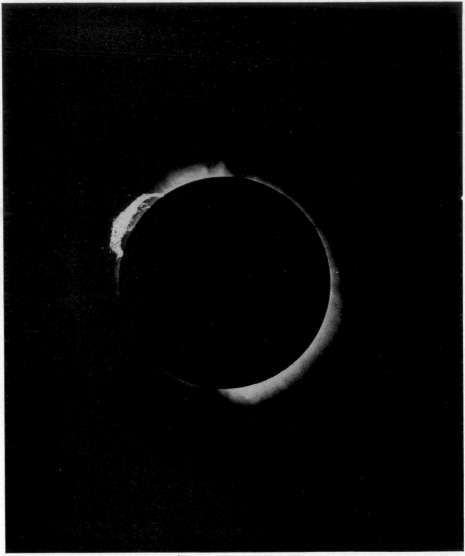

A. C. de la C. Crommelin

Fig. 78. The same as fig. 77, but with a shorter exposure. The prominence at the top left-hand edge is now seen quite clearly. It is found to have a length of more than 250,000 miles.

Such spectra are usually emitted by the atoms of a chemically simple substance—what the chemists describe as an element. Not only so, but all the atoms of any one element, such as hydrogen, give out one chord of colours; while those of any other element, such as oxygen, give out another and quite different chord. Some substances give out light which is almost entirely of one single colour; naturally these are very popular for use in electric signs and luminous tubes.

Now suppose we put a small amount of any substance, say a pinch of ordinary table salt, into a hot flame, and watch what happens to the spectrum of the flame. A number of new lines will at once appear, which must of course have originated in the salt. Possibly we may be able to recognise some of the lines. Sodium, for instance, contains a very distinctive chord, consisting of two lines of excessively bright yellow lying side by side very close together. If we recognise these in the spectrum of our salt, we shall know that the salt contains sodium.

This method of tracing out the chemical structure of substances is described as "spectroscopic analysis", and provides an extremely sensitive test for the presence of many chemical elements. It will, for example, disclose the presence of a hundred-thousandth part of a milligram (1/3,000,000,000 oz.) of lithium. It is of course not necessary that we should put the chemical substance into the flame ourselves. If we can break up the light from any flame, no matter how distant it may be, into its constituent colours, we can tell something at least as to the composition of the flame; the light which travels from it to us brings with it a message as to what substances are producing the light. This makes it possible to investigate the composition of the sun and stars.

When Newton broke up sunlight into its constituent colours, he obtained a spectrum which he believed to be continuous, consisting of all conceivable colours arranged in order. But when Fraunhofer repeated the experiment in 1803, he was surprised to find that the spectrum was crossed by a number of dark lines, which he designated as $A, B, C, \ldots, K$. The spectrum was not continuous, but shewed brief gaps in the sequence of colours. There is a very simple explanation of these gaps.

Each atom in the sun's atmosphere is capable of emitting a chord of light consisting only of certain special and quite sharply-defined colours, but it cannot do this until it has first absorbed light of these same colours. Generally speaking, the atoms of a hot substance are likely to be in what we describe as an "excited" state, in which they have stores of light of their own peculiar colours to emit. The atoms of a cool substance, on the other hand, are likely to be in an "unexcited" state, in which they are hungry for light of these colours.

With this in our minds, let us fix our attention on the confused torrent of light which comes pouring up from the hot interior of the sun to the comparatively cool layers near its surface. It contains all colours of light, so that each atom in the comparatively cool atmosphere of the sun must be continually bathed in light of just those particular colours, among a host of others, which it is capable and desirous of absorbing. The atom

PLATE XXXIX

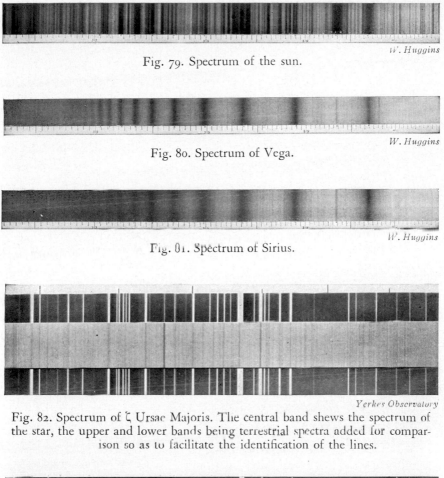

W. Huggins

Fig. 79. Spectrum of the sun.

W. Huggins

Fig. 80. Spectrum of Vega.

W. Huggins

Fig. 81. Spectrum of Sirius.

Yerkes Observatory

Fig. 82. Spectrum of ζ Ursae Majoris. The central band shews the spectrum of the star, the upper and lower bands being terrestrial spectra added for comparison so as to facilitate the identification of the lines.

Yerkes Observatory

Fig. 83. Spectrum of ζ Ursae Majoris. The central band shews the spectrum of the same star at a later date. Each line in the spectrum is now seen to be doubled shewing that the star is a binary system (see p. 187).

PLATE XL

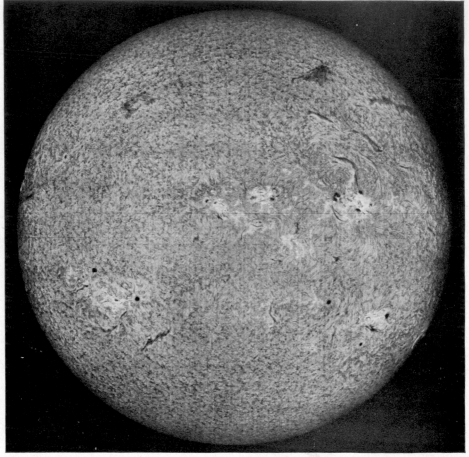

Mt Wilson Observatory

Fig. 84. The sun photographed in hydrogen light (Hα). This and the photograph shewn in Plate XXXI were taken simultaneously.

naturally absorbs some of this light, and the main torrent goes on its way weakened in light of this particular colour. By the time it has run the gauntlet of all the hungry cool atoms which lie in wait for it in the sun's atmosphere, and finally emerges into space, it will be deficient in all the colours associated with these atoms—the colours they emit when hot, and absorb when cool.

For this reason, the spectrum of the sun is necessarily crossed by a number of dark lines and bands; these are not evidence of hot atoms emitting light in the sun's interior, but of cool atoms in the sun's atmosphere absorbing it. Fraunhofer knew of only eleven such lines, but the modern astronomer knows many thousands, and it is the same with other stars. On Plate XXXIX (facing p. 166), fig. 79 shews a fragment of the sun's spectrum, while figs. 80–83 shew spectra of other stars.

The position of these lines and bands provides the astronomer with an enormous storehouse of information, to which he returns again and again when he wants knowledge about the stars—how bright they are, how massive, how distant, how fast they are moving in space, how rapidly they are rotating, and so forth. The important point for us at the moment is that the colours of light which are missing in the spectra of the sun and stars can almost always be identified with the colours of light emitted by known substances on earth. When this can be done, we know that atoms of these same substances are at work in the sun's atmosphere, absorbing light as it comes out, and so preventing it from reaching us. It is precisely the method by which we discover that ozone is present in the upper atmosphere of the earth (p. 62).

It is very significant that practically all the thousands of lines in the spectra of the sun and stars can be identified with the lines of substances which are known on earth. This of course shews that the sun and stars are built up of the same kind of atoms as we are familiar with on earth—hydrogen, oxygen, nitrogen, iron, copper, gold, and so forth. If we travel to the sun or stars we shall expect to see many strange sights, but we must not expect to discover any new substances. The universe appears to be built of the same kinds of bricks throughout.

To return to our study of the sun's surface, suppose we now allow the sun to photograph itself in a certain colour of light which is emitted by, let us say, hydrogen atoms. We shall not, of course, get a photograph of the complete sun, nor even of all the hydrogen in the sun, but only of so much of the sun's hydrogen as is emitting this particular colour of light, and is at the same time near enough to the surface for its light to reach us. For instance, fig. 84 (facing p. 167) shews the sun photographed in a certain kind of hydrogen light, that of the line which Fraunhofer designated C, but which we now describe as Hα.

This photograph was taken at precisely the same moment as fig. 69 (facing p. 156). But in the earlier photograph all the colours of light were shouting together, and the only information which they tell us in common is "sunspots"; in fig. 84 the hydrogen light is quietly telling its own story, alone and undisturbed by the others. And an interesting story it is.

We learn how the hydrogen is not uniformly distributed in the sun, but occurs in a mottled formation of clouds, which look as though they were drifting, or being pushed about, rather like the clouds in the earth's atmosphere. Yet this comparison does not extend to size, since many of these clouds are far larger than the whole earth. Here and there, the mottled formation gives place to the long lines described as filaments, three of which can be seen near the top right-hand corner of the picture, while still another formation appears in the vicinity of sunspots. We notice that groups of sunspots affect an area of the sun's surface which is incomparably larger than the actual spots of blackness which superficial observation discloses. Fig. 85 shews the vicinity of a group of sunspots photographed in this same hydrogen light; we notice how closely the cloud formation is related to the positions of the dark spots.

Figs. 86 and 87 (facing p. 171) shew the sun photographed simultaneously in hydrogen light of a special kind ($H\delta$) and in calcium light (H_2). The pictures look very different, for the simple reason that one is a picture of hydrogen in the sun and the other a picture of calcium in the sun.

So long as the atoms of a gas are at rest and undisturbed they will not give out light at all. To make a gas light up we must do something to it, just as we must with an electric-light bulb, or a horse-shoe. For instance, we may pass an electric current through it—almost the only method available under terrestrial conditions—or we may heat it up; just as a solid horse-shoe begins to glow and then light up when we heat it, so it is with the atoms of a gas. It is in this way that the collection of atoms which forms the sun is made to give out light.

The blacksmith tells the temperature of a piece of hot iron by its colour. As he heats it up, its colour gradually changes—red hot, yellow hot, white hot, and so on. The same colour always denotes the same degree of heat, and this is true whether the emitting substance is iron or not.

It is much the same with a gas : we can tell its temperature from the kind of light it emits. All the atoms which have impressed their mark on the photographic plate reproduced in fig. 86 were excited in the same way, and so were all, within limits, at the same temperature. Thus their light, in recording itself on the photographic plate, has presented us with a picture of precisely those parts of the sun's atmosphere which are at this special temperature and no other, and so emit the special kind of light which we call $H\delta$. The atoms which are shewn in fig. 87 were at the different temperature at which the kind of light is emitted which we call H_2. We may say, then, that figs. 86 and 87 shew atoms of the sun which are at different temperatures.

As the sun's heat flows from a hot interior to a cooler surface, the hottest layers are naturally also the deepest. We have described our pictures as photographs of different parts of the sun which are at different temperatures, but we might equally have described them as photographs of different layers which are at different depths. When pictures of different layers of the sun are obtained in this way, the light they emit shews that many of their atoms are in a special state which is very well known to physicists—in

PLATE XLI

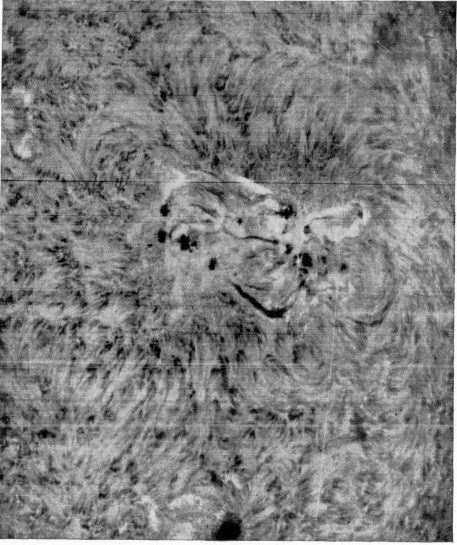

Mt Wilson Observatory

Fig. 85. A complicated group of sunspots photographed in hydrogen light (Hα).

PLATE XLII

Mt Wilson Observatory

Fig. 86. The sun photographed in hydrogen light (Hδ).

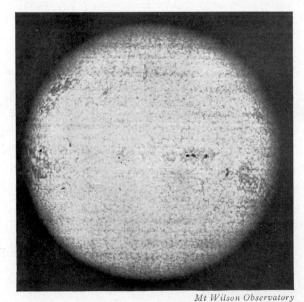

Mt Wilson Observatory

Fig. 87. The sun photographed in calcium light (H₂). This
and the photograph above were taken simultaneously.

brief, they are partially broken up by the heat. And the deeper we go into the interior of the sun, the more the atoms are found to be broken up.

When we heat solid ice, it turns into liquid water; the molecules move more easily, because the bonds which have hitherto gripped them closely together have been broken down by the heat; as soon as they can slip quite freely past one another, the ice has turned completely into water. When we heat liquid water, it turns into gaseous steam; the bonds are still further weakened, so that the molecules can now move quite independently of one another. If we heat up the steam, even the bonds which hold the atoms together inside the molecules are loosened, so that the molecules themselves break up into atoms of oxygen and hydrogen. And if we could heat these atoms still further, until they reached the temperature of the sun's atmosphere, we should find that even the atoms themselves were breaking up —as they actually are in the outer layers of the sun.

If we take our rocket near to the sun's surface and analyse a sample of the sun's atmosphere, we shall find that it consists of atoms which are beginning to break up. But if we proceed inward to the sun's lower layers, we find the atoms breaking up more and more until, when we get near the centre, very little is left except completely broken atoms. It is a state of matter of which we have no experience, and we hardly know whether it is best described as solid, liquid, or gaseous.

We have seen how the pressure at the centre of our earth must be one of millions of atmospheres; that at the centre of the far more massive sun must be about 50,000 million atmospheres. Such a pressure as this packs the broken fragments of atoms so closely together that something like a pound of substance would go into a thimble. It is only because the atoms are broken up that they can be packed as closely as this.

It will never be possible to experiment with matter in this state in our laboratories—indeed, it would kill us if we tried. For, at a rough calculation, the temperature at the centre of the sun must be some 40 or 50 million degrees. And even a pinhead of matter at this temperature would radiate so much energy off into space, that we should need an engine of about 3000 million million horse-power to make good the wastage, and keep up the temperature of the pinhead of matter. This would emit its radiation in the form of a terrific blast against which nothing could stand. Quite close to the pinhead, the flow of radiation would produce a pressure of millions of tons to the square inch. This pressure plays its part in keeping the sun from collapsing, and plays an even more important part in the more massive of the stars, which it blows out until they are as tenuous as immense bubbles. Even a hundred yards away from our pinhead, the blast of radiation would be so strong as to blow over any fortifications which have ever been built, and it would speedily shrivel up any man who ventured to within a thousand miles of the pinhead from which it issued.

CHAPTER VII

THE STARS

We all know now that our sun is a very ordinary star, but it took men a long time to discover this. Perhaps this is not surprising, for certainly it does not look much like an ordinary star to us. The reason is, of course, that it is enormously nearer than any of the other stars.

We have seen how the ancients imagined the earth to be the fixed centre of the universe, round which everything else moved. The stars merely formed a background of light, against which they could map out the motions of the sun, moon and planets. They thought of the stars as attached to the inside of a hollow sphere, which turned round over the earth much as a telescope dome turns round over the floor of a telescope, or "as one might turn a cap round on one's head". And although a few of the more philosophical of the Greeks gave reasons for thinking that the earth moved round the sun, they had no means of making their opinions or arguments known to a wide circle of people, so that these were forgotten as the world gradually became submerged in the intellectual darkness of the Middle Ages. Then, in 1543, a Polish monk, Copernicus, advanced views and arguments which were very similar to those which Aristarchus of Samos had propounded 1800 years earlier, although the extent to which he was indebted to his Greek predecessors is not clear.

In brief, Copernicus declared that the sun, and not the earth, formed the centre of the solar system, that the earth was merely a planet, and that it, like all the other planets, moved round the sun.

Against this 1800-year-old thesis the eminent Danish astronomer, Tycho Brahe, as well as many others, raised an objection which was itself nearly 1800 years old. Indeed, Archimedes had previously brought forward precisely the same objection against the similar opinions of Aristarchus of Samos. The objection was, in brief, that if the earth were really moving round the sun in space, the apparent arrangement of the stars ought continually to change. If I walk about in a garden, I see the arrangement of the trees continually changing; one seems to move behind another, a third to step out into view, and so on. Yet a greenfly crawling about on a rosebud is not likely to notice any such changes in the arrangement of the trees—his rosebud is too small. Those who opposed Copernicus argued that, as no such changes were observed to occur in the arrangement of the stars, the earth must be standing still in space. They did not know that, viewed as objects in the celestial garden, the earth's orbit and even the whole of the solar system are less than the smallest of rosebuds. As Aristarchus had said 1800 years before Copernicus, the whole of the earth's orbit round the sun stands in the same relation to the universe as the centre of a sphere to its surface.

Nevertheless, when the positions of the stars are measured with the help of a powerful telescope, their apparent arrangement is found to be continually changing. The changes are of two distinct kinds. As the sun is continually forging ahead through the stars, and dragging us with it, the stellar scenery changes in the way in which terrestrial scenery changes when we drive through a forest. But besides this, the motion of the earth round the sun produces change of another kind. The sky of July will look different from the sky of January, because between January and July we shall have moved 186 million miles round the sun to the opposite end of the earth's orbit. When January comes round again, things will be back as they were in the previous January, because the earth will have completed its orbit, and we shall have come back to our original position relative to the sun.

If we continue to think in terrestrial terms, this 186 million miles' motion of the earth seems a fantastically long journey; on the astronomical scale it is so minute that for a long time astronomers were unable to detect the small apparent rearrangement of stellar positions which it caused. Indeed this was not detected until 1838, and it then became possible to measure the distances of the stars.

Exact modern measurements shew that the nearest stars are almost exactly a million times as distant as the nearest planets. We have already seen how sparsely scattered the planets are in the solar system; it now appears that space is even more empty of stars than the solar system is of planets. Five fruits placed in the five continents of the earth—an apple in Europe, a pear in Asia, a cherry in America, and so on—will give us a scale model shewing relation between the sizes of the stars and their distances from one another. We readily understand why the stars can only be seen as points of light, and we can further see that, even if the stars were surrounded by planets as is our own sun, these planets would be much too faint and also much too near to the central sun to be seen as separate objects.

If we take six wasps and set them flying blindly about in a cage 1000 miles long, 1000 miles broad and 1000 miles high, we shall again have a model of the distance of the stars. We can also make it represent the speeds of their motions if we slow down our wasps until they move only at about a hundredth part of a snail's pace.

We may be sure that, as the wasps fly about their big cage at this speed, they will not bump into one another, or even pass near to one another, at very frequent intervals. Yet it is most probably only when stars do this that planets like our earth come into existence—by the process we have already described (p. 155). For this reason, the birth of planets must be a rare event, and also, since the universe has not existed for ever, planets themselves must be very rare. People used to think of each star as giving light to, and supporting life on, a retinue of planets, but it now looks as though planets are the rare exceptions; at the most favourable computation, it seems likely that only about one star in every hundred thousand can have a family of planets to take care of.

We have already seen how greatly the stars differ from one another in apparent brightness. There are two distinct causes for this—the stars are intrinsically of different brightnesses in themselves, and are also at different distances from us. A star may look bright because it is near to us, as in the conspicuous instance of our own sun, or because it is a very bright object in itself, or of course from a combination of these two reasons.

As soon as we know the distance of a star, we can say how much of its apparent faintness or brightness is attributable to distance, and how much to intrinsic faintness or brightness. This makes it possible to compare the intrinsic brightnesses—or luminosities, to use the technical word—of the different stars.

The procedure is as follows. According to a well-known law of physics, light falls off as the inverse square of the distance; to take a simple illustration, if I walk to double my present distance from a street light, it will look only a quarter as bright. In the same way, if we place the sun at a million times its present distance, it will look a million million times less bright than now. At its present distance the sun has a brightness of twelve million million of the units we introduced on p. 95, so that if it receded to a million times its present distance, its brightness would be reduced to twelve units; we should still be able to see it, but only as a rather faint star.

A great number of the stars in the sky shine with more than twelve units of brightness, and all except three of these—Sirius, α Centauri and Procyon—are known to be more than a million times as distant as the sun. All these stars, then, must be intrinsically brighter than the sun. Sirius, α Centauri and Procyon are also known to be intrinsically brighter than the sun, and the same is true of most of the stars we can see with our unaided eyes. Broadly speaking, all the stars which look bright in the sky are intrinsically brighter than the sun.

Sirius, which appears the brightest star in the whole sky, is at a distance of 51 million million miles, or about 550,000 times the distance of the sun. If the sun were placed where Sirius is, it would have a brightness of only 40 units, whereas Sirius has a brightness of 1080 units. Thus Sirius is a very luminous star—twenty-seven times as luminous as the sun. Its brilliant appearance results from a favourable combination of the two factors which make for brilliance. It is both very bright in itself, and also very near, only one of the 5000 stars we can see without a telescope being nearer to us than Sirius.

Many of the nearest stars are of such low intrinsic luminosity that, in spite of their nearness, they cannot be seen at all by our unaided eyesight, but need a quite powerful telescope. The nearest of all known stars, Proxima, with a brightness of only a sixtieth of a unit, is so faint that it was only discovered quite recently. Its intrinsic luminosity is so low that it only gives out about a 20,000th part as much light as the sun, and even less heat. If it were put in place of our sun, the earth would become far colder than Pluto now is, and we should all be frozen solid in a very short time.

At the other end of the scale we find innumerable stars which are intrinsically more luminous even than Sirius, but look less bright in the sky because they are more distant. The brightest of all (*S* Doradus) gives out at least 300,000 times as much radiation as the sun, so that if it were suddenly to replace the sun, we should all be roasted in a fraction of a minute, and turned into vapour—sea, rocks, earth, and all—in a very few hours.

Nevertheless, the majority of stars prove to be fainter than the sun. Of the thirty stars which are nearest to it in space, only three are more luminous than the sun, while most of the remaining twenty-seven are very much less luminous. Even this is not the whole story, for it must be added that we happen to inhabit a part of the sky in which the stars are very distinctly above the average in luminosity.

We have seen how the apparent brightness of a star depends on two factors, namely, its nearness and its intrinsic luminosity. The latter of these two factors, the intrinsic luminosity of the star, itself depends also on two factors—the size of the star and the amount of radiation it emits from each square inch of its surface. We have found, for instance, that Sirius is twenty-seven times as luminous as the sun. But this leaves it an open question whether Sirius has twenty-seven times as much surface as the sun, or whether it is of the same size as the sun and gives out twenty-seven times as much radiation per square inch, or what other combinations of size and emission of radiation result in its total output being what it is.

The star's spectrum provides the means of answering this and all similar questions. For it tells us how much radiation the star emits from each square inch of its surface, and from this we can deduce the actual size of the star.

We have already seen that the quality of a star's spectrum depends on the temperature of the surface of the star. Different varieties of spectra correspond to different temperatures, with the result that, except for minute differences in detail, all spectra can be arranged in one single continuous series. As we pass from one end of this series to another, we are passing through a continuous range of temperatures of stellar surfaces. If we could gradually heat up the surface of a single star, we should find its spectrum passing through the whole of the sequence in succession. Indeed, sometimes nature performs this experiment for us; certain stars known as "variables" change in this manner spontaneously and of themselves, and we have only to watch the event happening to see the continuous sequence of spectra demonstrated in nature's own laboratory.

The amount of radiation which any surface emits also depends on the temperature of the surface; as a substance is heated up, it radiates out more and more energy. A really hot coal fire, such as we see in the firebox of a locomotive, may perhaps give about a quarter of a horse-power per square inch. The far hotter carbon in an electric arc may give as much as 6 horse-power per square inch.

When two stars shew identical, or very similar, spectra—as for instance Sirius and Vega (Plate XXXIX, facing p. 166)—we know that their surfaces must be at the same temperature and so are emitting the same amount of energy per square inch. Thus any difference in the intrinsic luminosities of two such stars can only result from a difference in their sizes. On the other hand, when two stars have different spectra, their surfaces must be at different temperatures and so must emit different amounts of energy per square inch. The spectra which form the sequence already mentioned may be identified with different temperatures and different emissions of energy to the square inch.

The spectra which form one end of this sequence indicate temperatures of not more than about 1400 degrees Centigrade, at which each square inch of the star's surface gives out only about a quarter of a horse-power—about the same as a really hot coal fire. We have seen how heating up a mass of iron causes its apparent colour to change in the sense of passing along the spectrum from the red end towards the violet. It is much the same with the stars, and these coolest stars of all are at such low temperatures that their radiation is almost entirely at the red end of the spectrum; they are in fact merely red hot. Many of them look red, or at least reddish, to the eye, so that they are frequently described as red stars.

About half-way along the sequence we come to spectra like that of the sun. These indicate a temperature of about 5600 degrees Centigrade, and at such a temperature each square inch of surface gives out about 50 horse-power. We can check the accuracy of this estimate in the following way.

If we measure how much sunshine falls on a square inch of the earth's surface, we can calculate first how much falls on the whole earth, and then how much is given out by the whole sun. If we divide this last number by the number of square inches on the whole surface of the sun, we can find how much sunshine is given out by each square inch of the sun's surface. We find that the energy equivalent of the sunshine given out by each square inch of the sun's surface is just about 50 horse-power—enough to run a powerful car all day and all night for millions of years, although of course not for all eternity, since even the sun's colossal stores of energy must come to an end some time. The area on which a single locomotive could stand would give out enough energy to run all the railways in the British Isles.

The spectra which lie at the remote end of the sequence indicate temperatures of perhaps 60,000 or 70,000 degrees Centigrade, so that each square inch of the star's surface will give out anything from 500,000 to 1,000,000 horse-power of energy—the amount of star that we could cover with a postage-stamp radiates out enough energy to run all the liners on the Atlantic Ocean. The main bulk of the radiation from these stars is invisible, lying far beyond the violet end of the spectrum. The visible radiation is largely concentrated in the violet end, so that the stars are often described as blue stars.

In this way the spectrum of a star informs us how much energy each square inch of its surface emits. Knowing the intrinsic luminosity of the star is of course the same thing as knowing the total amount of energy that its whole surface emits. A simple division will now tell us how many square inches of surface it has, from which it is an easy matter to calculate the diameter and size of the star.

The results of such calculations are very interesting, the more so as they shew that the sizes of the stars are not mere random quantities, but are closely connected with the physical states of the stars. Let us discuss this relation by working down gradually from the largest stars to the smallest.

The largest stars of all are without exception found to be red and cool. They only give out about a quarter horse-power of radiation per square inch, and so need a great many square inches to work off their heat. They are the immense stars, blown out like colossal bubbles by the pressure of radiation, to which we have already alluded (p. 172). We have recorded the disastrous consequences which would follow if *S* Doradus or Proxima were substituted for our sun. If one of these large red stars were to re-place our sun, the results would be even more disastrous, since we should find ourselves inside it; the stars are larger than the whole of the earth's orbit. Indeed the largest yet known (Antares) has a diameter 450 times that of the sun—or about 400 million miles. We could pack about 60 million suns inside it, and there would still be room to spare. Our rocket, averaging more than 5000 miles an hour, took 2 days to reach the moon. If we tried to travel through the sun at the same rate it would take us a whole week, but if we tried to travel through this big star at the same rate, it would take 9 years. It is perhaps not surprising that astronomers describe these stars as "giants".

Let us now imagine that we measure all the stars, and place them in a row in order of size. We shall find that to a large extent we have also arranged them in order of colour. As we have just seen, the very large stars are all red; as we pass from these to rather smaller stars, we shall find the colour becoming less red. So it goes on, until finally we come to stars which are quite a lot smaller, having perhaps only ten or twenty times the diameter of the sun. These have only about a thousandth part as much surface as the red giants, so that to give out the same amount of radiation, they must give out a thousand times as much energy from each square inch. This being so, it is not surprising to find that these stars are at excessively high temperatures; they are the very hot blue stars of which we have already spoken.

We now seem to have used up the whole range of possible colours, and so of course of spectra, for stars, although we have only travelled a small way along the range of possible sizes—for the majority of stars are far smaller than the blue stars we have just described, with ten or twenty times the diameter of the sun. In actual fact as we pass to these still smaller stars, we find the range of colours and spectra merely repeating themselves. Instead of the smaller stars getting still hotter and bluer, we find them getting cooler and redder again, so that they not only have fewer square inches of surface, but also emit less radiation from each square inch. Clearly, they are far feebler stars than the red giants from which we started. In the end, we come to stars which are just as red and cool as the huge giants, but far smaller in size. These are known as red "dwarfs"—with justice, since most of them are much smaller than our sun, and have only about a thousandth part of the diameter of the red giants. If we take a full stop on this page to represent one of these red dwarfs, the red giants will be represented by a cart-wheel.

So far we have found three main types of stars:

Very large (giants)—red and cool.
Middle size—blue and hot.
Very small (dwarfs)—red and cool again.

But the limit of smallness has not yet been reached, and stars even smaller than the red dwarfs are known to exist. The smallest of red dwarfs are still about the size of Jupiter or Saturn—only a thousandth part as big as the sun, but still a thousand times bigger than the earth. The smallest of all known stars are only about the size of the earth. These are described as "white dwarfs", because they are mostly white in colour, with spectra which usually correspond to temperatures of 10,000 degrees Centigrade or even more. Such high temperatures cause each inch of their surfaces to radiate intensely, and yet their surfaces are so small that their total radiation is very small indeed; they are so faint that only a few have so far been discovered.

We have already seen that the sun gives out light of all wave-lengths, although only about four octaves of light are given out in large amounts, and only one octave reaches us in abundance. We have also seen that a number of stars are far cooler than the sun. If we describe the sun as being white hot, these stars must be described as only red hot, and the radiation they give out is one or even two octaves lower than the radiation of the sun. If our sun had given out such radiation, we may perhaps suppose that our eyes would have adjusted themselves to it so that our visible spectrum would have been one or two octaves lower. We should not have been able to see our present green, blue, etc., at all, but only colours for which our languages contain no names, because we cannot see them. Grass, which now absorbs all colours except green, would look white, while the sky would look black. The scenery in general would look like the infra-red photograph shewn in fig. 37 (Plate XV, p. 76), while the infra-red pictures shewn in Plate XLIII suggest that many of the minor details of life would be different from what they now are.

These red stars, being cooler than the sun, give out light on the infra-red side of the sun's spectrum. Stars which are hotter than the sun naturally give spectra on the other, the ultra-violet, side. Sirius, for instance, with a temperature roughly double that of the sun, gives out a spectrum of light which is about an octave higher than the sun's. It may not appear to be so in an ordinary photograph, such as is shewn in Plate XXXIX (facing p. 166), because such photographs only shew the tail end running towards the red—most of the light is ultra-violet, and so is shut out by the ozone layer of our atmosphere. If Sirius had planets, the eyes of their inhabitants would probably have adjusted themselves to ultra-violet colours, for which again we have no names because we cannot see them. Life would be very different for such people. To take a trivial instance, glass is opaque to ultra-violet light, so that they could not use it for windows in their houses. On the other hand, it would do very well for the walls of the houses— except for the dangers referred to in the proverb. Air is nearly opaque to ultra-violet light because of scattering, and is quite opaque if it contains much ozone, so that if the Sirians had an atmosphere at all like ours, their sky would look perpetually black.

The hottest stars of all give spectra which lie three or three and a half octaves above that of the sun. If we want to find light of

PLATE XLIII

Ilford Co.

Fig. 88. Portrait of a Hottentot, taken by infra-red and ordinary light respectively. The characteristic dark pigment is seen to be transparent to infra-red radiation.

F. C. Bawden. Ilford Co.

Fig. 89. A potato leaf photographed in infra-red and ordinary light respectively. The black marks in the infra-red picture indicate the presence of potato blight, and cannot be seen in the picture taken by ordinary light.

PLATE XLIV

Herbert Flower. Ilford Co.

Fig. 90. Star-fish as seen by X-radiation.

Herbert Flower. Ilford Co.

Fig. 91. Poppy-heads as seen by X-radiation.

wave-lengths even shorter than this we must go inside the stars. If we sample the radiation a few thousand miles inside the sun, we shall find a spectrum like that of Sirius; a little farther in, the spectrum will have gone yet another octave up, and so on. At the centre of the sun, and probably of most stars, it is something like thirteen octaves up; the radiation here is of the kind we describe as X-radiation. Most substances are transparent to this, so that if we lived inside a star, shells, flowers, etc., would look like the photographs shewn in Plate XLIV, opposite.

So far we have been dealing only with those qualities of a star which can be seen by inspection, such as its temperature and size. We now pass to something more fundamental—the amount of substance the star contains, which we call its "mass". When we want to find out how much substance an object contains on earth, we usually weigh it, which means that we measure the gravitational pull between it and the earth. We can weigh the stars in much the same way, and so find out how much substance they contain.

Most stars pursue solitary paths through space, but occasionally we find them travelling in pairs, forming what is described as a binary system, or a double star. Each star grips the other fast in its gravitational pull, so that the two move through space together, each describing an orbit round the other. They keep together for just the same reason as the sun and earth; gravitation is too strong to permit of their separating—neither of them has speed enough to jump clear of the other.

We shall soon see that such binary systems are often very

interesting in themselves, but they are specially interesting as providing an opportunity for weighing the stars.

Each of the component stars of a binary system moves round the other somewhat as the earth moves round the sun, but with one very significant difference. The earth's mass is so much smaller than the sun's (1 to 332,000) that the sun's motion is hardly disturbed by the puny gravitational pull of the earth. In a true binary system, on the other hand, the two stars are much nearer to one another in mass. Consequently there is much more of an equal partnership in the matter of gravitational pulls, so that neither star is just making the other run round it, but rather the pair revolve about some point between the two. By noticing how much each star pulls on the other, we can find the ratio of their weights, and if we can also measure the dimensions of the orbit, we can find the actual weights of both the stars.

Sometimes the two stars which form a binary system are fairly similar in respect of size, colour and luminosity, so that the pair may properly be described as well matched. Such well-matched pairs are particularly frequent among the brightest and hottest stars of all. Indeed more often than not these brightest and hottest stars of all form constituents of binary systems. In such cases, the two constituents are often found to be very close indeed to one another; they may even touch, or—in extreme cases—overlap. It seems likely that stars whose constituents are as close as this originally formed a single mass, which has broken up as a result of spinning too fast for safety—rather as a fly-wheel is apt to break if it is spun too fast.

In other cases the two stars are exceedingly ill-matched and incongruous. A conspicuous instance is provided by Sirius, which forms a binary system with a white dwarf star. The principal star, the Sirius which shines so brightly in the sky, has a diameter half as large again as the sun, while its white dwarf companion has only a thirtieth of the sun's diameter. The red giant o Ceti provides an even more extreme instance of the same thing. It has about 400 times the diameter of the sun, and forms a binary system with a white dwarf companion whose diameter is unknown, but can hardly be more than a ten-thousandth part of that of the principal star. If the principal star is represented by a cart-wheel, its white dwarf companion is a mere grain of sand—perhaps only a speck of dust.

Even when there is an extreme disparity of size, the masses are often found to be fairly equal, the immense star perhaps having only five or ten times the mass of its minute companion. Generally speaking, it is likely that even white dwarf stars have masses which are comparable with ordinary stars. They resemble the earth in size, but the sun in mass. This of course means that the substance of a white dwarf star must be packed enormously more compactly than the substance of the sun. The average ton of matter in the sun occupies about a cubic yard, but the average ton of matter in an ordinary white dwarf would all go inside a thimble. By contrast the average ton of matter in the big star of o Ceti occupies about as much space as the interior of Waterloo Station.

Under such conditions as we encounter on earth, it is impossible to crush matter together as closely as it is in the white dwarf stars. The secret of these stars is that their atoms are broken up into their separate constituent particles. As we passed downwards in the sun, we saw the temperature becoming hotter and hotter, and the atoms more and more broken up (p. 171). At the centres of the white dwarfs, the temperature is incomparably hotter even than at the centre of the sun, so that the atoms are completely broken up, and can be packed into a very small space indeed.

The majority of binary systems do not belong to the sensational types which have so far been described, but consist of two components which are usually neither excessively close nor excessively dissimilar. For instance, fig. 92 (facing p. 196) shews photographs of the very ordinary binary star Kruger 60 taken in the years 1908, 1915, and 1920. When a large number of observations of the kind are available, it is easy to complete the orbit and then calculate the masses of the two constituents; in the case of Kruger 60 they are found to be one-quarter and one-fifth of that of the sun. Few binary systems are found in which the constituents have masses much smaller than these, but in the other direction we find masses ranging up to hundreds of times that of the sun.

The two components of the star Kruger 60 take fifty-five of our years to move round one another. Even this is a fairly rapid period of revolution for a binary star; many such systems have periods of thousands, and sometimes hundreds of thousands, of years.

At the other extreme are systems in which the period is very short, perhaps only a few days or even hours. Such systems cannot be seen or photographed as anything but single points of light, since the two components are too near to be seen as distinct stars in the telescope. Sometimes the orbits of such a binary system are so located in space that one component comes between the earth and the other component once in every complete revolution. At such moments the light of the second component is eclipsed and the total light of the star is temporarily diminished. A binary system of this kind is described as an eclipsing variable, and in favourable cases the observed changes in the total light may enable us to reconstruct the whole motion and calculate the size of the orbit, and also the diameters and masses of the two component stars.

We shall not of course see any eclipsing effect in a binary system unless the orbits of the components lie so that one component passes directly in front of the other as seen from the earth. But there are other ways of knowing that a system is binary.

When a train or motor-car rushes past us sounding its whistle or horn, we notice a fall in the pitch of the note as it passes by. This fall of pitch results from the wave-like nature of sound; our ears necessarily pick up more waves a second when the train is coming towards us than when it is receding from us.

Light also is of a wave-like nature, so that when a star is approaching us, our eyes pick up more waves per second than they would if the star were at rest, and the light of the star appears more blue in colour. If the star is receding from us, fewer waves are picked up, and the light appears more red in colour than it would normally do. Thus we can tell whether a star is receding from us or advancing towards us by studying its spectrum. When the spectrum contains sharp, clearly-defined lines, we can measure the amount by which they are displaced with great accuracy, and from this can deduce the exact speed of advance or recession of the star.

The spectral lines may be displaced by precisely the same amount year after year; in such a case we know that the star is moving towards or away from us at a perfectly uniform speed. In other cases the displacement varies continually, so that the star's speed of motion must continually be changing, and we conclude that the star is describing an orbit about a companion which is either entirely dark, or so faint that we cannot see its spectrum. Sometimes, as in the case of the star ζ Ursae Majoris whose spectrum is shewn on Plate XXXIX (facing p. 166), the spectra of both constituents can be seen, and we can then calculate the orbits of both as definitely as though we saw the stars themselves moving in space. Knowing the orbits, we can again calculate the masses of the constituent stars.

Thus we see that there are a great many ways of estimating stellar masses. Whichever method we use, the giant and blue stars are always found to be enormously more massive than the dwarf stars. The most massive star of which the weights are known with any certainty is a blue star known as Plaskett's star, in which the components each have about a hundred times the weight of the sun.

From methods such as those just described, we obtain a tremendous store of information as to the masses, sizes and temperatures of the stars. A few years ago astronomers could tell us very little about the stars except their names and positions in the sky, but they can now add a tremendous amount of information about each star. It adds enormously to the interest of our study of the sky if we can think of the stars in terms of their size, motion in space, weight, colour and other physical characteristics.

When we do this, we often find that a constellation is not a mere haphazard division of stars; its principal stars frequently prove to be very similar in their physical constitution, and at the same time are found to be all moving in the same direction with the same speed, thus shewing that they are physically connected.

A conspicuous instance is to be found in the stars of the constellation Orion. With the exception of the brightest star of the whole constellation, *a* Orionis or Betelgeux, practically all the brighter stars are moving in the same direction and at about the same rate. Also their physical characteristics are so similar that it becomes natural to compare them to a flock of well-matched birds. Apart from the exceptional star Betelgeux, the twelve next brightest stars are all exceptionally hot, exceptionally bright and exceptionally massive. They are all blue in colour, and belong to the class of stars whose members are exceptionally prone to break up into binary systems; and in fact all but one of these twelve stars are either known or suspected to be a binary. The brightest of the twelve, Rigel or *β* Orionis, is of special interest as being one of the most luminous stars known, its intrinsic luminosity being about 15,000 times that of the sun.

We obtain a slightly different story, although one in much the same style, when we turn from the constellation of Orion to that of the Great Bear. Again nearly all the stars are of one colour, but this time it is white. They form a group of stars which are less magnificent than those of Orion, a group which is much nearer to us and altogether a more homely affair, although still impressive enough. Six out of the seven of the stars which form the well-known Plough are white, and rather like Sirius in their physical characteristics. They are all larger, hotter, more luminous and more massive than the sun, although far less so than the Orion stars. Again, the brightest star in the whole constellation, α Ursae Majoris, or Dubhe, stands apart from the rest, being a rather large, cool, red star moving in a path of its own. Only three of the seven stars of the Plough are binary, for the stars of the Great Bear are already below the level of luminosity and temperature at which almost every star is binary.

We have already noticed that the conspicuous stars which form the constellations are mostly more luminous than the sun. They are also quite near home on the astronomical scale. For even the most luminous of all stars cannot be seen with our unaided eyes if they are at a great distance from us, and yet most of the conspicuous stars of the constellations can be seen very easily with our unaided eyes. Thus we may be sure that they are both exceptionally luminous and exceptionally near. Indeed it would be rather surprising if the most conspicuous stars in the whole sky did not owe their exceptional brilliance to a combination of favourable circumstances.

If we want to study the average star we must seek the aid of a telescope. We have already seen how this collects light, and so effectively increases the diameter of the pupil of our eye. A telescope with ten times the aperture of our eye ought to enable us to see every class of astronomical object to a distance in space ten times greater than that to which we can see without its aid. Thus, if the stars were uniformly distributed in space, we ought to see a thousand times as many stars as with our unaided eyes. With a telescope of twenty times the aperture of our eye, we ought to see eight thousand times as many stars, and so on indefinitely. When we actually perform this experiment, we find that the law holds good up to a certain distance only. After that it begins to fail; we see fewer stars than the law would lead us to expect, as though some stars were missing from their places. This must of course mean that space is not uniformly filled with stars. If we go far enough, we shall come to a limit where the stars begin to fall off, and we discover where this limit occurs by noticing where the law first begins to fail.

The five photographs of star-fields on Plates XLV–XLVII (following p. 196) will shew how the method is worked. The same field of stars is photographed with different exposures, these being adjusted so that each plate (except the last) shews stars three stellar magnitudes fainter than the plate before it. Now a star which is three stellar magnitudes fainter than another has approximately a sixteenth of the brightness of the latter (see fig. 42, p. 97). It is easy to shew that if space were uniformly filled with stars each plate except the last would contain 64 times as many stars as the preceding; for the last plate the ratio would be 16.

Actually the increase in the number of stars on successive plates falls far below these numbers, shewing that the limit to the system of stars is touched quite early in the sequence.

The two Herschels, father and son, used a similar method for mapping out the shape and the limits of the system of stars to which our sun belongs. If the sun were at the centre of a globular mass of stars, the limit would obviously occur at the same distance in all directions. Actually the limit is found to occur at different distances in different directions.

If we are caught in a snow-storm when we are at sea, or crossing a flat plain on the earth, we may see snow-flakes surrounding us on all sides and apparently forming an opaque barrier of snow, while up above the sky may be comparatively clear. The reason for the difference is of course that the snow surrounds us for many miles in every horizontal direction, whereas it extends for one mile at most in the vertical direction.

The Herschels found that the stars were arranged like the snow-flakes in a snow-storm—i.e. in a flat disc—and concluded that the system of stars must be shaped somewhat like a snow-storm, or a coin or like a cart-wheel. They believed that the sun was somewhere near the centre, but we know now that they were mistaken in this, their telescopic power being utterly inadequate to reach anywhere near to the edges of the system.

PLATE XLV

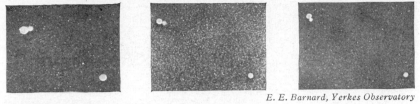

E. E. Barnard, Yerkes Observatory

July 1908   September 1915   July 1920

Fig. 92. The binary system Kruger 60 (at top left-hand corner) as seen in the summers of 1908, 1915 and 1920 respectively. The two components perform a complete rotation around one another in 55 years, so that by 1963 they will be back in the position shewn in the figure on the left.

Mt Wilson Observatory

Fig. 93. A small part of the constellation Auriga, shewing the only star brighter than the ninth magnitude (indicated by pointers). This forms the first picture of a sequence which is continued on Plates XLVI and XLVII, overleaf.

PLATE XLVI

Mt Wilson Observatory

Fig. 94. The same field as in fig. 93, shewing stars
down to the twelfth magnitude.

Mt Wilson Observatory

Fig. 95. The same field again, shewing stars down to the fifteenth magnitude.
(The pattern which is forming around the brightest star is of course merely
an instrumental defect.)

PLATE XLVII

Mt Wilson Observatory

Fig. 96. The same field again, shewing stars down
to the eighteenth magnitude.

Mt Wilson Observatory

Fig. 97. The same field again, shewing stars down
to the twentieth magnitude.

The sun is very far from the centre, although it is very nearly in the central plane of the system.

If we look in the direction which lies along the central plane of this coin or cart-wheel of stars, we are looking through the greatest possible thickness of the system and so ought to see an almost solid wall of stars, like the wall of snow-flakes we see when we look towards the horizon in a snow-storm. This solid wall of stars is the Milky Way, which we can see spanning the sky as a faint band of glimmering light on any clear, moonless night. The constitution of the Milky Way had been something of a mystery up to the time of Galileo, but his telescope at once shewed that it consisted of stars, as indeed Anaxagoras and Democritus had conjectured more than 2000 years earlier. These stars are so far away that we cannot hope to see them at all as separate individuals, but the light of millions of millions of distant faint stars combines to produce the illusion of a continuous cloud of light.

The sky we see without telescopic aid consists of this background of very faint distant stars overlaid with a foreground of the few bright stars which form the constellations. Telescopic study at once connects up this background and foreground by shewing that a middle distance exists, consisting of stars which are both too faint to be seen individually and too sparsely scattered to form a continuous cloud of light. In this way the sun is found to be a member of a single system of stars which is shaped, as we have already said, like a disc or a coin or a cart-wheel.

We have already spoken of the surveyor's method of determining the distances of the stars—we travel over 186,000,000 miles from one end of the earth's orbit to the other and notice by how much the apparent direction of a star changes in consequence. Unfortunately, this method is only successful for quite near stars. The nearest star of all, Proxima Centauri, is at a distance of 25 million million miles; to avoid using big numbers we often specify this distance as $4\frac{1}{4}$ light-years, because light, which travels nearly 6 million million miles in a year, needs $4\frac{1}{4}$ years to travel from the star to us; we see the star, not as it is now, but as it was $4\frac{1}{4}$ years ago.

Now the surveyor's method enables us to find the distance of such stars as this with good accuracy, but it is, naturally enough, less successful with stars at a greater distance. It begins to fail badly for stars whose light takes more than a few hundred years to reach us, and is quite useless for stars which lie anywhere near the outer confines of our system of stars. Other methods must be found for determining the distances of these.

The most useful method depends on estimating the intrinsic brightness of a star from its general physical characteristics. For as soon as we know the intrinsic brightness of a star, a comparison with its apparent brightness will at once tell us the distance of the star.

There are three special types of star whose intrinsic brightness can be determined with fair, although varying, degrees of accuracy. We have already noticed that all the blue stars are very luminous, and in actual fact their intrinsic luminosity is found to depend almost exclusively on what we may call the degree or blueness, or in other words on the exact spectral type of the star. The same is true of the very large stars that we have described as red giants.

Consequently by studying the spectra of stars of either of these kinds, we can discover the intrinsic brightness of the stars and hence deduce their distances.

There is, however, a third class of stars whose distances can be fixed with even greater accuracy. These are the stars known as Cepheid and long-period variables; they do not shine with a steady light, but their brightness varies continually from day to day. This cycle of changes of brightness repeats itself at perfectly regular intervals, and the intrinsic luminosity of a star is found to depend almost exclusively on the length of the interval; stars which change most slowly are intrinsically the brightest; those which change most rapidly are the least bright. However distant such a variable star may be, we can measure the length of time from bright to bright or from faint to faint. This simple observation discloses the intrinsic brightness of the star, and from this we can deduce its distance.

Yet even with all these methods at our disposal it would be a difficult matter to map out the system of stars without adventitious aids. Such aids are provided by the objects known as "globular clusters". These are themselves minor systems of stars, far smaller than the main system, and yet each containing hundreds of thousands of stars. Each of these clusters contains great numbers of Cepheid variables, which make it easy to determine the distance of the cluster. When we know the distance of a cluster it is of course an easy matter to determine its size, and it is interesting to find that the globular clusters are almost exactly similar to one another in shape, size and general arrangement— we do not know why.

When the positions of these clusters are mapped out, it is found that they form a coin-shaped or disc-shaped aggregate; this is roughly circular in shape, and lies equally and symmetrically on the two sides of the Milky Way. It seems reasonable to suppose that the general arrangement and position of the system of globular clusters coincides with that of the system of stars, so that where the clusters come to an end, the system of stars also comes to an end. If so, the system of stars must have a diameter of roughly 200,000 light-years. But so far from its centre being near the sun, as the Herschels thought, it is something like 40,000 light-years' distant.

Thus we may think of the galactic system as a disc or coin or cart-wheel with the sun lying in its central plane, but perhaps a third of a radius out from the centre. The centre of the system is so remote that we cannot even see its brightest stars with our un-aided eyes; these can at the best only see stars whose light takes 3000 years to reach us. This explains why the bright constellation stars appear to be uniformly spread in all directions; we only see a tiny piece of the whole structure, and inside this tiny piece the stars really are spread fairly uniformly.

It has recently been discovered that the motions of the stars are neither random motions nor uniformly arranged; indeed it now seems to be established that the whole system is rotating round a centre, much as a cart-wheel rotates about its hub. This rotation of the great wheel of stars whirls the sun through space at a rate of about 200 miles a second, yet the wheel is so vast that the sun must travel at this speed for about 250 million years before it has made one complete circle round the hub.

Such a rate of spin as this is almost inconceivably slow—one turn in 250 million years. To try to realise what it means, let us compare our rotating cart-wheel to the hour hand of a clock which turns completely round once in 12 hours. If we now slow the hour hand down until it turns at the same rate as the system of stars, the jump which at present occurs every second would take more than 5000 years—almost the whole of human civilisation. Yet a study of the ages of the stars seems to shew that our wheel must have made thousands, and perhaps hundreds of thousands, of complete revolutions.

The sun would fly off the whirling wheel into space, like the speck of mud off a bicycle wheel, were it not that the gravitational pull of the other stars restrains it. This gravitational pull keeps the sun moving in an orbit, just as the gravitational pull of the sun does the earth. And just as our knowledge of the earth's orbit makes it possible to calculate the mass of the sun, so our knowledge of the sun's orbit makes it possible to calculate the total mass of the stars which constitute the great wheel. We find that the number of stars in the wheel is certainly greater than a hundred thousand million, and may well be double this.

Our unaided eyes can distinguish at most about 5000 of this multitude of stars as distinct points of light—one in 40,000,000. Thus for every star that we see as a star, there must be 39,999,999 others that are either completely invisible or are merged in the general faint glimmer of the Milky Way. There are about 2000 million inhabitants of the earth, so that if the stars were divided equally among all the earth's inhabitants, there would be about 100 for each person. Yet if we choose our stars by drawing lots at random, each of us will find that there are odds of about 400,000 to 1 that he will not be able to see a single one of his stars without using a telescope.

CHAPTER VIII

THE NEBULAE

The moon and planets look very conspicuous objects in the sky, but we know that these are very near neighbours which only look bright and big because they are near. For the rest our unaided eyes can see nothing of the universe except stars.

A small telescope or field-glass will shew us more stars in abundance, but it will shew us something else as well. A new class of object comes within our ken, the fuzzy indefinite patches of faint light which we describe as "nebulae".

The word "nebula" is of course the Latin word for a mist or cloud. In the early days of astronomy it was used indiscriminately to describe any object of misty or fuzzy appearance—any object, indeed, which did not exhibit a clear outline. Since then it has been found that the nebulae fall into three distinct classes.

The first consists of objects known as planetary nebulae, which lie entirely within our system of stars. It is now known that these are themselves stars which, for reasons not altogether understood, have become surrounded by very extensive atmospheres. Examples are shewn in fig. 98 (facing p. 204). We described the red giant stars as large, but when their atmospheres are counted in, these stars are beyond all comparison larger. Our rocket, travelling at 5000 miles an hour, would take 9 years to travel through the biggest of red giants, but about 90,000 years to travel through one of these planetary nebulae. This means that if we regard the planetary nebulae as stars, they are some 10,000 times larger than the largest stars we have yet mentioned.

Strictly speaking, these nebulae are the atmospheres of stars rather than the stars themselves. Peering through these atmospheres, we see the stars themselves at the centres of the nebulae, and these are, if anything, more remarkable than the vast atmospheres which surround them. To begin with they are surprisingly small, with an average diameter of only about a fifth of that of the sun. Their surfaces are at excessively high temperatures, which range up to about 70,000 or 75,000 degrees Centigrade. These are the highest temperatures that can actually be observed in the universe, although we know that the interiors of stars—which we cannot observe—must be at still higher temperatures. In a sense the temperatures we have just mentioned are themselves internal temperatures, because they are measured at the bottom of the big atmospheres surrounding the stars and not at their surfaces. These small sizes and excessively high temperatures shew that the central stars of the planetary nebulae belong to the same general category as the white dwarfs we have already discussed (p. 185).

The second class of nebulae also consists of objects which lie within the system of stars bounded by the Milky Way. The nebulae of the first are atmospheres surrounding single stars; those of the second class may be described as atmospheres surrounding whole groups, and sometimes even whole constellations, of stars. Fig. 99 shews the familiar stars of the Pleiades, photographed with a long exposure. A casual glance at these

PLATE XLVIII

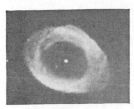

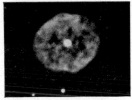

Mt Wilson Observatory

Fig. 98. Three planetary nebulae—N.G.C. 6720 (the ring nebula in Lyra), N.G.C. 2022, and N.G.C. 1501.

Kerolyr, Forcalquier

Fig. 99. The stars of the Pleiades, with the nebulosity surrounding them.

PLATE XLIX

Mt Wilson Observatory

Fig. 100. The nebulosity which surrounds, and is lighted up by, a single star in the constellation of Auriga.

stars, either with our unaided eyes or through a telescope, shews no nebulosity of any kind, but when the constellation is photographed with a long exposure each star is found to be surrounded by a nebulous cloud of light. Fig. 100 (opposite) shews the intricate detail of the nebulosity surrounding a single star.

With still longer exposures the nebulosities surrounding the different stars would join up to form a continuous cloud of light and we should find an enormous number of stars all immersed in one great unbroken sea of nebulosity. An example of such a sea of nebulosity is shewn in fig. 101 (facing p. 206). In many cases the nebulosity does not take the form of clouds of light, but of patches of darkness, a conspicuous example being shewn in fig. 102 (facing p. 207). It seems fairly certain that these dark patches are produced by absorbing matter which shuts out the light of the stars behind, and the absorption may well be of the same general kind as produces dark lines in stellar spectra and deprives our own atmosphere of its ultra-violet radiation. The light is absorbed by cool gas but is emitted by hot.

These nebulae look very sensational, but only in the way in which the moon and planets may look sensational—because they are comparatively near to us. The nebulae of the third class, to which we come next, are sensational in themselves. A planetary nebula may give out ten or perhaps a hundred times as much light as the sun, one of the "galactic" nebulae just described may give out perhaps hundreds or thousands of times as much, but the third class of nebulae, the "extra-galactic" nebulae, give out thousands of millions of times as much. They are enormously larger than the galactic nebulae in size, but look smaller and less impressive because of their great distance from us.

These three kinds of nebulae are so different in shape and general appearance that there is usually no difficulty in distinguishing between them. But their spectra provide a further means of discrimination, if this is needed. When the light of either the planetary or galactic nebulae is analysed in a spectroscope, it is found to give the same spectra as the various kinds of atoms we know on earth. This shews that these nebulae are mere clouds of luminous atoms—gas lighted up by the stars embedded in them.

The extra-galactic nebulae, on the other hand, give spectra like those of the stars. It is, then, natural to suspect that these are clouds, not of atoms but of stars. For a long time, this was nothing more than a plausible conjecture, but there can no longer be much doubt as to its truth. For, just as Galileo's telescope broke up the Milky Way into separate points of light which he at once identified as stars, so the modern high-power telescope resolves the outermost regions of these nebulae into separate points of light, which may, without hesitation, be identified as stars.

There can be no reasonable doubt that they really are stars, for they reproduce practically all the characteristics of the stars of our own system. Many, for instance, do not shine with a steady light, but fluctuate in the same characteristic and quite unmistakable way as the Cepheid variables of our own system. Quite recently other objects have been detected, similar to objects with which we are familiar in our own system of stars. Not only have variable stars of all kinds been found, but also "novae" or new stars

PLATE L

Mt Wilson Observatory

Fig. 101. Nebulosity in the constellation of Sobieski's shield.

PLATE LI

Kerolyr, Forcalquier

Fig. 102. Nebulosity in the constellation of Orion. The bright object half-way up the plate is the star ζ Orionis, the southernmost of the three stars of Orion's belt. The photograph was given an exposure of 11 hours, which is enough to shew all details of the clouds of obscuring nebular matter.

which suddenly flash out to thousands of times their ordinary brightness, and then, after undergoing several fluctuations of brightness and darkness, become faint again. Globular clusters have also been discovered very similar to those of our own galactic system. There is, then, no reason to doubt that these extra-galactic nebulae are, in part at least, systems of stars very similar to those of our own galactic system.

We have seen how variable stars and globular clusters occur throughout the galactic system of stars, and so make it possible to estimate the distances of the remotest parts of this system. The distances of the nearer nebulae can be estimated in precisely the same way. Cepheid and other variable stars can be recognised in these nebulae by the peculiar character of their light variation. They behave in just the same way as variable stars nearer home, but look enormously fainter because of their greater distance. And, as we have already seen, the difference in faintness at once tells us the difference in distance.

In this way, it has been estimated that the two nearest nebulae are both about 800,000 light-years' distant—the light by which we are now seeing them started on its journey through space about 800,000 years ago, when man was first appearing on earth. Fig. 104 (facing p. 208) shews one of these two near nebulae, the great nebula in Andromeda. In spite of its immense distance, it occupies quite a large part of the sky; if the full moon were in the same photograph it would only appear the size of a sixpence. And even this does not shew the whole size of the nebula. The more it is studied the larger it is found to be, and already it has been found to extend to several times the dimensions shewn in the photograph.

An object which is at so stupendous a distance and yet fills up so much of the sky must clearly be of immense size. Our rocket which took 2 days to reach the moon, would have taken a week to travel through the sun, 9 years through an ordinary big star, 90,000 years through a planetary nebula—but it is not much good saying how long it would take to travel through this nebula. Actually the nebula is about 100,000 light-years in diameter, so that the time would be about 12,000 million years. We should have to enlarge our photograph of the nebula to the size of all Europe before an object of the size of the sun could be seen in it.

We notice that this nebula has a sort of cart-wheel shape, such as we have already attributed to our own galactic system of stars. Indeed, the size, shape and general constitution of this nebula combine to suggest that it may be very similar to our own system. This, and a large number of other nebulae, are not only like cart-wheels in shape, but are also found to be rotating like cart-wheels about their hubs or centres—again like our own system of stars. Each wheel is held together as a compact structure by the gravitational attraction of its parts, so that we can calculate its mass by the method we have already used to calculate the masses of the sun and of the galactic system, although it is not possible to claim much accuracy for such a calculation. The Andromeda nebula is found to turn about the hub of its wheel once in every 20 million years, and from this it is

PLATE LII

Mt Wilson Observatory

Fig. 103. The "whirlpool" nebula in Canes Venatici.

Yerkes Observatory

Fig. 104. The great nebula in Andromeda.

Mt Wilson Observatory

Fig. 105. A nebula (N.G.C. 4565) in Berenice's Hair.

Three nebulae, all of characteristic cart-wheel shape, and probably somewhat similar in structure, viewed from different angles.

PLATE LIII

Mt Wilson Observatory

Fig. 106. A close group of nebulae in the constellation of Pegasus. The nebulae near the centre of the plate all look of about the same size and brilliance, and so are all at about the same distance—they form a close group in space. Other nebulae, which look smaller and fainter, are probably at a greater distance, and so are not physically connected with the principal group.

calculated that its mass must be equal to that of several thousands of millions of suns—it is safest not to say precisely how many.

The extra-galactic nebulae are not all of cart-wheel shape; indeed they shew considerable diversity both of shape and general appearance. It is found however that almost all of them can be arranged in a single continuous sequence. This sequence begins with nebulae which are fuzzy in appearance, globular or nearly so in shape, and in which no stars can be discerned; it ends with pure clouds of stars like our own system. Only the nebulae in the latter half of this sequence are shaped like cart-wheels, and here the comparison is specially appropriate, since many of them are rotating around a sort of central boss or projection, which looks surprisingly like the hub of a cart-wheel. This cart-wheel shape may be more or less disguised when the nebulae happen to be seen from unsuitable angles (see Plate LII, facing p. 208), but it is very obvious when we view them edge-on, as in the nebula shewn in fig. 105. When we allow for actual nebulae being seen at all possible angles, we find that the sequence in question is simply an arrangement in order of flatness, the shapes ranging from spheres to cart-wheels.

When we take a walk through a forest of oaks, we come upon trees of all sizes, ranging from full-grown forest trees down to saplings, and even to young shoots just growing out of acorns, and acorns lying on the ground. Here again we find that all the stages we encounter can be arranged in order to form one continuous sequence, starting with the newly-fallen acorn, passing through the sprouting acorn, the baby oak-tree, the sapling, and the young tree to the full-grown forest tree. We naturally suspect that the different appearances may represent different stages of growth, and so constitute an "evolutionary sequence". But this must remain only a suspicion; oaks grow slowly, and we cannot wait long enough to watch the change occur.

It is the same with the nebulae. Any appreciable change must occupy millions of years. Thus we cannot wait to watch them change, but we may conjecture that as they change they move on from one state to the next in the sequence. If this is so, the sequence becomes a sort of cinematograph film, exhibiting the life-history of a nebula. All the nebulae which come earlier than any particular nebula in the sequence are pictures of what this nebula has already been at some time in the past; those which come after it are pictures of what it will be at some time in the future.

The sequence of nebular shapes has a further interest, since calculation shews that it almost exactly coincides with the sequence of shapes which a huge ball of gas would assume as it gradually shrank, increasing its speed of rotation as it did so. The faster the ball of gas rotates, the flatter its shape—just as with the planets of the solar system. In time the shape becomes so flat that it cannot flatten any more; a further increase in the speed of rotation then causes matter to fly off from the equator—as we imagined might happen on our earth (p. 10) if this were set spinning fast enough. We imagine the rim and spokes of the cart-wheel to have been formed in this way, the hub being the much-flattened remains of the original ball of gas. The final end of this sequence is of special interest, since by the time it is reached the whole of the gas is condensed into detached globules, and calculation shews that each globule would have about the same mass as an actual star. It becomes natural to conjecture that each nebula started as a rotating mass of gas, that this mass passed through, or will pass through, the sequence of changes we have already described, and ended, or will end, as a cloud of stars. Thus the nebulae are the birth-places of the stars; in them rotating masses of gas are moulded into stars such as we know and find in our own galactic system.

If these conjectures are sound, we can trace our earth back to the sun, and the sun back to a nebula, but how did the nebulae themselves come into being?

Most cosmogonies have taken as their starting-point the sup-position that the universe started as a chaotic mass of gas. It can be shewn that such a mass of gas could not stay uniformly spread throughout space. The cloud of steam from a kettle or from the chimney of a locomotive does not stay uniformly spread out, but tends to condense into tiny drops, and we find that it would be the same with gas of any kind spread through space. A uni-formly spread gas, whatever its nature, would be unstable in the sense that any slight disturbance or irregularity would tend to increase indefinitely instead of smoothing itself out. Finally, the whole mass would condense, or break up, into detached masses of denser gas. Calculation shews that these would be on something like the scale of the actual nebulae, and would form at about the average distance apart of the observed nebulae. This makes it possible to travel conjecturally yet one stage farther back in time. Having already travelled back from earth to sun and from sun to nebulae, we can now complete our story by tracing the nebulae back to a mass of chaotic gas filling all space.

If the nebulae came into existence in some such way as this, we should expect them all to be of about the same size, weight, and intrinsic brightness. This is found very approximately to be the case. Two nebulae of the same shape often look very different in size and brightness, but the difference of appearance can usually be attributed almost entirely to their being at different distances from us.

If this is a general law, as at present it appears to be, then nebulae of any assigned shape may be treated as standard articles, just as Cepheid variables are, and their distances can be estimated from their apparent faintness (Plate LIII, facing p. 209). The faintest nebulae which can be photographed in the great 100-inch telescope at Mount Wilson prove to be so distant that their light takes 140 million years to reach us, and so are about a thousand times as distant as the farthest star in the Milky Way. Some two million nebulae lie within this distance.

Telescopically, these nebulae are of interest as forming very beautiful and interesting objects. Cosmogonically, they are of even greater interest as giving us a sort of cinematograph film shewing how we believe the sun and stars to have come into existence. Yet they have recently acquired an even stronger interest from the circumstance that they all appear to be running away from us—and this at perfectly terrific speeds.

We have already noticed how the motion of a star results in the lines of its spectrum being displaced—towards the red if the star is receding from us, and towards the violet if it is advancing towards us. Many of the lines in the spectra of the nebulae also are found to be displaced to abnormal positions, and this is most simply explained by supposing that the nebulae are themselves in motion.

Until recently, it was only possible to study the spectra of a few of the nearer nebulae, and these seemed to indicate that the nebulae were coming and going almost at random. Gradually it began to be noticed that the motions were not altogether chaotic; the approaching nebulae were mostly in one half of the sky, the receding nebulae in the other. All this could be explained if it were possible to suppose that the sun was advancing through space towards the former group of nebulae, and so of course receding from the latter group, at a speed of some hundreds of miles a second.

The cart-wheel rotation of the galaxy has now provided exactly the motion needed to justify this supposition. But the apparent motions of the nebulae prove to be something more than a mere reflection of the sun's motion through space. When the sun's motion is subtracted from the apparent motions of the nebulae, the nebulae are not brought to rest, and neither are they found to be moving at random, like the molecules of a gas. Instead of this we find that all the nebulae are receding from us with speeds which are almost, and possibly even quite, proportional to their distances.

In round numbers, each million light-years of distance is found to be associated with a speed of 100 miles a second. Nebulae which are a million light-years' distant from us recede with this speed, those at two million light-years' distance recede with double this speed, and so on. The largest speed of recession which has so far been observed is 15,000 miles a second—about a million times the speed of an express train. The nebula which holds this record is estimated to be at a distance of 135 million light-years, and so is very near to the limit of vision of the telescope.

When a shell bursts on a battlefield the fragments travel at different speeds, those which travel fastest also travelling farthest. At any particular moment after the explosion, each fragment will have covered a distance which is exactly proportional to its speed of motion. This is the same thing as saying that its speed is proportional to its distance from the point at which the shell burst. This is exactly the law of the receding nebulae, and makes it look as though, at some instant in the past, the universe had suddenly burst into fragments, our whole galactic system being one of the fragments—the particular one to which we are clinging.

There is however another way in which the motions of the nebulae can be explained. Imagine a number of straws floating down a river in company. If the river narrows at any particular spot, we shall notice the straws coming closer to one another, and where the river widens again, they will spread farther apart. When such a spreading apart occurs, an insect living on any one bit of floating straw will see all the other straws receding from it. And if the river has just passed through a very narrow bottleneck, their speed of recession will be exactly proportional to the distance, which again is the law of the nebulae.

Thus there are two possible explanations of the motions of the nebulae which look very similar, and yet there is a fundamental difference between them. When we compare the nebulae to the fragments of a burst shell, we imagine the nebulae to be moving *through* space. But when we compare them to straws floating in a river, the river must be space itself; the nebulae are not moving *through* space, but *with* space—they are straws shewing us in what way the currents of space are flowing, and the law that speed is proportional to distance suggests that space is expanding uniformly.

Probably the latter explanation is the best, because we now think that space is curved, and round, and finite in amount—rather like the surface of a balloon. Space is not to be compared to the air inside the balloon, but to the rubber which forms its surface. Thus we can travel on and on in space for ever, just as a fly could walk on for ever round the surface of this balloon. It would of course have to repeat its tracks, but it would never come to any obstacle that prevented its going on.

In the same way, we believe that if we tried to travel on for ever through space, we should never find anything to stop us, although sooner or later we should come back to our starting-point, as Drake did when he circumnavigated the globe. Needless to say there is no use in trying to circumnavigate space—for one thing life is too short. A ray of light might have a better chance, for it travels at 10 million miles a minute and is not limited to a lifetime of threescore years and ten. It was at one time thought that a sufficiently powerful telescope might let us look round space and see our own earth by light which, starting many millions of years ago, had travelled round the whole of space and finally come back to its starting-point. Naturally such an experience as this would give us a very direct and convincing proof of the curvature of space, but we no longer believe it to be possible to travel so far through space as this, even though we travel on the wings of light. Various astronomers have devised methods for estimating the size of the whole of space, and, however much they may differ from one another, they at least all agree that space is far too large for us to dream of seeing round it. The big telescope at Mount Wilson looks so far into space that we can see nebulae whose light started when our earth was inhabited by the weird animals we saw in our first chapter, and has been travelling over 140 million years to reach us. Yet it shews us only a tiny fraction of space, so small that it may perhaps bear the same relation to the whole of space as the Isle of Wight does to the surface of the earth.

Thus we see that not only is space almost inconceivably large, but it is continually becoming larger. It doubles its linear dimensions every 1300 million years or so, so that there is already eight times as much space as when the earliest radioactive rocks solidified, and perhaps more than a hundred times as much as when the earth was torn out of the sun. With every tick of the clock, its diameter increases by at least several hundreds of thousands of miles.

Possibly, however, we are more interested in matter than in mere empty space. Even in the tiny bit of space we can see there are some millions of nebulae, while in the part we cannot see there are probably millions of millions of nebulae, each containing thousands of millions of stars. Each nebula contains as many stars as there are grains of sand in a good handful, so that all the nebulae between them must contain about as many stars as there are grains of sand on all the seashores of the world. When we survey the vast universe as a whole, we see our sun reduced to a grain of sand, and our earth to a millionth part of a grain of sand—a tiny speck of dust circling round a grain of sand which is a million times bigger than itself, and yet is only of infinitesimal size in the universe as a whole. We may take pleasure in finding that the universe is such a very grand affair, but we cannot flatter ourselves that our mundane affairs play any large part in it.

Such is the universe of our travels. If we have not been able to construct a complete cinematograph film, at least we have seen a series of pictures on which something of its past history has been sketched. We first saw a primaeval universe which consisted merely of a mass of chaotic gas. As we watched, we saw this gradually condensing into nebulae. It seems very probable—although I do not think this has been strictly proved as yet—that such a condensation of chaotic gas into nebulae would of itself start space expanding. At any rate, for this or for some other reason, space itself began to expand, which means that even while the nebulae are forming, as well as for ever after, they must move steadily farther away from one another.

During all this time, the nebulae are changing their shapes in the way we have noticed, until finally they end by breaking up into stars. One particular nebula was the birth-place of our own familiar friends, Sirius, Aldebaran, Arcturus, and so on, as well as a far smaller and less brilliant object—our own sun. For millions of years, these and millions of other stars move blindly past one another, until finally we see our sun wander into the danger zone of a bigger star, and a cataclysm results out of which the planets are born—our earth among others. At first it is simply a ball of hot gas—as the sun is now, but much smaller. In time it cools down, liquefies and finally forms a solid surface; we see steam condensing into water, and forming seas and rivers. Then— greatest mystery of all—life appears. It is very humble at first but gradually increases in complexity until finally, only a few minutes back on the astronomical clock, man emerges, and starts gradually and slowly to climb the long steep ladder of civilisation. Yet only within the last few ticks of this clock has he concerned himself with the meaning of the nightly pageant of the sky. Then Egyptians, Chinese, Babylonians and Greeks began in turn to wonder what it all meant. Only one tick ago the telescope was invented and gave us the means of finding out. Within that one tick almost all I have told you has been discovered, and many thousands of times as much besides. And with our knowledge of the skies increasing at its present rate, who shall say what strange surprises the next tick of the clock may have in store for us?

INDEX

Heraclides of Pontus, explanation of
    planetary motions, 85
  rotation of earth, 3
Heraclitus, nature of sun, moon and
    stars, 79, 80
Homer, 2, 89, 102
Hottentot photographed in infra-red
    light, Plate XLIII (facing p. 186)
Hydrogen in sun, 168 ff.

Igneous rocks, 21
Inertia, 3
Infra-red photography, 75 and Plates XV
    (facing p. 76) and XLIII (facing
    p. 186)
Infra-red radiation, 54 ff., 185
Ionisation of gases, 66 ff.
Isaac Newton, cometary motions, 102
  gravitation, 126, 127
  motion of bodies, 4
Isostasy, 23, 27

Jeffers, 125
Jupiter, 83, 97, 99, 100
  atmosphere of, 146
  gravitational pull of, 147
  moons of, 125, 151
  physical condition of, 145 ff.
  shape of, 144
  size of, 124, 156
  temperature of, 144, 145, 146
Jurassic Era, 41, 47
"Just-So" stories, 44, 153

Kennelly-Heaviside layer, 66
Krakatoa, eruption of, 74
Kruger, 60 (binary star), 190 and Plate
    XLV (facing p. 196)

Life, in solar system, 148 ff.
  on Mars, 141, 142
  on moon, 115
  on Venus, 135
Light, nature and properties of, 49

Light-year (defined), 198
Limb of sun, 157
Line-spectrum, 164
Lithosphere of earth, 17
Little Bear, constellation of, 90
Luminosity of stars, 177 ff.

Machaerodus, 44 and Plate XII (facing p. 45)
Mars, 13, 97, 99, 100
  atmosphere on, 136 ff.
  canals on, 140 ff.
  climate of, 139
  days and seasons of, 138
  gravitation on, 136
  life on, 141, 142
  water on, 136 ff.
Marsh-gas, 140
Megatherium, 45 and Plate XII (facing p. 45)
Mercury, 83, 97, 100
  absence of atmosphere, 131
  climate, 130, 144
  orbit of, 124
  rotation of, 130
Meteor craters, 105, 118
Meteorites, 7, 104, 105
  composition of, 105
Meteors, 104, 117
Methane in atmospheres of planets, 146
Milky Way, 197, 200, 202
Molecules, 113
Moon, 77 ff., 107 ff.
  absence of air and water on, 109, 114
  composition of, 118 ff.
  distance of, 107
  future of, 153
  gravitation on, 112
  mountains on, 110, 115, 116
  seas on, 108
  temperature of, 120
  tidal action of, 150

Nasmyth, 115
Nature of sun, moon and stars, early
    views as to, 79 ff.

BURT FRANKLIN: RESEARCH & SOURCE WORKS SERIES 557

CHAMBER AND ORCHESTRAL MUSIC OF
JOHANNES BRAHMS

HANDBOOK TO THE
CHAMBER & ORCHESTRAL
MUSIC OF
JOHANNES BRAHMS

HISTORICAL AND DESCRIPTIVE ACCOUNT OF EACH WORK WITH
FXHAUSTIVE STRUCTURAL, THEMATIC AND RHYTHMICAL ANALYSES,
AND A COMPLETE RHYTHMICAL CHART OF EACH MOVEMENT

COPIOUSLY ILLUSTRATED IN MUSIC-TYPE

BY

EDWIN EVANS

Complete Guide for Student, Concert-goer and Pianist

First Series to Op. 67 inclusive

BURT FRANKLIN
NEW YORK

Published by LENOX HILL Pub. & Dist. Co. (Burt Franklin)
235 East 44th St., New York, N.Y. 10017
Originally Published: 1912
Reprinted: 1970
Printed in the U.S.A.

S.B.N. 8337-10885
Library of Congress Card Catalog No.: 76-129468
Burt Franklin: Research and Source Works Series 557

THE CHAMBER & ORCHESTRAL WORKS.

GENERAL TABLE OF
CONTENTS.

(A) DIDACTIC.

(B) THE HANDBOOK.

Being a detailed account of all the Orchestral and Chamber Works of Brahms in the order of Opus number.

(Op. 1, Sonata in C, for piano. Op. 2, Sonata in F sharp minor, for piano. Op. 3, Six Vocal Pieces. Op. 4, Scherzo in E flat minor, for piano. Op. 5, Sonata, in F minor, for piano. Op. 6, Six Vocal Pieces. Op. 7, Six Vocal Pieces.)

OP. 8. FIRST PIANO TRIO.

(Op. 9, Variations on a Schumann Theme in F sharp minor, for piano. Op. 10, Four Ballades for piano.)

OP. 11. SERENADE (ORCHESTRA).

(Op. 12, "Ave Maria." Op. 13, "Begräbnissgesang." Op. 14, Eight Songs and Romances. Op. 15, First Pianoforte Concerto in D minor.)

OP. 16. SERENADE (ORCHESTRA).

OP. 17. FOUR FEMALE CHORUSES.

OP. 18. FIRST STRING SEXTET.

(Op. 19, Five Songs. Op. 20, Three Vocal Duets. Op. 21, Two Sets of Variations for piano solo. Op. 22, Seven Marienlieder. Op. 23, Variations on a Schumann Theme, for piano duet. Op. 24, Variations and Fugue on Handel Theme, for piano.)

OP. 25. FIRST PIANO QUARTET.

(C) ANALYTIC.

Including classification of Works, Index to Music Examples, Rhythmical Tables, etc.

BRAHMS HANDBOOK.

(A) DIDACTIC.

CHAPTER I.

INTRODUCTORY.

1. THE present volume, though corresponding with its predecessors in general plan, necessarily differs from them in certain particulars to which we must first draw attention. The multiplicity of the vocal works required that in Vol. I detailed accounts should be reserved for the greater choral productions; whilst the pianoforte compositions treated in Vol. II, though presenting great variety of feature, were scarcely of a calibre to necessitate minute analysis. With the chamber and orchestral works in Vol. III however the case is different. It is true that highly interesting accounts of these are extant, giving a wonderfully clear impression of their nature and value, and even in some instances instructively entering upon technical detail. Such excursions have however been made at the fancy of authors and have consequently little value for the student who, being thoroughly determined to possess an accurate knowledge of these creations, requires an account of them so exhaustive as to comprise everything he can reasonably desire to know. To supply this nothing can be effective but analysis reaching to the rhythmical significance of every bar; accounting for all material, whether subjects or intermediate motives; laying bare all formal proportions and developments; and fully describing all contrasts and characteristic features.

2. By describing the plan adopted in carrying out this labori-

ous scheme we shall best prepare the reader for use of the
"Handbook" or B section of the present volume, the immense
detail contained in which reduces both the Didactic and Analytical sections to very small dimensions.

3. The plan of the "Handbook" is therefore as follows :—

Firstly to certain works of extra importance a "Preliminary
Note" is attached for the purpose of including particulars either
of general or historical character. The object of this is to
exclude from the articles under movement-headings (such as
"allegro," "andante" and so forth) everything which is not
strictly technical comment.

Such comment upon the very early works will be found to
be more than usually copious. This arises from the necessity
of treating each Brahms feature as it arises at sufficient length
to enable the explanation of it to be referred to in future cases.
On the other hand there are a few works* the account given of
which is rather more concise, though never to the exclusion of
essentials.

The foremost feature of the entire work is the complete rhythmical chart given of every movement. The manner of preparing
and using the various rhythmical tables is explained under
Op. 8, as the first work in order. In this the phrases are mostly
taken at full length, but later on the number "2" has been relied
upon as sufficient—either to indicate strong and weak bars, to
locate extensions or to combine for phrase-groups. Any trouble
devoted to forming the habit of using these tables will repay
the student a hundredfold.

The next feature consists of the quotation of subjects in such
manner as to correspond with their table description; and its
effect, if properly used as it should be in combination with the
table, will be to convert the latter into a musically illustrated
map of the whole movement.

The "epitome" and "outline" of each movement (placed for
convenience at the end of each article) give rapid views of what
has been previously stated at length; and they complete the list
of constant features appertaining to our plan. There is also
however the important occasional feature of examples and elucidation of technical subjects involved in the descriptions.

4. A condition of successful use of the rhythmical tables is
that the student should count his bars; and it is necessary, in
any case, that he should understand the method of enumeration

---

* Opp. 38, 77, 78, 99 and 108.

here employed. For instance, the initial notes of opening phrases are here disregarded altogether, the counting commencing with the first complete bar. As against that the final bar, though it may be incomplete, forms with us a unit. In the case of repeated sections with alternative endings (indicated by "first" and "second time") the printed bars are simply counted mechanically. The estimated addition for repeats therefore includes the bars of such sections *without either ending* —because of the bars occupied by such endings already forming part of the number.* As a consequence of the second ending of first section appearing after the double-bar the *real* is naturally shorter than the *apparent* length of the Durchführung by whatnumber of bars may have comprised the "1ma Volta."

5. It is recognised that there is room for many differences of opinion upon some of the subjects treated; as for instance the method of construing the rhythm, location of the groups, of extensions of the phrase, and so forth. The object being to give a sufficiently lucid explanation to enable the reader to form his own view, praise or blame of any feature is not advanced without the details which have served to such conclusion. Generally speaking, the point of view taken up is that of Brahms himself, who, as is well known, attached supreme importance to the musical thought and less to mere sensuous effect.

6. In respect of terminology the term Durchführung† (to the use of which we have persistently adhered) is the only one not generally understood; such words as bridge, overlap, approach, intermediate motive, etc., being used in their everyday signification.

7. Finally, we may claim to have adopted a plan well calculated to restrain all play of personal feeling on our own part. To subject a musical composition to minute analysis is to place it upon the scales of justice—a procedure not greatly in favour with either class of extremist. The results of this method of judgment are various; but that the general verdict to which they point admits of no doubt cannot at all events be imputed to any advocacy of partisan character.

---

* The above assumes the "2da Volta" to consist of a complete bar; which, though generally, is not always the case. It is necessary to mention therefore that when (as in the slow movement of Op. 36) it consists of only a portion of the bar, that portion is disregarded in the counting.

† Neither "development," "working out," "free fantasia," nor any other English term available, conveys the idea of conducting the listener, as it were, upon a journey, to the return groups.

CHAPTER II.

BRAHMS AS A COMPOSER OF CHAMBER WORKS.

1. IT was evident from the first that Brahms would become a great composer of chamber music, and to this day even the first version of the Trio, Op. 8, published in 1859, has thoroughly held its own. It was followed by his cultivation of this school being somewhat delayed by the Serenades for Orchestra, Op. 11 and 16; but the result of the beautiful string Sextet, Op. 18, was even more convincing of the composer's special genius for chamber music. The two piano Quartets, Op. 25 and 26, can scarcely be said to occupy such high ground; but the perfection of Op. 18 is not to be expected in each successive work even from the greatest genius.

2. The retention of early material in the quartets may account for their falling short of the perfection which Brahms had already taught people to expect, but with the piano Quintet, Op. 34, he at once assumed that position of ascendancy in present-day chamber-music which he has ever since enjoyed. On the other hand there remained certain obstacles to his general acceptance in that sense. These are fully detailed in the Handbook.

3. The second string Sextet, Op. 36, was scarcely calculated to lessen these obstacles though it did much to confirm the high opinion formed of the composer by his own immediate surrounding. His extensive indulgence in polyphony for this particular work was followed up by a proportionate contrapuntal display in the 'cello Sonata, Op. 38; and it is noticeable that several works reflect in this way the character of those they immediately follow.

4. Then came a new departure in the horn Trio, Op. 40. The conditions of the composition of any chamber work to which a wind instrument is admitted are so fully dealt with under the headings of the clarinet works that description here would be superfluous. It is enough to say that in the horn trio they are met with perfect success, and only the resultant constitution of this work prevents its full comparison with those for piano and strings.

5. Up to this point Brahms had not indulged in the favourite combination of the string quartet—that at which composers are generally first to try their hand—but in 1873 he entered also upon this field, having previously, as we are told, written many quartets which he had not chosen to publish. Even without this information we should know from the very finish of the two Quartets of Op. 51 that they were no first attempts at writing for this combination, but in them Brahms does nothing to propitiate those who had previously found fault with his peculiar style. The only work hitherto in which any desire to hold out a hand to opponents can be said to have appeared is the Sextet, Op. 18, the geniality of which was however probably due to quite other causes.

6. It is doubtful whether even up to this point Brahms had completely shaken off his attachment to early material and the third piano Quartet, Op. 60, beautiful as it is, bears traces of influences not quite to its advantage. But with the third string Quartet, Op. 67, we have his style in full maturity; which is equivalent to the highest praise possible to be given to any work.

7. His indifference to the customs of other composers, as shown by the late appearance of his first string quartet, is confirmed by the much later appearance of his first violin Sonata, Op. 78—a work which contributed so powerfully to the spread of his reputation that the opinions it immediately called forth are now of special value for comparison between them and those held at the present time.

8. After another orchestral diversion Brahms again returned to chamber music with the third piano Trio, Op. 87, in 1883. This work may be said to be one of the least appreciated; though the reasons for this naturally appertain to its own review, to which the reader is referred. In the general sense this neglect merely betokens an incorrect standpoint and is not therefore contributed to by the real Brahms student, for whom this work presents no difficulty whatever. On the other hand, it is

doubtless true that appearance of the lovely first string Quintet, Op. 88, in the same year did much to divert attention from the trio.

9. After this we have some relaxation of effort in the second 'cello and violin Sonatas, Op. 99 and 100 respectively—each of them works of high purport and full calibre for the means employed. These were followed by the fourth piano Trio, Op. 101, appearing in 1887, in which the composer almost surpasses himself in his endowment of sonata form with new means of variety. This perpetual investment of one form with new features of interest may in fact be said to be that which most distinguishes him from other composers; and the same trait appears, though necessarily on a reduced scale, in the third violin Sonata, Op. 108. After this only one work precedes what we may venture to call the "clarinet period"—this being the second string Quintet, Op. 111. Special attention is due to this quintet as really marking the conclusion of Brahms's labours within the domain of pure chamber music. For an epitome of the value of this work and of its relation to Brahms's entire output of its class the reader is referred to the digest of criticism given with its "Preliminary Note."

10. The first clarinet work is the Trio, Op. 114, ranking as fifth piano Trio, but really standing apart. In it Brahms seems somewhat to have overrated the instrument's powers, but in the Quintet following as Op. 115 he shows a marvellously ripened experience. This fine result is considerably aided by the increased number of strings rendering it possible to reserve the clarinet for a special vocation throughout, whereas in the Trio he had been obliged to treat it on equal terms with its associates. The whole clarinet group shows that his experience tended in the direction of isolating the wind instrument; and this is finally borne out by the last work (Op. 120), consisting of two Sonatas for piano and clarinet only—both highly successful. But the most beautiful of the clarinet group is undoubtedly the Quintet; which as a clarinet work is supreme, and comes very near to rivalling the best of the pure chamber works.

11. In a general view of Brahms's works of this class the clarinet group should be regarded as an extra; especially as in them the ascendancy of sonata-form is less apparent. This naturally follows from the tendency to variation style which is an inevitable consequence of use of the wind instrument, but it scarcely agrees with what seems to have been the composer's grand object—namely, to glorify sonata-form by offering a

revelation to the modern musician of new possibilities within it. The same field had already been so ploughed by Beethoven that it was natural to deem its resources exhausted. Brahms not only proved the contrary but the fact of each successive work of his right up to the very latest containing something new in this regard goes far to show that even he has not exhausted it.

12. He has however exhausted it for the time being. No composer of chamber music has appeared to dispute his right to a supreme position in that school, the combination of his love of formal beauty with a full measure of both science and inspiration being too rare an event. Should his rival ever appear in this field, and should the world of chamber-music ever have to rejoice over further revelations of the same kind the glory will be largely his for having so effectually pointed the way.

CHAPTER III.

BRAHMS AS ORCHESTRAL COMPOSER.

1. BRAHMS'S first orchestral work was the serenade for orchestra, Op. 11; which, though differing materially from the Op. 16 serenade, combines with it to represent what we are bound to deem an apprenticeship in orchestral writing. The peculiar style which he afterwards developed is not apparent in either of these works, notwithstanding that they consist of many movements and are very variously scored.

2. The evident effort involved in these first works for orchestra is the first indication that orchestral writing was not to become this composer's peculiar field. His total output of the class numbers accordingly but nine works, even including the serenades just mentioned. Of the remaining seven no less than four are symphonies; a circumstance which those familiar with the bend of his mind must regard as a matter of course. In the symphony so much depends upon material and construction that necessities of scoring are largely pre-determined, and therefore do not depend upon any special orchestral bent. This could not fail to be a great attraction for a composer who excelled mostly in form and characteristic. Breadth of the bearings in a free style of composition throws a composer completely upon his orchestral resource, whereas in a symphony the material is already largely provided for.

3. The three remaining orchestral works are represented by the variations on a Haydn-theme and the two overtures. As to the first, which was also the first mature orchestral venture, it fully confirms the symphony argument, on account of the allocation of material being even more rigid in variation-form than in the symphony. The overtures therefore form the outstanding

item; and that, all things considered, they further result in a strengthening of the same conclusion may be proved by reference to their chapters.

4. It may therefore be assumed that in writing for the orchestra Brahms always sought the protection of an outline the filling up of which depended more upon the skilful use of fixed material than upon fantastic application of orchestral effects. There are two reasons for bearing this well in mind; because it not only explains the absence from his orchestral works of all spasmodic and extravagant effect but shows how his renunciation of these led also to his avoidance of all stock mannerisms. It is not so much the former as the latter of these traits which has led to fault being found with his orchestration, the ordinary listener being better able to dispense with his accustomed thrills than to accept new styles of ordinary accompaniment and amplification. For a long time it remained undiscovered that Brahms had practically invented a new style, people being content with calling his instrumentation "thick" or "muddy" and there letting the matter end. By degrees however the idea dawned that common traits of orchestration had been quite purposely avoided, and that a sort of filigree style had been set up the beauty of which could only result from very finished execution; but which, when once realised, appeared to possess a new and peculiar charm. Whether this feature is ever to become widely appreciated or no it will be seen that at all events it is not to be confounded with faulty workmanship and that those who so regard it simply lack information.

5. The characteristic in question will be found frequently referred to in the following pages under the name of "Gothic" instrumentation—a term invented for it by Dr. Riemann and extremely apt for its description. The very exhaustiveness with which the symphonies are individually treated under their several headings renders it unnecessary to proceed further with this subject in the present chapter. Enough to say therefore that Brahms was by no means prolific as an orchestral composer; that his works acquire the orchestral character more distinctly through breadth of outline than by special choice of material; and that he renounced conventional use of the orchestra in favour of a style peculiarly his own. The reader who is interested in the elucidation of these questions will find abundant food for reflection in the following pages.

(B) THE HANDBOOK.

THE CHAMBER AND ORCHESTRAL WORKS

OF

JOHANNES BRAHMS

IN THE ORDER OF THEIR OPUS NUMBER

With Analyses, full explanation of Technical Detail and
appropriate Biographical and Historical Information.

NOTE.—The numerical succession of the Opus List is completed in the
companion volumes, containing a similar account of the PIANO-
FORTE AND ORGAN (Vol. II) and of the VOCAL (Vol. I) Works
respectively.

OP. 8.   FIRST PIANO TRIO.

(For Piano, Violin and Violoncello.)

I. ALLEGRO CON BRIO.
II. SCHERZO, ALLEGRO MOLTO.
III. ADAGIO NON TROPPO
IV. FINALE, ALLEGRO MOLTO AGITATO.

Published by N. Simrock in 1859.*   Revision by the Composer,
published by N. Simrock in 1891.

PRELIMINARY NOTE.

1. THE consistency of Brahms's career renders it desirable to dwell upon the subject of the early works to an extent somewhat out of proportion to the attention devoted to others of greater importance; but the convenience of this proceeding will be experienced later on when various matters, instead of having to be described at length, will be found capable of being disposed of by mere reference to the explanations now and shortly to be given.

2. But it is not only as an early work that this trio claims attention as it is also the only one which the composer revised to the extent of a new printed version, the nearest approach to anything of the same kind occurring in the case of Op. 16 (q.v.); and, though we naturally accept the revision as an expression of the composer's final desire (besides which it is now the version almost universally in vogue) we must also remember Brahms's own warning to the effect that

It is rare for a work which has once reached conclusion to become better by revision.†

---

* This is the date as stated in Simrock's Thematic Catalogue but Kalbeck gives it as 1854.

† Selten wird eine Arbeit, einmal zu einem Abschluss gekommen ist, durch Umarbeitung besser.

3. We cannot moreover dismiss the case by assuming this to
be one of the rare exceptions which he admits, considering the
variety of opinion with regard to it; or insist upon superior
value attaching to the original version as representing historical
interest, if greater musical interest belongs to the new version.
Upon the whole it is the latter which we have to consider, though
it will be interesting to quote opinions upon both.   Thus Fuller-
Maitland calls the revision

an interesting example of self-criticism characteristic of the very greatest minds, and very rare amongst musicians. In the last years of the
composer's life he revised this, his first chamber composition; and a comparison of the two versions is in the highest degree instructive to students
of his methods.   One subject was evidently discarded for too close a resemblance to Schubert's song, " Am Meer "; a new development of the
Finale is substituted for the old; and in the other movements many details
are to be noticed, all of which are improvements in the direction of
breadth and simplicity.

4. On the other hand, we have the following from Miss
Florence May.

This trio remained for many years but little known; but now with its
beautiful youthful qualities it is dear to those who have yielded their
hearts to the spell of Brahms's music.   The composer's fertile fancy has
betrayed him in the first Allegro into some episodical writing which somewhat clouds the distinctness of outline and impedes the listener in his
appreciation of the distinguished beauties of the movement, and there
are places in the finale where a certain disappointment succeeds to the
conviction inspired by the impetuous opening subject: but in wealth of
material, in the rare beauty of its principal themes, and in noble sincerity
of expression the trio occupies a distinguished place even among the
examples of Brahms's maturity.
*The revised edition of 1891 does not seem likely to diminish the affection
with which the original is regarded.**

5. Erb confirms Fuller-Maitland in the following terms.

Thirty years after the production of this work Brahms recomposed it,
the corrections in nearly every case taking the form of simplifications—a
proof that his growth was towards clearness and the abandonment of those
characteristics least pleasing to superficial hearers.

6. But most instructive of all is the opinion of Brahms's great
friends the Herzogenbergs, whose admiration for the new version was curiously mingled with regret for the old. In a letter
from Elisabeth v. Herzogenberg dated from Berlin, October 9,
1890, for instance, she gently chides the composer for applying
his master-hand to the revision of the delightful productions of
his youth

because no one can be imbued with the same spirit after so long a time.

---

* The italics are ours.

A few weeks later Heinrich v. Herzogenberg writes to say that

> though we both now understand the new form we quietly bemoan the traits of loveliness which have been taken away;*

and that this became his permanent opinion is clear, for in the following year he makes a remark which is evidently the result of study.

> The power of adaptation of the elder Brahms to the younger is some-times† perfectly astonishing, but sometimes† also I cannot get rid of the impression of a collaboration of two inherently unequal masters.

7. The fact is that no other composer was ever so well equipped for taking the productions of his youth in hand, Brahms's life-programme remaining ever the same. He did not chafe at the restrictions of form, having quite early in life achieved a complete mastery which enabled him to combine with their observance more legitimate liberty than had been hitherto exercised. He was not, like so many composers, a mere traveller and wanderer upon the face of the earth; but one who, contented with his dwelling-place, spent his life in rendering it more and more beautiful. His return to this particular work can therefore only be construed as proof of his special affection for it; and though it may be true, as sometimes urged, that instruction is to be derived from comparison of the two versions, it is also true that the same may be obtained by comparison of any other two similar works, if sufficiently removed from one another in point of time.

I. ALLEGRO CON BRIO.

8. In dealing with this movement certain digressions will be necessary in explanation of rhythmical tables and other features of our work; for although a separate chapter might have been given to this subject an object-lesson will be found more useful. It will also be more useful if we set eulogy completely aside; and, considering what Brahms himself once said to Jenner:

---

* Wir verstehen nun die Idee der Umarbeitung wenn wir auch einzelnen Lieblingen leise nachweinen.

† He mentions the movements to which the remark applies.

You will never hear a word of praise from me. If you cannot bear
that it shows that what you have in you is not worth saving ;*

we have the master's own approval of that course, as well as
the certainty that he would have been the first to welcome a
verdict passed upon his works, based not upon mere likings and
dislikings, but upon a reasoned assessment of their artistic value.

9. The plan will therefore be—first, to gauge the structure of
each work, and by the proportions of its outline to judge of its
claim to symmetry and unity. Next, to take the thematic
material which is the composer's basis of action and examine
the contrasts which it provides both integrally and as a result
of developments. These procedures combined should enable us
to account for every rhythmic pulsation, trace its relation to the
sub-phrase or motive—thence to the period—thence to the section, movement and entire work. We have to deal with creations
which are rich in evidence of the immense amount of thought
bestowed upon their production, and it is ridiculous in such a
case to suppose that even accomplished performers can by mere
listening at once arrive at a proper judgment. This will explain
the high degree of importance here attached to the rhythmical
table.

10. In submitting these tables to the student we do not of
course pretend that there can be no difference of opinion upon
the dissections submitted. Even the broader rhythmical dispositions sometimes admit of being construed differently, and
this is naturally more the case the narrower they become. But,
should the use of the tables bring such differences to light, far
from diminishing, it will but prove their value in concentrating
attention to a matter of supreme importance, and yet one very
much neglected.

11. The great bulk of musical creation is finally reducible to
the two-bar phrase as represented by the strong and weak bars.
Sustained three-bar rhythm is extremely rare and five-bar
scarcely to be considered at all, so that phrases of equal numbers
may be safely taken for practical purposes as composed of so
many times two. Later on we shall therefore adopt 2 as fixed
component, but at first it will be better to distinguish between
say two twelve-bar phrases which though each consisting of
2×6 might be formed respectively of $8 + 4$ and 4×3. The
present trio, for instance, opens with twelve bars which we in-

---

* Sie werden nie ein lobendes Wort von mir hören. Wenn Sie das nicht vertragen
können, so ist das was in Ihnen steckt, nur wert dass es zu Grunde geht.

dicate in the rhythmical table as 8 + 4, notwithstanding that they might with equal correctness have been construed as 4 × 3. The difference between the two significations is that the former reads the period as 8 bars to which 4 are added—that being the meaning of the plus sign; whereas the latter reading is of 3 four-bar phrases—that being the meaning of the multiplication sign. There is an artistic difference however; for, if the sentence is taken as three phrases of entirely similar character, the beauty of the extension disappears from view.   This will no doubt be rendered clearer by an example; which will also serve as statement of first subject.

Ex. 1.   Op. 8, Allegro con brio, first subject.

To locate the phrase-extensions and to make quite sure that our reading is in accord with the composer's intention is impossible without the full rhythmical analysis which brings one part of a movement to the elucidation of another.   The scanning moreover should not at first be in phrases so short as to allow a mere extension to appear as one.   Here for instance the first eight bars might easily have been dissected into short phrases of two bars each, but this simpler method cannot prudently be employed until after experience has been gained.

13. It sometimes happens (and especially during episodial treatments) that the phrases indicated by table do not appear rhythmically detached and that the continuous flow of such working might be held to leave it an open question whether they really are phrases in the ordinary sense of the term.   From the broader rhythmical standpoint however they must be held to form part of the same category as those of the ruling rhythmical pulsation of the movement, providing they contain no internal evidence to the contrary.

14. The rhythmical table being therefore a chart of the movement we proceed to list its principal uses. These are to ascertain

1. The proportion of the entire extent which is assigned to statement of first, second or third subjects separately.
2. The relation between thematic material as stated in opening and at the return respectively.
3. The proportion allowed to Durchführung and Coda separately and the relation of these to one another.
4. The extent of purely episodial matter and that of theme development.
5. Particulars of all phrase-extensions.

RHYTHMICAL TABLE.

Ex. 2. Op. 8. I, Allegro con brio. Statement of first subject.

PORTION OF MOVEMENT.	DESCRIPTION OF MATERIAL	NO. OF BARS	COMPOSED OF	EXTENDING TO BAR
First ⎫ Section ⎬ (part of) ⎭	1st subject	12	8 + 4	12
		8	4 × 2	20
		15	8 + 4 + 3	35
		9	8 + 1	44
	Episodial principally	10*	8 + 2	54
		8*	8	62
		5	4 + 1	67
		8	4 × 2	75
	Introducing 2nd subject	8	4 × 2	83
Totals.		83		83

15. We see from this that Brahms has indulged in episodial working to an extent scarcely consistent with a first statement; and the student is thus introduced to an apparent defect which may or may not be justified by contents; just as, later on, when we come to our analysis of the return, he will see whether Brahms has given unity to his work by treating this in some manner to be reconciled with the present development. The common knowledge that this Trio is open to the charge of diffuseness should not deter us from making the discovery for ourselves, but in order to do that we require to see the entire movement at a

---

* See par. 18.

RHYTHMICAL TABLE.

Ex. 3. Op. 8. I, Allegro con brio. Statement of second subject.

PORTION	MATERIAL	BARS	COMPOSED OF	EXTEND- ING TO BAR
1st section (part of)	2nd subject	8	4 × 2	91
	Intermediate motives	18	4 × 4 + 2	109
	3rd subject	8	2 × 4	117
	Extra*	3	–	120
Totals.		37		120

glance. We shall not therefore in future divide the subjects from the rest of the movements, which we have only done in this instance for extra simplicity by way of introduction.

RHYTHMICAL TABLE.

Ex. 4. Op. 8. I, Allegro con brio. Statement of Durchführung, Return and Coda.

PORTION	MATERIAL	BARS	COMPOSED OF	EXTEND- ING TO BAR
Durchführung	Bridge	9	2 × 4 + 1	129
	,,	10	2 × 5	139
	1st subject	5	4 + 1	144
	,,	7	4 + 3	151
	Episodial	8	2 × 4	159
	,	5	single bars	164
	,,	3	2 + 1	167
	,,	8	8	175
	,,	12	8 + 4	187
	1st subject	12	8 + 4	199
Totals.		79		199
Return	1st subject	9	8 + 1	208
	,,	9	8 + 1	217
	,.	8	4 × 2	225
	2nd subject	8	4 × 2	233
	,,	18	4 × 4 + 2	251
	Bridge	6	2 × 3	257
Totals.		58		257
Coda	Episodial	32	4 × 8	289
	,,	3	3 + ⌒†	292
Totals.		35		292

---

* For 2da Volta. See Introductory Chapter, par. 4.

† See par. 17.

16. The separation into groups frequently occurs at an extension* of the phrase, and obviously the total number of bars would otherwise be sufficiently accounted for in dividing it by the recognised phrase-length. Simple movements in lyric form often do admit of being so treated, and even in this case we have an instance in the coda, which, dissecting as $4 \times 8 = 32$, indicates an absence of phrase-extensions in that department. Its last phrase however is one of three bars the apparent irregularity of which we must explain.

17. The phrase in question is really only a prolongation of the final chord, and its contents of $3 + \frown$, if stated in words, would amount to "3 bars, plus a reliance upon the intuition of the performers to prolong the final chord (and sometimes also to allow for silent bars thereafter) in a manner to satisfy rhythmic requirements." The fact is that, although this Coda is correctly indicated as 4×8, there is a rhythmic superiority of alternate four-bar phrases, counting from the first—as the reader will easily perceive upon hearing the work played. In other words it would be equally correct to state this Coda is 8×4; in which case the final three-bar phrase would obviously be the commencement of one of eight, and the pause simply a short way of indicating prolongation of the final chord and subsequent silence during the time which these eight bars would, if written out, have occupied. They are here presented thus written out for the student's guidance. The case affords also

Ex. 5. Rhythmic significance of the pause.

an illustration of what was said in par. 10, viz., that whether this rhythmic dissection be agreed to or no, the usefulness of its explanation remains.

18. In episodial treatments the rhythm is liable to be somewhat free in a manner of which an account of the number of bars gives no accurate record. Thus, in the present statement

---

* Contraction, either simple or as caused by the overlapping of two phrases, does not occur in the present movement.

of first subject there are phrases of 8 and 10 of which certain bars, instead of being in allabreve are in $\frac{3}{2}$ time.   This points to the difference between a pause which is rhythmically essential (such as that shown in Ex. 5) and one which is desirable merely as a means of expression.   The precise length of the latter is of course indefinable, as it will naturally vary with the feeling of individual performers; and, in cases where the composer is willing to allow this latitude no one else can object.   The reference here is however merely to the expressive holding of a single note or chord.

19. But there is also a *holding back of the rhythmic unit while motion continues*—a fact which has hitherto been most strangely overlooked in description though not in feeling.   There is abundant evidence of this in the favour accorded to changes in the bar-value by modern composers who have naturally become restive and impatient at the servility imposed upon them by having their music mechanically sliced up and served out in precisely equal time-portions.   We have referred elsewhere to the superiority of Gregorian notation in this respect and there can be no doubt that the future has in store for us some reform of our notation calculated to meet the need here shown.*   That of the moment however is to explain that the extra contents of these $\frac{3}{2}$ bars are merely elaborations of their first beats by which the next first-beat entry is delayed, or in other words they are a mere continuation of motion while the rhythmic beat is being held back.   In all such cases we must first examine the rhythmic basis of the musical thought before occurrence of the melodic incentive to elaborate.

20. The student can only properly appreciate the melodic incentive to extend the bar value at the points marked * by re-

Ex. 6.   Rhythmic basis of bars 45-62, Op. 8.

---

* It may not be amiss here to quote a few words from the author's short treatise on "Modal Accompaniment of Plain Chant," bearing upon this subject.

At page 136 (§ 134) we read : Our slavish division into equal time-por-

ferring to the work itself, but the mere fact of such extensions being dependent upon melodic traits shows that as far as the general subject is concerned they might just as easily have fallen elsewhere. The point is that had an ordinary pause been employed, not only its duration would have been vague but motion in other parts would have simultaneously ceased; whereas by changing the bar-value the length of the pause is both defined and the motion continued. This alone will serve to show how

Ex, 7. Pause by delay of rhythmic pulsation with continued motion.

ridiculous it is to regard frequent changes of bar-value as an affectation on the part of the composer.

21. The expansion of a subject by means of auxiliary motives is for the time being included with the subject as a single item; which is perfectly correct as the two elements need never be separated except for purposes of greater detail. The reasons for deferring consideration of the intermediate motive are—first, that it is simpler to begin by regarding it as one with the subject, and secondly, that with so many incidental matters to explain it became desirable to shorten review of the present work, where possible. The subject of the "intermediate motive" will therefore be introduced with Op. 18, the next chamber work; and we now pass on to the present third subject. Strange to say, this subject is sometimes called a "codetta" to the first

tions very frequently causes modern composers to change the bar-value; thus showing that, in order to express their emotions with fidelity to nature they want the very freedom which Gregorian music already enjoys.

section; which is an evident misapplication of the term, considering that at the return it joins a "codetta" to the real coda of the movement. No doubt it is customary to round off the first section in sonata-form by a subject usually of cantabile character and designated on that account the "song-group"—which it must be confessed that the present third subject is not. But that can form no reason for embarrassment here; the group in question being not even of Coda character, as we shall endeavour to show.

22. The fact is that there is no real departure from the conventional third subject at all; what has happened being merely that instead of allowing it to appear in simple form, Brahms has elaborated it by means of an accessory figure—evidently with an eye to material for the Durchführung.

23. The "cantabile" of the third subject is in many sonatas of such cooling effect that, in order to attain to the necessary warmth during Durchführung, the composer is tempted to make the latter too long. Here, on the contrary, we start with the real business of the Durchführung from the moment of crossing the double bar; yet the subject when stripped of all elaboration

Ex. 8. Third subject of Op. 8 in crude form.

falls so entirely within the usual conditions that we can only wonder at so simple a figure having been misconstrued.

Ex. 9. Figure used for elaboration of third Subject. (Bar 1 of Ex. 8.)

etc.

24. This figuration enters largely into the Durchführung, which is earnest and enthusiastic, leading at bar 200 to the return groups; these being an abridgement of the first section. The Coda as stated is of simple design but of highly sensuous effect, and the whole movement in spite of its outdrawn first section a fine contribution to its class.

25. Epitome.

(a) Subjects. For first and third of these, see Examples 1 and 8. The second subject is here given as to four bars, which become eight by being followed up in sequence.

Ex. 10. Second Subject, Op. 8, I.

Strings
(doubled
in 8va)

Piano
(doubled
in 8va)

etc.

(b) Key B; changing (at bar 124 or seventh of the Durch-führung) to G, returning to original key at bar 184 (16 before return), changing to B minor at bar 211 (twelfth of the return), and regaining the original key at bar 252.

(c) Time, allabreve; single-bar changes to $\frac{3}{2}$ at bars 52, 54, 60, 62. These changes of bar-value occur only during the first statement of principal subject (see Ex. 6 and 7), the second statement being considerably abridged.

(d) Length, 292 bars, or 406 with repeat of first section.

Ex. 11. Outline, Op. 8.

FIRST SECTION	DURCHFÜHRUNG	RETURN	CODA
117	79	58	35
I II III		I II III	
83 26 8		26 26 6	

II. SCHERZO, ALLEGRO MOLTO.

26. A glance at the accompanying table will now show that the first section and Trio of this movement have each one subject only, that this subject is in each case slightly expanded after the repeat, that the phrasing is duple (with rare cases of extension, these being however also duple), and that the form is lyric.*

RHYTHMICAL TABLE.

Ex. 12. Op. 8, Scherzo, First Section.

PORTION	MATERIAL	BARS	COMPOSED OF	EXTENDING TO BAR
1st part	Subject	12	4 × 3	12
	,,	12	4 × 3	24
	,,	8	4 × 2	32
2nd part	2da Volta	4	4	36
	Expansion ⎱ of subject ⎰	4	4	40
	,,	48	4 × 12	88
	,,	36	4 × 9	124
Return	Subject	12	4 × 3	136
	,,	12	4 × 3	148
	,,	14	4 × 3 + 2	162
	Bridge to Trio	6	4 + 2	168
Totals.		168		168

Other items of observation concerning the symmetry of the movement will be the proportional space devoted to expansion of the subject, to return and to the graft of Trio and first section.

27. The sostenuto character of the Trio may be at once de-

---

* Full exposition of this subject for those who require it may be found in the author's "How to Compose within the Lyric Form."

RHYTHMICAL TABLE.
Ex. 13. Op. 8, Scherzo. Trio (Meno Allegro).

PORTION	MATERIAL	BARS	COMPOSED OF	EXTEND-ING TO BAR
1st part	Subject	16	8 × 2	184
	,,	16	8 × 2	200
2nd part	Expansion of subject }	18	8 × 2 + 2	218
	,,	34	4 × 8 + 2	252
	2da Volta	2	2	254
	Bridge to Re-turn section }	12	4 × 3	266
Totals.		98		266

duced from its rhythmisation in phrases of eight bars, as compared with those of four in the opening section.

28. There is no simple return as there was for the first section; but as against that the thirty-four bars forming the second item given to expansion of the subject unite within themselves the conditions both of expansion and return. As a matter of fact the theme does actually return; but it is with a new instrumentation which allows the excitement still to grow and to reach its climax at the bridge. This is a refinement in the observance of form which the student should note.

RHYTHMICAL TABLE.
Ex. 14   Op. 8, Scherzo, Return and Coda.

PORTION	MATERIAL	BARS	COMPOSED OF	EXTEND-ING TO BAR
Return	Subject	12	4 × 3	278
	,,	12	4 × 3	290
	,,	8	4 × 2	298
	,,	4	4	302
	Expansion	48	4 × 12	350
	,,	36	4 × 9	386
	Subject	12	4 × 3	398
	,,	12	4 × 3	410
	,,	14	4 × 3 + 2	42.
	Bridge	4	4	428
Totals.		162		428
Coda	Free	36	4 × 9	464
		2	2*	2
Totals.		38		466

* Equivalent with ⌒ to 4 rhythmically. See Ex. 5.

29. The treatment of the first section subject is so Beethovenish

Ex. 15. Op. 8, Scherzo. (Subject of first section.)

'Cello.   Pf.

that although the daintiness of the theme pervades the movement the logic of its expansion imparts something of a serious
character. We are intellectually borne along by the *moto perpetuo* of the crotchet-pulsation until, at the Trio, the latter is
displaced by pulsation of the *bar*. The climax of expansion is
signalised by continued quaver motion; and if fault could be
found it would be with the delay which ensues after subsidence
of the quaver motion before re-entry of the theme (bars 89 to
124). The latter is however beautifully approached, so that any
undue delay is well atoned for.

30. It would perhaps be going too far to assert this Trio-sub-

Ex. 16. Op. 8, Scherzo (subject of Trio).

ject to have been a deliberate counterpoint of the leading theme,
but it certainly bears that appearance. Thus bars 129 to 133

Ex. 17. Op. 8, Scherzo First and Second Subjects combined.

Violin

Piano

form a passage in which both subjects are combined.   Apart from its contrapuntal interest this observation is amusing; for, if true, it corresponds with what we once remarked of Tchaïkovsky in his Trio, Op. 50, and shows that notwithstanding his adverse opinion of Brahms he did not scorn in 1882 to follow a plan which the alleged "composer of no inspiration" had initiated in 1859.*

The coda is distinctly more florid than the movement generally, its "piano-solo" element almost overstepping consistency. It is in fact only redeemed by its occasional reminders of the leading theme.

31. Epitome.

(a) Subjects.   See Exs. 14, 15.

(b) Key B minor, with Trio in B major.

(c) Time ¾, without change.

(d) Length 466 bars, or 544 with repeats.

Ex. 18. Op. 8, Scherzo. Outline.

FIRST PART	TRIO	RETURN	CODA
163	98	162	38

III. ADAGIO

32. The disposition of parts in this movement is scarcely that of a trio of instruments; the thematic material being so persistently treated as a dialogue between the piano as a self-sufficing instrument and the two strings, taken collectively as a separate self-sufficing combination.   This procedure is always interesting; and though it is not peculiar to Brahms, the steadfastness with which it is here maintained imparts such reality to the imaginary conversation that the effect seems new.

---

* The reader for whom this question of the evolution of themes may have a special interest will find it somewhat fully dealt with in the author's analysis of the Tchaïkovsky Trio, Op. 50. (See "Tchaïkovsky, His Life and Works," pp. 272 to 287).

RHYTHMICAL TABLE

Ex. 19. Op. 8, Adagio.

PORTION	MATERIAL	BARS	COMPOSED OF	EXTEND-ING TO BAR
Opening	1st subject	18	$(4 + 2) \times 3$	18
	,,	6	6	24
	,,	8	4×2	32
Totals.		32		32
Development	2nd subject	11	$\left.\begin{array}{l} 4 + 1 \\ 4 + 2 \end{array}\right\}$	43
	Expansion	8	4×2	51
	,,	6	$4 + 2$	57
	,,	8	4×2	65
Totals.		33		65
Close	1st subject	18	$(4 + 2) \times 3$	83
	,,	7	$6 + 1$	90
	,,	9	$4 \times 2 + 1$	99
Totals.		34		99

33. In course of the movement we meet with

(a) Chorale for piano; answered by meditative interludes for strings.

(b) Independent meditative interludes for strings; with piano either *tacet* or supplying light elaborative accompaniment.

(c) 'Cello cantabile; with piano accompaniment, violin tacet, the last of these being used only for statement of second subject. In this the violin has no share, besides which it holds no prominence throughout the movement other than that inseparable from an upper part. In the expansion following this 'cello solo the phrases and their component motives become however more detached; this conventional feature being maintained until the return, which differs much in aspect but little in substance from the original statement. This variety of treatment for return groups is a great charm specially befitting an earnest movement, which is thus enabled without coda assistance to reach a perfectly satisfactory conclusion.

34. If the plan of interspersing the chorale with string interludes were pursued mechanically it would obviously lead to a complete melody broken up by non-integral interludes—a merely perfunctory and inartistic affair. But Brahms avoids

Ex. 20. Op. 8, Adagio, Piano Chorale, with string interlude.

this by making his string interlude independent just at the moment when the chorale would otherwise be expected to conclude.

Ex. 21. Op. 8, Adagio, Independent string interlude.

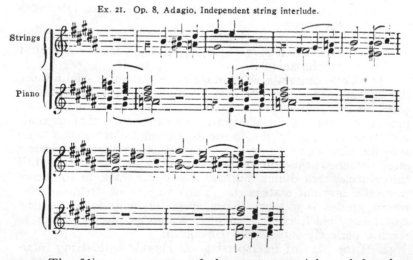

35. The filigree treatment of the same material used for the return group renders coda unnecessary, especially with a diminuendo cadence in view.

Ex, 22. Op. 8, Adagio, variety of return group without change of material.

36. The 'cello cantabile of the second subject serves the useful purpose of exhibiting one of the phrase-extensions recorded in

Ex. 23. Op. 8, Adagio, Second Subject.

the rhythmical table* as congenial to the Brahms style of composition; for here, though the phrase extension is obvious the
extra bar is no mere repetition, the repeated motive being in-
vested with just the difference of harmony sufficient to impart a
new tint, but without adding anything calculated to hide the
gracefulness of the rhythmical addition.

37. The agitato consequent upon detachment of motives,
which leads to the return, being managed upon the usual lines,

Ex. 24. Op. 8, Adagio. Expansion cf Second Subject.

etc.

offers little for technical remark, though much for artistic appreciation, as exhibiting a judicious self-restraint, though unfortunately the lesson which it conveys is least likely to be accepted
by those who are most in need of it.

38. Epitome.

(a) Subjects. See Examples 19 and 22.

(b) Key, B major. No change of key and amount even of
transient modulation but slight. On the other hand much use
is made of relative minor especially during the middle section.

---

* Ex. 19 (opening of the development). The extension in question is
the "+ 1" indicated at the appearance of second subject.

There is a lack of key-contrast in this trio as a result of all its
movements being in B, either major or minor. See paragraph 40.

(c) Time, common; without change.

(d) Length ninety-nine bars, no repeats.

Ex. 25. Op. 8, Adagio. Outline.

FIRST SECTION	MIDDLE SECTION	CONCLUDING SECTION
32	33	34

That these sections are rhythmically divisible into three, four
and three groups respectively may be perceived from the Table,
Ex. 19.

IV. ALLEGRO.

39. Rondo form is comparatively unfavourable to the display of the Brahms individuality, and accordingly it is in these
movements that we find most trace of the influence of other
composers. The outline seems more or less incompatible with
ideas of heroic or noble character and scarcely lends itself even
to those of any superior earnestness. Hence in this movement
we have a treatment not subserviently but distinctly Mendelssohnian; the development being of the genteel character with
which that master has made us familiar, the effects mostly monophonic; and the piano part, without being so egregiously out of
balance as that of Mendelssohn's D minor Trio, being too pro-
fuse for its material and too largely given to mere accompaniment. The objection is that the three instruments are here
employed not for the production of an ideal *trio*, but for the
glorification of what might have been essentially presented by
one. As against this however there can be nothing but praise for
the manner in which this lower ideal has been pursued; besides
which it is admittedly open to contend that a lighter style is
desirable for finale.

RHYTHMICAL TABLE.

Ex. 26. Op. 8, Finale (Allegro).

PORTION	MATERIAL	BARS	COMPOSED OF	EXTEND-ING TO BAR
1st statement	1st subject	17	$\left.\begin{array}{l} 2 \times 4 \\ 4 \times 2 \end{array}\right\} + 1$	17
	,,	20	$\left.\begin{array}{l} 2 \times 4 \\ 4 \times 3 \end{array}\right\}$	37
	,,	16	$(2 + 2 + 4) \times 2$	53
	,,	10	$4 \times 2 + 2$	63
Totals.		63		63
Middle section	2nd subject	24	$\left.\begin{array}{l} 4 \times 2 \\ (2 \times 2 + 4) \times 2 \end{array}\right\}$	87
	,,	23	$\left.\begin{array}{l} 4 + 1 \\ 4 \times 4 + 2 \end{array}\right\}$	110
Totals.		47		110
2nd statement	1st subject	18	$\left.\begin{array}{l} 2 \times 4 \\ 4 \times 2 \end{array}\right\} + 2$	128
	,,	24	$\left.\begin{array}{l} 2 \times 8 \\ 4 \times 2 \end{array}\right\}$	152
	Bridge to 3rd subject	18	$4 \times 4 + 2$	170
Totals.		60		170
Middle section	3rd subject	34	$4 \times 8 + 2$	204
	2nd subject ,,	37	$\left.\begin{array}{l} 4 \times 2 \\ (2 \times 2 + 4) \times 2 \\ 4 + 1 \\ 4 \times 2 \end{array}\right\}$	241
Totals.		71		241
Coda	Bridge 1st subject	20	$\left.\begin{array}{l} 4 \\ (2 \times 2 + 4) \times 2 \end{array}\right\}$	261
	Free	12	4×3	273
	,,	36	$\left.\begin{array}{l} 2 \times 4 \\ 4 \times 7 \end{array}\right\}$	309
	1st subject ,,	13	$\left.\begin{array}{l} 2 \times 4 \\ 4 + 1 \end{array}\right\}$	322
Totals.		81		322

40. In this trio Brahms seems to set the principle of contrast
in tonalities completely at defiance, each of the four movements
being in B—either major or minor. We shall certainly not set
out to defend this practice; yet we must remember that the
variety principle owes its origin to a period when movements
were more diatonic than at present. Nowadays when the call

made upon foreign keys in the course of every movement is so
extensive the importance of the parent tonality question is not
only considerably reduced, but even the motive for its observance is somewhat changed.   Formerly the contrast of keys was
as that of tints in a design—a desideratum now entirely supplanted by our boldness and freedom in modulation.   If we now
require a scheme of related keys it is not for purposes of contrast but in order to give unity to the entire scheme.

41. Granting this we must allow that, in adhering to a B
tonic, if Brahms committed a fault at all it was in adhering too
closely to the unity principle.   Moreover, and as usual with
him, there are modifying features.   Here, for instance, at the
opening, so far as the mere sense of hearing is concerned the
effect is that of being in G major.   The desired sensuous contrast is there; being secured by the simple process of suspending
the fifth in the chord of B minor.   Hence it is sometimes in the
listener's interest to be deceived; though this can scarcely be
said of the critics whom Brahms has thus beguiled into describing this movement as opening in G major.   The mistake is
useful however as proving the treachery of merely superficial
observation.

42. That there is no affectation of the key of G will be obvious
upon examination of the subject, which is of dual character;

Ex. 27.   Op. 8, Finale, First subject.

its second member being subsequently utilised as a separate
theme.   The continuation seems here to pose as a development;
but this it cannot be rightly considered, because of being used
under the same principle as that described in par. 7 of Op. 16
—the only difference between the two being that in this case
coherence in working hides mechanics completely from view.
This second member of the first subject may have even had
something to do with the evolution (for the new version) of the
second subject in D.   The reader can easily form his own opinion hereupon by comparing them as under; but such coincidences
in the Brahms works are too numerous to allow of mention
except on special occasions.

Ex. 28. Op. 8, Finale, Second member of First Subject.

Ex. 29. Op. 8, Finale, Second Subject.

43.   The third subject (bar 171) may be considered either as a subject or a development of certain traits of the opening theme.   Thus refinement of workmanship is often the analytical critic's embarrassment, such mutuality of relationship rendering classification difficult.

Ex. 30. Op. 8, Finale, First Subject (conclusion of first period).

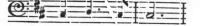

Ex. 31. Op. 8, Finale, First Subject. (Passages leading to conclusion of statement).

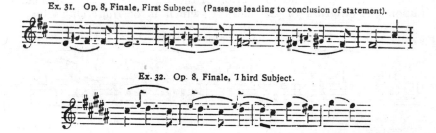

Ex. 32. Op. 8, Finale, Third Subject.

44. Much elasticity and grace is imparted to the movement by means of phrase-extension, the occasions of which are to be ascertained from the rhythmical table   The principal theme is of decidedly square-cut character; and, in the hands of a less gifted composer, it would have probably resulted in an equally square-set formal outline; whereas in this case the strength of the rectangular work is united with the grace of a varying phrase-length.   This shows the importance of being able to survey the whole at a glance; for, in listening to the work, whilst conscious of the pleasure derived, we can know nothing of the beautiful symmetry to which our enjoyment is largely due.

45. But, over and above what may be ascertained by mere scrutiny of measurements, there is the variety of object for which these extensions are employed. Sometimes they have merely the effect of a written out pause. At other times the composer is purposely holding the listener in suspense (as, for example, during the two bars immediately preceding second subject); or, it may be, restraining rhythmic motion preparatory to its increase. In matters of this kind nothing can take the place of a close examination of the work itself; though for the general reader the main conclusion to be derived will no doubt be sufficiently clear.

46. Epitome.

(a) Subjects. See Ex. 26 to 31.

(b) Key, B minor, with change to B major and retention of that key from entry of introduction to third subject to commencement of the Coda. Much transient but no extensive modulations.

(c) Time, $\frac{3}{4}$, without change.

(d) Length, 322 bars; no repeats.

Ex. 33. Op. 8, Finale. Outline.

FIRST STATEMENT	DEVELOPMENT	RETURN	DEVELOPMENT	CODA
63	47	60	71	81
I	II	I	III II	I

OP. 11. SERENADE IN D.

(For two Flutes, two Oboes, two Clarinets, two Bassoons, four Horns, two Trumpets, Drums and Strings.)

I. ALLEGRO MOLTO.
II. SCHERZO (No. 1) ALLEGRO NON TROPPO.
III. ADAGIO NON TROPPO.
IV. MENUETTO I AND II.
V. SCHERZO (No. 2), ALLEGRO.
VI. RONDO. ALLEGRO.

Arranged by the Composer for piano duet. Published by
N. Simrock in 1860.

PRELIMINARY NOTE.

(a) The " Period " question.

1. THE Serenades are of simple character as compared either with the Trio we have just left or with the piano solo Sonatas, Op. 1, 2 and 5, critics therefore generally regarding them as a new departure. But this is doubtless also due in part to the well-worn habit of dividing a composer's output into " periods," as a convenient method of review; one useful enough in cases where at certain dates there is an evident change of style but scarcely applicable to the Brahms works in respect of which people are not even agreed about the position of the landmarks they desire to set up.

2. It is curious too to observe the readiness with which slight differences are caught at for this " period " purpose. Thus, one might suppose the simple character of the present Serenade to be sufficiently well explained by its being Brahms's first writing for wind instruments; but Erb considers it to mark " emancipation from romantic tendency, over-maturity and display of erudition." Fuller-Maitland calls the small movements of these

works a "series of monochromes," a description which seems to
admit that wind instruments are used in them only in a tentative
manner; but even if we take it that they merely illustrate the
Colles dictum of Brahms "caring comparatively little for the
rapid passing from colour to colour which contributes so much
to the charm of modern music" the period-theory fares no better,
for Morin, another critic, draws the line, not at this work at all,
but at the Sextet, Op. 18.

3. The only Brahms "period" with any definite meaning is
that which relates to his habit of giving himself up for a time
to one class of composition; and it is in this way that we sometimes speak of the choral period (1868-72) or of the "symphonic
decade" (1877-86)—both usefully compact expressions. For
practical purposes therefore all that we have to consider is that
Brahms, who was now about twenty-three years of age, had
already produced several works of high character, but mostly
open to the reproach of outrunning the means selected for their
expression. Conscious of the necessity for action upon a broader
scale he had devoted four years to meditation and study the
value of which he was now about to test.   The creative faculty
not having full play in such circumstances the works are naturally simple, but as to any changed views we need only recall the
piano-concerto of the same period to recognise in it all the
original exuberance.

(b) The Serenades as a revival.

4. Treating the Serenades, Op. 11 and 16, collectively, it is
necessary first to observe that such productions are what were
formerly called "Divertimenti"—a class somewhat midway
between chamber and orchestral music; one which included also
the "Cassation," was rather freely cultivated in the eighteenth
century and consisted mostly of pieces intended for performance
in the open air.

5. The prudence of choosing this class of composition for a
first essay in orchestral writing becomes evident when we remember that the composition of Divertimenti was upon the wane
even in Mozart's time, and that but for him this form would by
now have become completely forgotten.   He not only rescued
it from oblivion, but his specimens of it are practically all that
we know; the result being that his name is so identified with it
as to cause a difficulty in even thinking of it apart from him.
Naturally a revival of this kind not only justifies but calls for
a Mozartean style, and therefore provides opportunity for its
exercise quite unassociated with any restriction.

6. There would appear therefore to be some want of thought on the part of those who describe the Mozartean features of these works as a retrograde step, a beneficent example of self-restraint, self-criticism and what not. The basis of all these views is probably the laudable desire to pay court to these works from respect for Brahms's other achievements; but while respecting this feeling we are bound to hold that the master is best honoured by a frank exposition of whatever his works may contain. It is unquestionable that these works are inferior to his other output and that, as we shall presently show, he himself was aware of that fact.

7. This is not however to call in question Brahms's habit of severe self-restraint; which, however motived, was a piece of real good fortune to him as a composer—if not indeed necessary to him as a defence against indiscriminate praise. Take, for instance, the friendly judgment of Dietrich upon these Serenades, describing them as the

first results of Brahms's industry after seclusion at Detmold and Hamburg,

and followed up by an interesting account of his meeting with Brahms after their long separation.

After six years of silence Brahms had brought with him a number of new and splendid compositions to which we were now introduced. These were the Serenades in A and D, the "Ave Maria," the Funeral Hymn, some songs and the piano Concerto in D minor. We had frequent gatherings in company with Professor Jahn (the biographer of Mozart) for the purpose of performing chamber music. How keenly we relished these musical treats!

8. Anyone familiar with Brahms will at once perceive the jumble of bracing the Serenades with the D minor Concerto and ascribe such generalisation to desire. But Brahms himself was not misled into believing the Serenades to be finished works; for in writing to Joachim (from Detmold, December 8, '58) and asking him for some special music-paper he says that he requires it

in order finally to change the first Serenade into a symphony, for I perceive that, as it is, it is neither one thing nor the other and is all wrong.*

9. Even in 1860, moreover, when after much deliberation the work was about to be published many qualms still survived and were expressed to Joachim. The strictures to which both of these Serenades are subject are specially mentioned under the heading of the opening movement of Op. 16; and, though we

---

* Ich sehe es ein dass das Werk eine Zwittergestalt, nichts Rechtes ist.

cannot also reproach them with having failed to realise the "Divertimento" character (not being sure whether Brahms intended them as Divertimenti) internal evidence shows that the composer's individuality would have been too strong to enable him to do this even had he so intended—his rhythmic proclivities being entirely at variance with the typical mode of expression.

I. ALLEGRO MOLTO.

10. Though the prominence given to elementary harmonies in this movement may help to give it something of the Divertimento character, modern traits intervene to destroy all eighteenth century allusion. It may be urged on behalf of these features that, after all, they are not really new; but, on the contrary, very old. That may be so; but we have at least to remember that they were in abeyance during the Divertimento period, and are therefore as inconsistent with reproductions of that form as if now introduced for the first time.

11. For example, Folk-song and Gregorian music possess a freedom of rhythm not to be found in the Cassation in spite of the latter's more recent origin. The objection to such freedom is not therefore that it is new, but rather that it is too old. It is only "new" because modern musicians have travelled beyond the ideas of the rococo period and sigh for a return to Nature; and, if it appear to be new, it is only as any old fashion may appear new, if, after a long period of disuse, it is suddenly revived.

12. To take a case in point the division of the allabreve bar into three minims is a rhythm, conceivable perhaps in development, but not as part of a subject of eighteenth century suggestion.

Ex. 34.   Divergent rhythm.

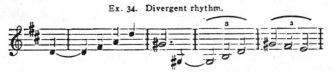

We can only picture the fops and gallants of the period as being embarrassed by it, or an exquisite as waiting for it to be over before attempting to bow, or pirouette, or kiss his lady's hand.   In short, the Divertimento character is not there; and this result should cause us no surprise, considering that the form was chosen not for historical but for purely technical associations.

13. Another point is that whilst these Serenades indulge much freedom of rhythm *within* the bar the broad outline of the pieces is of quite elementary kind—too elementary in fact to justify our giving tables of them.*   The Movements being mostly of simple lyric character may generally be rhythmically summarised by mere division of the total number of bars by the recognised phrase-length.   Such extensions or contractions as do occur have moreover not the interest of those to be found in later works; besides which the extraordinary length in several cases is quite deterrent.   With maturer productions the intermediate motives are interwoven, but here they occupy the place which should be given to development of the subjects proper, and result both in depriving the Durchführung of all climax and in rendering the whole desultory.

In this particular movement the pastoral effect is marred by changeful bar-subdivision; and, as the subjects merely suggest a development which does not happen, feeling remains in the condition appropriate to a technical exercise.

14. Epitome

(a) Subjects.

Ex. 35. Op. 11, Allegro, First Subject.

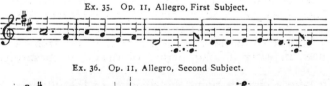

Ex. 36. Op. 11, Allegro, Second Subject.

The general character being pastoral, pedal basses occur frequently.   There are also instances of *basso ostinato*—though none remarkable.

---

* These Serenades are the only works of which we have not judged it necessary to give Rhythmical Tables.

(b) Key D major—one continuous movement, with free modulation in Durchführung causing enharmonic changes into D flat and B flat.

(c) Time, allabreve. Retained throughout, though much varied by triplet division of bar $\left(\d\;\d\;\d\right)$ and half-bar $\left(\bullet\;\d\;\bullet\right)$.

(d) Length, 576 bars; or 768 including the 192 for repeat of first section.

Ex. 37. Op 11, Allegro. Outline.

FIRST SECTION	DURCHFÜHRUNG	RETURN	CODA
204	151	140	69
Intro. I II III 4 110 65 25		I II III 60 70 19	

II. SCHERZO (No. 1).

Allegro non troppo.

15. A reserve of power is here apparent in spite of the delicacy with which material is handled; the polyphony being like a giant at play—gambolling light-heartedly enough but failing to hide the learned presence.

16. The crotchet motion is so incessant that the tiniest quaver-group becomes a relief; besides which the length of the movement exceeds its interest and the contrast of the Trio is insufficient. The latter however has at least the merit of offering a good defence of Brahms against the unjust charge of over-use of syncopation.

17. Why should Brahms have been specially dubbed "Syncopen-Komponist," considering the prior claim of Schumann to that title? Why, again, should either of them have to be reproached for the use, however free, of this means of expression? This is a mystery; but it is also a question which concerns us too closely to be passed by. The flippancies we sometimes hear upon this entirely omit to notice that a whole movement may be syncopated without necessarily suffering any alteration thereby. Syncopation in such a case merely affects the accentuation of

accompanying parts (assuming these to retain the normal beat) and need not otherwise interfere with either melody, harmony or rhythm.

18. Extreme use of syncopation would therefore tend to approach and finally to arrive at the point from which we started. This, however, presupposes that we are dealing with the thing itself, and not with the mere mode of its presentation to the eye. Thus there is no difference between (a) and (b) in the following example

Ex. 38.   Non-effect of Syncopation.

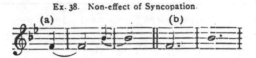

except as to the manner of writing   But such syncopation, though leaving the melody unchanged, is of the utmost service to the composer when it comes to a question of phrasing—as may be seen by comparing (a) and (b) in application.

Ex. 39.   Use of Syncopation.

Here not only the syncopations at (a) confer greater freedom, but their absence, at (b) compels us to impoverish the second emphatic utterance in order not to displace the bar-line; from which we see that, in order to be rationally applied, the term Syncopen-Komponist should be entirely reserved for the composer who syncopates without motive.   Bar-lines are as mere niches upon a foot-rule; and to demand that turns of the musical phrase should coincide with them is like expecting the pattern of a carpet to coincide with crevices of the floor-boards.

19. This movement is in simple lyric form and subject to the common shortcoming of these early orchestral works—that of suggesting more than is realised.   To those able to appreciate mere suggestion they accordingly seem to bear a message which is quite different from that conveyed to those forced entirely to rely upon what they hear.   It may be natural to ardent musicians to give the composer credit for the full force of ideas to them apparent, but criticism can only take account of what is provided in full.

20. Epitome.

(a) Subjects.

Ex. 40. Op. 11. Scherzo No. 1.

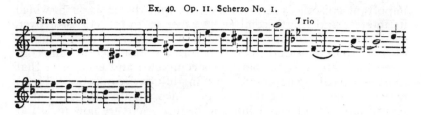

Several others might be quoted, but without advantage. Mention may be made however of the graceful and melodious second subject of first section, which by leading to some free modulation (at "poco ritenuto") and thus re-introducing the theme gives a good instance of miniature development.

(b) Key. First section in D minor; Trio in B flat.

(c) Time ¾. "Un poco ritenuto" for 20 bars preceding return of theme in first section.

Trio, "poco piu animato." No Coda; the Da Capo being "senza replica" with close at end of first section.

(d) Length 335 bars; or 363 including the repeat of first part of Section 1, but without D.C. (senza replica).

Ex. 41. Op. 11, Scherzo, No. 1. Outline.

FIRST SECTION	TRIO
‖: 27 :‖ 129	179

III. ADAGIO NON TROPPO.

21. This movement is generally accepted as the best of the work in respect both of contents and instrumentation, but to concede this leads to no conclusion of any value. In regard to scoring the opening by lower strings and bassoons and the wave-tremolo for second violins and 'cellos which forms the accompaniment during an episode leading to second subject are features. But the episode in question has unfortunately all the importance of a new subject; and, though doubtless in the composer's mind the second theme consisted of the grade cantabile in F delivered by the horn later on, the intervention of this

important episode is fatal to the principal theme as such, which
its interest and length combine to cause us to forget. Moreover,
even after the horn melody we have to wait during a long fugato
of more than episodial interest before the first section (unrecog-
nised but happening at bar 88) is complete; and even after that
there are still some interesting modulative figurations based
upon the fugato before the portion which we are here obliged to
regard as a sort of Durchführung begins. We are now in D flat
after traversing over 100 bars in Adagio, but not even during
this new portion is there any reference to our opening melody,
the vocation of which as principal theme is simply thrown to
the winds.

22. The Durchführung is however very beautiful in itself and
while it lasts, which is only for 30 bars. This unsymmetrical
dimension appears due to the composer's belated anxiety to get
back to his theme, and to this having caused him so to compress
matters that within this small space he has managed to give us
the fugato subject combined with a new alternating figure, as
well as the horn subject in a new dress. Then, wonderful to
relate, but quite in keeping with the above anxiety, the principal
subject reappears in B—a semitone higher than the original
key; leaving nothing for it but to scramble into B flat quickly.

Ex. 42. Op. 11. Adagio. Syncopated Bass.

Undoubtedly the syncopated bass is good, but it fails to take the place of the logical feature; and though the themes may be skilfully joined they are not evolved.   Moreover, the episodes by their length and interest usurp the position due to main subjects, and combine with the complicated rhythm to give to the whole a want of coherence; whilst the phrasing admits of being too variously construed to render its tabular exposition in any one form advisable.

23. Epitome.

(a) Subjects.

Ex 43. Op. II, Adagio, First Subject and Episode.

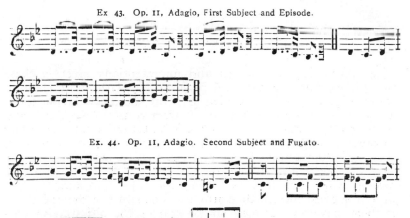

Ex. 44. Op. II, Adagio. Second Subject and Fugato.

(b) Key B flat, one continuous movement, with frequent transient modulation but only one recognised change of key—that to B mentioned in par. 22.

(c) Time $\frac{2}{4}$ with extension to $\frac{3}{4}$ of one bar only.   Rhythmic pulsations of crotchet value for opening theme; of quaver value for all other subjects.

(d) Length 250 bars.   This dimension compared with that of the slow movement of Beethoven's C minor Symphony, one of vastly greater purport, shows

Beethoven, 738 quavers andante.

Brahms, 1,000 quavers adagio.

Ex. 45. Op. 11, Adagio. Outline.

	FIRST SUBJECT	EPISODE	SECOND SUBJECT	FUGATO	EPISODE	DURCHFÜHRUNG	CODA
First Statement	38	25	15	10	16	30	——
Return	49	16	15	10	——	——	26

IV. MINUETS (1 AND 2).

24. Of traditional pattern and unpretentious in style these two pieces, cast for alternate performance with short coda to follow No. 1, may be regarded as good specimens of the form. They have a simplicity which is attractive in its way, as being conformable to antique style; but the imitation is not of a nature to cause us any danger of mistaking these for old-time productions. Frequent use of the under-changing note for example would alone suffice to create a suspicion of modern origin; besides which the rhythmic bounds of No. 1 (10 and 15 bars) do not suggest the old-time article. The spirit of the old dance is there, however. It may not be that of the old stately court dance, being rather that of specimens with which the "suite" has made us familiar. But that is no reproach, these little movements being thoroughly in keeping with the only association they have in view.

26. Epitome.

(a) Subjects.

Ex. 46. Op. 11, Minuets, Subjects.

No. 1   No. 2

Reduced score: flute, two clarinets, bassoon and 'cello; with addition of viola for No. 2.

(b) Key, No. 1, G major; No. 2, G minor.

(c) Time, $\frac{3}{4}$.

(d) Length, 63 bars (including 3 for "second time" bars). Add 44 for repeats.

Ex. 47. Op. 11, Minuets. Outline.

NO. 1	NO. 2	BRIDGE TO D.C.	CODA
|: 10 :|: 15:|	|: 8 :|: 16 :|	4	7

V.   SCHERZO (No. 2), ALLEGRO.

27. This Scherzo is planned upon a much smaller scale than No. 1—and is all the better for it. Brahms here scarcely appears, as the lack of development gives his individuality no chance of display; and it almost seems as if Beethoven had taken his place, so forcibly are we reminded of that composer.

28. The respective crotchet and quaver motions of the two sections form, no doubt, an intentionally marked contrast; and the slight development allowed to the conclusion of the first is not only thoroughly remindful of old-style, but is put to a charming use by rendering Coda unnecessary when occurring after the Da Capo. Regarded as in antique style, this piece is a success; even such matters as the thinness of the instrumentation contributing to the illusion.

29. Epitome.

(a) Subjects.

Ex. 48.   Op. 11, Scherzo No. 2, Subjects.

(b) Key, D major throughout. Only transient modulation
—that into relative minor during middle portion of Trio.

(c) Time, $\frac{3}{4}$. No departures from the strict beat. Rhythmic
pulsation, that of the bar.

(d) Length, 90 bars, plus 74 for repeats and 60 for D.C. senza
replica; total, 224.

Ex. 49. Op. 11, Scherzo, No 2. Outline.

FIRST SECTION	TRIO
16 + ‖: 48 :‖	‖: 8 :‖: 18 :‖

VI. RONDO (ALLEGRO).

30. The length of this rondo is not inordinate upon the whole,
but the period which elapses between recurrences of the principal
theme is such that only two returns (at bars 103 and 241) are
possible. In some circumstances this might be held to be sufficient, but here the principal subject is a mere rhythmical figure
of which we soon tire—and should tire even sooner were it not
for some episodial work which again does duty for development.
As it is, our welcome of second subject is at the expense of the
first, the form is disturbed, and the happy return of the principal
theme which is so great a charm of the perfect rondo is in abeyance. We bow to its ultimate return as inevitable but are past
giving it any welcome.

31. With more variety of subject between returns the rondo
spirit might have survived. But, even then, the first subject
would have remained a serious handicap. Moreover, the retention during the whole movement of the new theme entering at
bar 64 (as shown by a first appearance in A, another at bar 139
in C and yet another at bar 182 in D) would in any case have
compromised the result.

32. It is true that after the third statement of principal theme
this second subject entirely disappears, and that the elaborate
Coda is exclusively given to the first subject—that is if we
include under that term the episodial passages already referred

to. To do so however is extremely difficult, seeing that they also attach to the statement of second subject, at bars 157 and following.

33. This constant use of the same auxiliary subjects is a great cause of weariness, besides which the returns themselves are not happily induced—appearing rather to pounce upon us unawares. Being no fulfilment of any gradually awakened expectation they are only mechanically conformable to rondo-form—truly a most singular reproach to have to make in the case of Brahms.

34. To sum up, we can find no worthiness in this rondo beyond that to be expected of ordinary musicianship; and even that not always tempered by the best judgment. The semiquaver moto-perpetuo accompaniment to second subject (bars 180-222) for instance, is good, but too prolonged. Being, throughout the movement, only released from one obsession to be delivered over to another, we are entitled to say that it is the composer himself who compels us to overlook the beauty of the second subject, the adroitness of the figurations and the enthusiasm of the Coda; all of which are atoning features. But the real student, disregarding all this, looks beyond it to a virility of style which he knows will survive all else.

35. Epitome.
(a) Subjects.

Ex. 50. Op. 11, Rondon, Subjects.

(b) Key, D major, no recognised change.
(c) Time, $\frac{2}{4}$. No changes of movement though much variety of bar-subdivision, each successive kind of which is remarkably sustained. In this way we have quaver-motion, triplet quaver

figurations and semiquaver motion successively employed as
accompaniment to second subject; giving to the whole piece
something of the aspect of a contrapuntal exercise on two, three
and four notes for each rhythmical pulsation.

(d) Length, 357 bars.

Ex. 51. Op. 11, Rondo. Outline.

I	II	I	II	I	CODA
64	38	37	101	16	101

OP. 16. SERENADE IN A.

*(For Piccolo, two Flutes, two Oboes, two Clarinets, two Horns,
Violas, 'Cellos and Basses.)*

I. Allegro moderato.
II. Scherzo vivace.
III. Adagio non troppo.
IV. Quasi menuetto.
V. Rondo allegro.

Arranged by the Composer for piano duet. Published by
N. Simrock in 1875.

PRELIMINARY NOTE.
On Brahms's early orchestral work.

1. A VERSION of the present work appeared at Bonn as early
as 1860, but was withdrawn by the composer. As it stands
therefore this Serenade is a revision after fifteen years' experience and cannot in respect of orchestration be fairly compared
with Op. 11. In order of publication it has everything up to
about Op. 65 behind it, and should therefore well enable us to
see how far the defects of the Serenades were capable of
retrievement.

2. The earlier version was scored for four horns, as compared
with two in the revision, in one movement of which however the
horns are silent. The subjects were probably not interfered with
as they clearly belong to the same period as those of Op. 11.
This is strikingly supported by affinity between subjects of the
two works—even in the case of movements of quite opposite
character.

Ex, 52. Affinity between Subjects of Op. 11 and 10,.

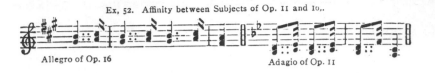

Allegro of Op. 16   Adagio of Op. 11

3. In comparing the two scores the first thing to observe is that, for the treatment of subjects which as we have seen are kindred, Brahms required, or thought he required, in 1860, four horns, trumpets and drums; but that in 1875 he wanted only two horns and neither trumpets nor drums. Exclusion of the violins was of course also a diminution, but that matter stands upon a different footing to explain which will be to dispose of the subject.

4. The themes are mostly of wind-instrument character and the violins if retained must have remained comparatively silent; have either usurped or doubled the wind-work; or have elaborated it out of character. Nothing would have been easier than elaboration of the ordinary kind, but Brahms had little respect for such means. He was never tempted to dress himself in the fine feathers which are responsible for so many fine birds of our modern collection; his appreciation being entirely reserved for ideas, and his later works showing a style of orchestral elaboration consistent with his faith and quite his own—one which when it becomes better understood will cause a great change in the view taken of his scoring. The suppression of the violins in the present case therefore means simply that there was nothing integral for them to do. It has been described as "bold" to adopt such a modified score, but surely it was bolder to earmark the entire orchestra for Op. 11.

5. A chamber-work must suffer by being scored for orchestra just as an orchestral work cannot be made to fit a chamber combination. The attempt to do either of these things means a disregard of the affinity necessary between the idea and its means of expression; and we may be sure that had Brahms not been moved by an affection for his early work his revision would have been more penetrating. As it is, we have before us a chamber-work for orchestra; proof of which lies in the unavoidable impression of undue length conveyed by several of the movements. The ideas not being of sufficiently genuine orchestral character the scoring cannot be reviewed in a manner leading to any solid conclusion.

I. ALLEGRO MODERATO.

6. Brahms, from the first, was a master in Sonata-form; but this is not to say that he was also a master in adapting either the dimensions of the form or the character of his material to the means employed. We know that he was not, and that on the contrary the discrepancy alluded to characterised his early work; including the Serenades which we are now treating. In view of the indiscriminate praise* which these works have received we are compelled to treat the matter at some length.

7. In great works of sonata or symphonic form, material is in inverse ratio to means; the vocation of the greater means being to amplify and glorify plain material, while that of the lesser means is to decorate and vary what has been already chosen for pliability. It is because of this that when a great sonata for the piano embarks upon material of the nobler sort it always seems to overcharge the instrument by requiring from it a demonstration beyond its powers. The tendency of noble material is to call for pure development, that of light material being to take refuge in variety. But the small means is incapable of giving to the logical development of a great sonata the dignity which is its due; and this remains true notwithstanding that there are many sonatas of powerful appeal in spite of inadequate expression. The last fact only shows that the defect of overcharging a solo instrument is, after all, one to be condoned; whereas employment of the orchestra for unsuitable work can find no manner of excuse. We will now apply these various considerations.

The first subject of this Allegro occupies 16 bars, extended to 19 by echoes which cadence it as perfectly in E as might be required for close of the first section. We have then a virtual new subject—appendage, episode, extension—the name is indifferent, except that it is certainly no development.

---

* Speaking of the instrumentation, for example, a well-known critic observes : "Here the composer actually renounces the use of the noblest and most expressive of all orchestral voices"; precisely as if Brahms had performed some act of heroic self-denial. The only effect is, of course, to call our attention to the fact of Op. 11 having been over-scored. Of the present movement moreover he goes on to say that "construction shows the perfect master"; having evidently mere mechanical construction in view, to the disregard of all relation between dimensions and kind of material.

Ex. 53, Op. 16, Allegro, Dual Character of First Subject.

We might perhaps call it an intermediate motive were there any
relation to the foregoing, but the rhythmic motion presented by
it is the greatest in the entire movement—not even the Durchführung going beyond the combination of normal with triplet
crotchets.

8. The first subject is arbitrarily extended by echo passages
which, altogether, occupy eleven bars before the second subject
appears. Eighteen bars more are taken up by modulative extensions of no interest and sixteen more by the material marked
(b) in the last example: all this out of a total of seventy given
to first subject.

Ex. 54 Op. 16, Allegro, Echo-passages in extension of first subject.

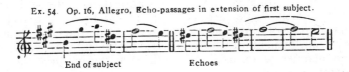

9. As against these seventy bars only forty-eight are given to
both the second and third subjects, neither of which is therefore
commensurately stated, though their compactness would be no
fault if it stood alone. The second subject after proceeding for

Ex. 55. Op. 16, Allegro, Second Subject.

eighteen bars comes to an interesting cadence; this being followed by a period conveniently to be regarded as still another
subject, and consisting of sixteen bars, or rather eight repeated

—the repetition being associated with melodic inflections remindful of second subject.

Ex. 56. Op. 16, Allegro, Third Subject.

10. During the echo passages attached to first subject we meet that disregard of position of the bar-line which is so often associated with rhythmic interest; and, though there is no such interest here, the eleven tedious bars which follow the third subject will equally well serve as an example. The subjoined divides at (a) (b) in order to show the contrast between the Brahms passage and ordinary rhythm.

11. The Durchführung opens with a blank repetition of first subject followed by 21 bars of second-rate contrapuntal work upon the extension (b) of Ex. 53. Then, being in D flat, we meet the first subject again—this time interwoven contrapuntally with the triplet figure of the extension. Having thus arrived at

Lx. 57. Op. 16, Allegro, Displacement of bar-line.

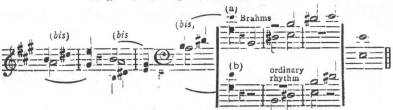

bar 165 (47 of the Durchführung, which begins at bar 119) we endure 26 bars which, for all connection with the main thought, might as well have been culled from anywhere. Their principal feature seeks to justify the extension of first subject which we have described as an intrusion, and is here shown.

Ex. 58. Op. 16, Allegro, Durchführung (Bars 133-4).

12. It is probably the effect of revision and re-revision that spontaneity is lacking. Thus at the return (bar 217) there is a feature which in later works invariably courts our admiration—the feature, that is, of shrouding re-entry of the theme by grafting it to the Durchführung. The intention is here, but it is not realised, and the paltriness of the effect produced by the very same device which Brahms afterwards employed so magnificently should show us how dangerous it is to fondle work merely because it has cost us labour.

13. The return is perfunctory and calls for no remark; but the Coda is altogether out of proportion. One particularly warm-hearted critic actually goes so far as to call it "almost a second Durchführung"—evidently intending this as praise. To overpraise the early works of a great man is pardonable, as it comes from a feeling of reverence; but to call a defect an excellence cannot be so regarded.

14. Epitome.

(a) Subjects, see Ex. 53, 55 and 56.

(b) Key, A major; no recognised change though much modulation.

(c) Time, allabreve, with constant minim pulsation. No quavers, the extreme subdivision of the pulsation being into triplet crotchets. Normal and triplet crotchets combined, however, give eight percussions within the bar, besides an increase of agitato on account of proceeding from two parts. The following example shows at (a) the pulsations, at (b) their normal crotchet division, at (c) their triplet-crotchet division, at (d) the two combined, and at (e) the same percussions given by a single part, but producing an effect not only different generally but less agitato in particular.

Ex. 59. Op. 16, Allegro, Subdivisions of the minim pulsation.

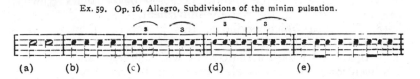

(a)   (b)   (c)   (d)   (e)

(d) Length, 372 bars, no repeats.

Ex. 60. Outline of Op. 16, No. 1.

FIRST SECTION	DURCHFÜHRUNG	RETURN	CODA
118	98	101	55
I II III 70 22 26		I II III 53 22 26	

II. SCHERZO, VIVACE.

15. We have now to return to the subject of the bar line, Brahms's special treatment of which has already been referred to; and to remind the student of its essential character as a merely outward and mechanical sign of rigidly accurate time-measurement, which is the same as saying that the beat which follows it coincides generally but not necessarily with a strong

pulsation within the phrase. But it is the phrase, and sub-ordinately the motives within it, which constitute the real measure; the bar-line being really nothing more than an assistance to the eye and conveying nothing whatever to the mind except what may be indirectly due to such assistance.

16. The fact that the beat which immediately follows the bar-line is *generally* a strong pulsation so leads the ordinary performer to assume that this must *necessarily* be the case, that it is comparatively rare to find musicians reading in phrases. Composers therefore have often, as a means of securing deference to the phrase, been obliged to resort to temporary change of the bar-value.

17. But, since composers have thus to reckon with the bar-habit when it stands in their way, they are clearly justified in turning it to advantage should occasion offer. This is what Brahms has done in the present movement.

18. The idea which underlies this is not at all new. It is only the attempt to utilise the vulgar accentuation of first beats in furtherance of high artistic aims which is new, and even this has been long and intuitively applied in the notation of certain dances. An example of this is presented by conventional notation of the Gavotte as compared with its bar-measurement.

Ex. 61.   Distribution of the Bar in Gavotte notation.

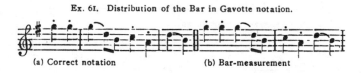

(a) Correct notation   (b) Bar-measurement

19. Here undoubtedly the bar-measurement would be perfect if mechanical regulation were the only object. But, as a means of securing the accentuation of the thirds beat, the notation is made to accord with the vulgar habit by so displacing the bar-line as to make the third beat become the first.

20. A duple rhythmical figure barred in triple time subjects the performer to two influences simultaneously; for, whilst he cannot altogether resist the duple character of the figure, he is also unable to cancel his ordinary inclination to emphasise first beats, and this conflict between the two produces a capricious effect happening in this case to suit the composer by favouring the Scherzo character.

21. That the Brahms motives are duple is at once evident, but their notation in duple time would, for the reasons given,

Ex. 62. Op. 16, Scherzo. Duple character of motives.

not further a desire to accentuate them alternately in a different manner. By adoption of $\frac{3}{4}$ this end is attained; the duple figure still remaining sufficiently assertive, though engaged in frolicsome conflict with the performer's habit of first beat accentuation.

Ex. 63. Op. 16, Scherzo. Conflict of duple motive with triple measure.

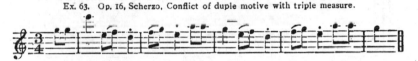

22. But opportunity for caprice is not limited to this advantage; for, with conventional accent once displaced, the composer enjoys the liberty of a wider choice of motive. This is proved by the bars immediately following the above, where the motives are really triple.

Ex. 64. Op. 16, Scherzo. Mixture of duple and triple motives.

23. In the Trio we have a combination of triple and duple rhythms, forming respectively melody and accompaniment. The former necessarily most engages the listener's attention and thus exposes the duple accompaniment to the chance of being insufficiently observed; unless the danger be avoided either by reserving melodic first-beat accentuation for alternate bars, where both commencements coincide (a), or by "thinking" $\frac{2}{4}$ time (b).

24. The movement as a whole, being lyric in form and therefore subject to conditions very different from the Allegro, is fairly successful; but its principal value to the student lies in the exemplification it offers of the points just mentioned. As a composition it lacks contrast, as may easily be gathered from the fact of the Trio being persistently accompanied by the pre-

Ex. 65. Op. 16, No. 2, Triple melody with duple accompaniment.

vailing rhythmical figure. There is accordingly neither any repose at the Trio nor any refinement in the manner of effecting the return; the latter being, in fact, quite crudely managed. The Coda is written upon a tonic pedal; and being highly spirited, forms a brilliant conclusion, presenting also the novelty of upward-rushing scale passages in triplet quavers. But this feature is too slight to redeem the tedium caused by the use of one rhythmic figure throughout, and contrast can only be looked for as between this movement as a whole and its companions.

25. Epitome.

(*a*) Subjects. See Ex. 63 and 65.

(*b*) Key, first section in C, Trio in F. Transient changes to E in first section and return; as also to C in Trio.

(*c*) Time, $\frac{3}{4}$. The conflict of rhythms described in the foregoing takes place during the first section horizontally, or between motives occurring in succession. During the Trio it occurs perpendicularly, or in the combination of melody and accompaniment.

(*d*) Length, 140 bars, or 175 with repeats.

Ex. 66. Outline of Op. 16, No. 2.

FIRST SECTION	TRIO	BRIDGE	RETURN	CODA
|: 10 :| 34 |	¦: 8 :|: 18 :¦	10	42	17

III. ADAGIO NON TROPPO.

26. The experimental character of the early orchestral works is evidenced in many ways, but never more strongly than in the style and form of this Passacaglia movement. The appeal of coincidences is apt to vary with different listeners, but we should imagine that no escape is possible from the reminder here offered of Bach's great organ-Passacaglia. The case is so remarkable that we feel bound to refresh the reader's memory by quotation of the Bach theme before proceeding to show how Brahms appears to have taken it for his model.

Ex. 67. Op, 16, Adagio, Theme-model from Bach.

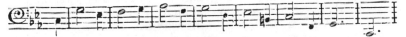

27. The contrast between the freedom of the early pianoforte works and the stiffness of the Serenades is of course due to the latter being for orchestra, and independently of the disadvantage under which the orchestration lies* it is largely borrowed. Thus Colles makes the observation that Op. 11 "bows in turn to each classical predecessor" in respect of orchestration; but the subservience so alluded to is slight in comparison with the manner in which Brahms here pays homage to Bach. He not only gives a reproduction of the proud strut of the Bach theme, but the actual notes of his subject are capable of serving as a Bach counterpoint. We may even take the counterpoint of his first setting as if it were intended for the Bach theme. More than that; for we can place the whole of these things together and, with the aid of a slight free part, present them as one setting.

28. The reader will surely agree that such an amount of coincidence is not to be explained otherwise than by supposing Brahms to have taken Bach's Passacaglia as his model. Moreover the divergences which arise do little to weaken this assumption, as they are precisely those to be expected. Brahms

---

* See par. 5.

Ex. 68. Op. 16,   Adagio, Combination of Brahms and Bach themes.

Free part (d)

Brahms counterpoint (c)

Brahms subject (b)

Bach subject (a)

never got far away from sonata-form whatever might be the professed outline of his work.   His lyric movement has generally a miniature Durchführung and his rondo an organised first-section parade.   But he never set himself a harder task than that of endeavouring to fuse sonata and passacaglia forms, as he has done in this movement; and it is noticeable that in the only other Passacaglia written by him, the finale to the Fourth Symphony, Op. 98, the experiment was not repeated.

29. The first result of the attempt is a zig-zag course, lasting for more than half of this A minor movement, through such incongruous keys as A flat and C minor.   Another is the use of phrase extension for division purposes, a device neither required by nor in keeping with pure passacaglia.   Finally, there is the "song-group," which, in spite of its individual beauty, imparts just the kind of rhythmical stagnation we should expect from any conflict of rigid passacaglia with pliable sonata-phrasing.

30. Though only successful whilst adhering to passacaglia-form, the experiment is always interesting.   Thus, what appears to be a second subject is introduced midway between the eleventh and twelfth settings (bar 23) as if to bend the passacaglia into sonata-service; and at the fifteenth setting (bar 30)

Ex. 69. Op. 16, Adagio, Second Subject.

we have a fairly evident song-group, the desire to give character to which has resulted in a halting rhythm inconsistent with either form.   The extension of both these themes beyond the limits of the passacaglia subject is another cause of obscurity,

Ex. 70. Op. 16, Adagio, Third Subject.

and the whole experiment's usefulness is in showing that no reconcilement is possible between passacaglia and sonata forms.

31. There are four single-bar phrase-extensions occurring at bars 17, 56, 67 and 74. The first of these is really beautiful and rounds off the first section of development with the effect of a solemn "Amen." But it is difficult to regard the others otherwise than as without object—the mere arrival at a desired key being totally inadmissible as such. A purposeless phrase-extension is a fault at any time; but altogether passes forgiveness in a Passacaglia.

32. The viola figure (bar 75, 36th setting) is merely elaborative, and does not prevent the settings 36 to 39 (bars 75 to 82) from being identical with the settings 1 to 4 (bars 1 to 8). But here the identity ceases, on account of the next four settings being influenced by the desire to conclude in A minor.

33. The generally placid character of the movement is only disturbed by the discordant outburst heralding a new departure after first section (bar 18); and the greatest bar-subdivision consists of viola semiquaver accompaniment to second, or horn, subject.

34. Epitome.

(a) Subjects. See Ex. 69-71.

(b) Key, A minor. Recognised changes to A flat and C minor.

(c) Time, ½. The rhythmical figure of the Passacaglia ♩ ♪ is practically constant, and the whole may be construed as in phrases of two-bar length (subject to the extensions already mentioned at pars. 29 and 31). For these, four bars must be allowed; besides three for prolongation of final cadence.

After deduction of phrase-extensions there remains the equivalent of forty-three passacaglia settings, many of which are rendered obscure, as above described; even the rhythm being but slightly in evidence for settings 15 to 20 (bars 30 to 41). But this is preparatory to the return, which from that point is gradual, until at the 28th setting (bar 57) it is boldly resumed.

(d) Length 93 bars; no repeats.

Ex. 71. Op. 16, Adagio. Outline.

FIRST SECTION	MIDDLE SECTION	CONCLUDING SECTION
Settings 1 to 8 16 + 1*	Settings 9 to 27 38 + 1*	Settings 28 to 43 32 + 1, 1 and 3*

IV. QUASI MENUETTO.

35. The term "quasi" may often be read as an apology. This applies however only to conventional movements, and not, as here, where there is bold departure from ordinary external feature.

36. The adoption of $\frac{6}{4}$ time for a minuet must not be confounded with merely throwing two bars into one. Slaves to custom will doubtless decide that it is not allowable at all; but even they may benefit by the enquiry whether the minuet character can be realised in $\frac{6}{4}$, and how far duple bar-subdivision affects the characteristics of a triple measure.

37. To begin with, we must not scan this movement in expectation of having the minuet character emerge from the triple half-bars; for the all-sufficient reason that these half bars are merely single rhythmical pulsations. They are therefore practically beats, proceeding at the same degree of motion as those of a stately minuet; the effect of the special notation adopted being simply to divide each of these dotted-minim beats into three crotchets. The use of $\frac{6}{4}$ therefore multiplies the ordinary notation by three, though it also does something else very much more important.

38. The bar and a half of $\frac{6}{4}$ being thus equivalent to the ordinary minuet bar of $\frac{3}{4}$, it follows that, when subdivided into nine crotchets, it is the equivalent of the $\frac{3}{4}$ when divided into triplet quavers. The only real distinction between the two cases is that in one the bar-line corresponds with the strong beat of the dance measure, and in the other it does not.

Ex. 72. Comparison of $\frac{6}{4}$ and $\frac{3}{4}$ minuet notation.

---

* The additions (+) are for the phrase extensions.

39. That force of custom does much to obscure this simple fact is evident from the way in which it is treated by critics who find themselves forced to give it some attention.   Thus Knorr, in allusion to bars 15-18, says that Brahms

here seems to have burst the bonds of the prescribed $\frac{6}{4}$ bar by changing it into one of $\frac{9}{4}$.†

Ex. 73. Op. 16. Quasi-Menuetto. Sample phrase in $\frac{6}{4}$, $\frac{9}{4}$.

For our own part we cannot see that the bonds of $\frac{6}{4}$ are more burst in this instance than elsewhere; in proof of which we invite the reader's attention to a phrase occurring several bars before Knorr made his discovery. Rather is it the bonds of $\frac{3}{4}$ which are burst by the use of $\frac{6}{4}$. The latter cannot bind in this instance, for the simple reason that the phrases refuse such bondage; and their freedom from the mechanics of ordinary first-beat accentuation is the result.

Ex. 74. Op. 16, Quasi-Menuetto, further phrase of $\frac{6}{4}$, $\frac{9}{4}$.*

40. Even if this were the only answer to the question—

Why, if this movement is really in $\frac{6}{4}$ should it be barred in $\frac{3}{4}$?

it would be satisfactory, therefore   But more remains; for there

---

† Sprengt sogar die Fessel des vorgeschriebenen $\frac{6}{4}$ Taktes die in einem $\frac{9}{4}$ Takt umgewandelt ist.

* The example consists of the second half of bar 5, bar 6, and the first half of bar 7 set in $\frac{9}{4}$ time for illustration.

is also the power of an occasional slight deviation from strict beat in accord with certain features of the dance to be taken into account.   By this means the third rhythmic pulsation is most gracefully delayed during continuation of the motion of sub-ordinate parts—and this very much in the same way (though the conditions are different) as that explained in connection with Op. 8.   An illustration of this feature occurs in the very opening bars, where the three pulsations are made up of two $\frac{6}{4}$ bars.

Ex. 75. Op. 16, Quasi-Menuetto, First Subject.

41. The difference between capriciously barring a $\frac{3}{4}$ movement in $\frac{6}{4}$ and doing so in refinement of triple rhythm is thus clear, though we shall not go so far as to defend the doubling of the pulsation length as presented by the Trio.   It may certainly

Ex. 76. Op. 16, Quasi-Menuetto, Trio-Subject.

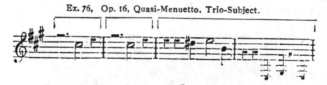

be pleaded that the instrumentation is charming,* that the general effect is of a gracefulness rarely attained and that the return is most happily effected; but these important features have no bearing upon the question whether the minuet pulsation will bear such augmentation.

42. Epitome.

(a) Subjects. See Ex. 75, 76.

(b) Key D, Trio in F sharp minor.

(c) Time, $\frac{6}{4}$, no change.

(d) Length, 132 bars, or 185 with repeats.

---

* The violas have a continuous tremolo whilst fragments of the opening subject added to it form an accompaniment to the oboe melody.

Ex. 77. Op. 16, Quasi menuetto. Outline.

FIRST SECTION	TRIO	RETURN	CODA
‖: 9 :‖: 23 :‖	‖: 24 :‖ 37	32	4

V. RONDO (ALLEGRO).

43. This movement is of painfully orthodox character—nothing but a few novelties of phrase-extension distinguishing it from mere rank-and-file specimens of the form. It is "good," something in the same sense as a demure child. It dutifully approaches sonata-form, is trim and prim in all its episodes and guides its modulations by time-honoured precept.

44. We of this wayward age, on the other hand, may not quite make it a virtue to fly in the face of holy tradition; but we certainly have a special love for those heroic sinners who reach their ends independently of its observance. What is genuinely old is matter for reverence apart; and imitations or reproductions require to be very happily conceived if they are to court admiration, or even attention. It cannot be said that the present Rondo fulfils that condition.

45. The movement starts with a "call" to attention for the first subject—a feature so insignificant in itself that the listener speedily forgets it. Long afterwards, however (at bar 142) he has to wake up to the necessity of accepting it as important.

Ex. 78. Op. 16, Rondo. The "call" (a) at opening and at bar 142; (b) first use
for development at bar 152.

The three subjects which intervene are entirely out of sympathy with this motive. The first is of the dual character indicated by (a) (b) in the example; and its treatment, which is mostly of student character, results in six appearances, either of formal or episodial character.

Ex. 79. Op. 16, Rondo, First Subject.

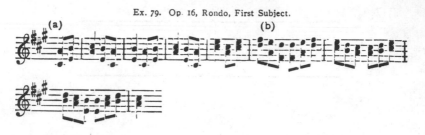

1. In A as first statement, at bars 2, 11 and 31.
2. In E as episode commencing at bar 122 and leading to the return.

Ex. 80. Op. 16, Rondo, Episode.

3. In A at bar 144 for the return.
4. In A at bar 273 corresponding in point of form to the original reappearance at bar 31.
5. In A for Coda, where it commences, as in Ex. 80, transposed into A.
6. In D (in augmentation) at bar 202 (Ex. 83).

Ex 81. Op. 16, Rondo augmentation of first subject.

46. To this subject the second offers no effective contrast, its rhythm being the same. Our only reasons for accepting it as a second subject at all is that, otherwise, the first-theme repetitions would reach an absurd number; and also that probably the canon shown in the example is relied upon for variety.

Ex. 82. Op. 16, Rondo, Second Subject

47. The third subject is stated in the dominant at bar 84, then in F sharp minor at bar 168, and finally in the tonic at bar 320. It consists of a phrase of seven bars (4 + 3) and certainly therefore offers a slight novelty of phrase-construction.

Ex. 83. Op. 16, Rondo, Third Subject.

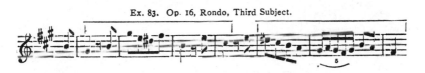

48. Returning now to the subject of the opening bars and of their revival at bar 142 (Ex. 78), logical treatment of the feature even when it does occur is of the poorest possible description, consisting merely of a modulative sequence following upon four bars of the first subject in C sharp. The use of the "call-pas-

Ex. 84. Op. 16, Rondo. Modulative sequence.

sage" as a means of phrase extension scarcely deserves mention under this heading, and we look in vain for any material of sufficient interest to account for nearly four hundred bars.

49. Epitome.

(*a*) Subjects. See Ex. 79-83.

(*b*) Key, A, no change

(c) Time, $\frac{2}{4}$, no change.
(d) Length, 396 bars, no repeats.

Ex. 85. Op. 16, Rondo. Outline.

FIRST SECTION				SECOND SECTION			THIRD SECTION			
I	II	III	episode	I	III	episode	I	II	III	coda
53	30	38	20	26	34	71	18	29	38	39
	141				131			124		

CONCLUDING NOTE.

50. We can neither confirm any of the foregoing adverse opinions upon the Serenades nor confront them with those of opposite character, on account of the very spare criticism which these works have called forth. Even Brahms's immediate friends had little if anything to say about them; and Max Bruch, writing in 1864, though he has a wealth of praise for other of Brahms's compositions, dismisses these by calling them " early works."* The faithful Joachim, however, though we have evidence that he was aware of necessity for the work's amendment, encourages Brahms, in 1858, by praising the Andante of Op. 11. It was only upon occasions when Brahms expressly sought his advice that he would venture upon such expressions as " badly orchestrated "—" too difficult for the violins "—" disagreeable false relation "—and so forth. At other times he would amiably attribute his impressions to outside causes, such as Brahms's fast playing and the bad piano at Göttingen.†

51. The critic with whom our review is most in agreement is the composer himself. We have already seen (Op. 11, pars. 8, 9) something of his dissatisfaction with these works; but even after

---

* An dem Andante Deiner Serenade habe ich mich eben wieder sehr erbaut. (Letters V, 207.)

† Du hattest den letzten Satz so ruschlig auf dem schlechten Klavier gespielt, dass ich in Göttingen nicht daraus Klug werden konnte. (Joachim Correspondence, V, 209.)

Op. 11 had been finally arranged and was about to be performed at Hanover under Joachim's direction, in 1860, there was
still considerable hesitation and further interchange of views;
similar conferences also preceding the publication of Op. 16
in 1875.

52. Frau v. Herzogenberg mentions having enjoyed the A
Serenade when "spending Sunday in her own way" in March,
1881, Knorr gives an analysis which can scarcely be said either
to praise or blame. Kalbeck's analysis is of greater detail.
Colles thinks that

From this experiment Brahms must have learnt a good deal of the art
of orchestration, although its actual matter is of slight importance,

and Fuller-Maitland describes Op. 16 as

Not of great importance for the general musical public.

OP. 18. FIRST STRING SEXTET IN B FLAT.

(For two Violins, two Violas and two Violoncellos.)

I. Allegro ma non troppo.
II. Tema con Variazione (Andante ma moderato).
III. Scherzo, Allegro molto.
IV. Rondo, Poco Allegretto e grazioso.

Published by N. Simrock in 1862.
Arrangement for Piano (four hands) by the Composer.

PRELIMINARY NOTE.

1. This genial work took five years to travel from the composer's studio to a London audience, and was produced as a "novelty" in Moscow five years after that; when Tchaïkovsky in making it the subject of a tirade against Brahms and all his works provided an excuse for others to doubt his merit. Even to this date a professed love of his compositions is eyed somewhat askance; as may easily be seen by Fuller-Maitland, in his recent work, deeming it necessary to render an account of his enthusiasm. How to explain this lack of appreciation, by some, of beauties which seem obvious to others, is a difficult matter; but there are facts bearing upon it which it may help us to consider.

2. Tchaïkovsky's was the case of a man of independent genius prevented by the strength of his own individuality from appreciating the standpoint of a nature opposed to his own; and the bulk of criticism, though not armed with any such excuse, also

proceeds from adopting a mistaken point of view. Its authors, by insisting upon their own standard of judgment, impose limitations upon the composer; and condemn, without understanding it, whatever may lie beyond their own horizons. This is always the great obstacle to the progress of any really new composer's reputation.

3. Brahms, unlike Wagner, was not given to defending himself by literary means; and lacking this powerful weapon could make but slow progress in general estimation. The propaganda which was specially necessary in his case he did nothing to establish.

4. Indifference to everything but integral value strikes his admirers as heroic, but it works quite differently as towards the public at large, whose principal desire is to be spared all trouble. Had the preceding works been less intense, the fame of this sextet would have spread more rapidly, its general attractiveness being, in fact, a stronger bid for popularity than Brahms was supposed capable of making. He had, however, already formed the intention of settling permanently at Vienna when at Winterthür in 1862. There the work was written, and its transparency is doubtless partly due to the necessity of converting the Viennese. They, at all events, proved sincerity by receiving it with a warm welcome, and why it should ever have encountered any other must remain a marvel to those who study it.

5. This being the first string work, we have to provide the reader with a few guiding principles, all the more necessary on account of having to deal first with a sextet; because when once the familiar combination of the quartet is exceeded, the danger appears of sacrificing some element of true chamber music. A natural result of increase of means is to bring with it the power, and therefore the temptation to treat combinations as units instead of allowing all conversations to remain those of individual voices. The evil lies in the consequent reaction upon ideas, which run great risk of turning out to be of quasi-orchestral character and therefore inconsistent with the true chamber-music ideal of evolving effects from equal and integral contributions by all instruments engaged.

6. The student will decide for himself in course of our review whether, or to what extent, this applies to the work before us; but falling short of the chamber-music ideal implies no reproach to the contents of any work. All musical ideas have a natural

destination; and, if suffered to reach it, these produce their maximum effect. If we transplant them we do not touch their integral value but we deprive them of the advantage of a suitable means of presentation. There are some combinations which are peculiarly liable to tempt a composer astray upon these points, and the sextet is one of them.

7. It is comparatively easy to observe whether in any given work orchestral or chamber treatment has been misapplied; the distribution of interest being, with the orchestral idea, a question of "scoring." Pure chamber-music is not scored in the ordinary sense of that term; because, if its material be of the right kind, we have no option but to give to each instrument its very own, whereas the act of orchestral scoring implies the exercise of a choice of colour. These principles are for general guidance, however, without special reference to any one work, and are here stated on account of Op. 18 being the first chamber-work of first-rate importance.

I. ALLEGRO NON TROPPO.

8. The student should first rhythmise the entire movement by aid of the summary, taking particular care to locate all phrase-extensions. The study of Brahms cannot be dissociated from the special study of rhythm, and upon that subject we shall now therefore lay particular stress.

9. The first ten bars for example offer an interesting case of phrase-extension, given in the table as 2 × 3 + 4; or, three two-bar phrases followed by one of four. It has been already mentioned that the fact of different readings of a musical sentence being possible does not diminish the usefulness of studying the results of any one in particular. Any reading to be justifiable must offer the means of being explained, and it is the explanation, not the reading, by which the student benefits. If he examine the first subject he will either see that the period naturally divided in the manner stated or be obliged to exercise some thought in construing it differently.

RHYTHMICAL TABLE

Ex. 86. Op. 18, Allegro, First Section and Durchführung.

PORTION	MATERIAL	BARS	PHRASES	EXTEND- ING TO
1st section	1st subject	30	$(2 \times 3 + 4)\ 3$	30
	,,	12	$2 \times 4 + 4$	42
	,,	18	$4 \times 4 + 2$	60
	Intermediate motive	24	$\left\{\begin{array}{l}2 \times 2 + 4 \\ 2 \times 4 \\ 4 \times 2\end{array}\right\}$	84
	2nd subject	18	$\left.\begin{array}{l}2 \times 2 \\ 4 + 1\end{array}\right\}\ 2$	102
	Bridge	5	5	107
	3rd subject	15	$\left.\begin{array}{l}4 \times 4 - 1 \\ 4 \times 3 + 2\end{array}\right\}$	140
	,,	14		
	Bridge	4	4	
Totals.		140		140
Durchführung	1st subject	33	$4 \times 8 + 1$	173
	3rd subject	18	$4 \times 4 + 2$	191
	Intermediate motive	16	$\left.\begin{array}{l}(2 \times 2 + 4)\ 2 \\ 4 + 2\end{array}\right\}$	213
	,,	6		
	Bridge	20	$8 \times 2 + 4$	233
Totals.		93		233

Ex. 87. Op. 18, Allegro, First Subject.

10. Rhythmical dissection has a very distinct influence upon performance, and that it should be even necessary to urge this shows how the advantages of rhythmical study are commonly disregarded, for it would certainly not be requisite to impress upon an actor the need of studying the rhythm of his lines. Can we even imagine him relying upon his ordinary capacity to read as a means of interpretation? We cannot do so; yet this is what the rank-and-file of musicians do every day. With a facile reading of notation and technical equipment they consider themselves prepared to render anything.

11. The musician's intuition naturally comes to his aid, and is often marvellously acute, but we shall have no difficulty in showing that it is insufficient. Here, for instance, if the violins who enter at the tenth bar do not know that their first bar is the mere taper-end of a phrase they are certain to begin too loud.

12. In the case of the solo performer the obligation to rhythmise is absolute. How, otherwise, can he be sure that his expression accords with the composer's intention? When two phrases overlap, for instance, the performance should make this clear; but is it at all likely to be clear if the performer himself is unaware of the fact? We know that even within the composer's intention there is room for differences of interpretation which are merely temperamental and might be indulged in by

the composer himself according to his mood.   There is no room, however, for any interpretation which ever so slightly distorts the rhythmic outline.

13. As to the conductor, without keen knowledge of the rhythm of what he conducts he does not even exist.   The score is allotted to him only in the second place for details of instrumentation; its first object being to give him a survey of rhythmical bearings.   Players from individual parts have no such means of observation and are therefore exempt.   The guiding rhythm may of course appear in any of their parts for a time; but in general the most assertive parts are least employed and the busiest those most engaged with rhythmical subdivisions. It has been the fashion to refer to the percussion instruments as "rhythmical," but all instruments are rhythmical, the responsibility for their rhythm being focussed upon the conductor.

14. We come now to the bearing of this upon the subject, not only of rhythm in general but of that of chamber music in particular.   If in the orchestra subservience to the conductor is absolute and all rhythmical waywardness of the individual forbidden—if, in orchestral music though everything in the way of musical device is permitted to the composer, anything of the nature of rhythmical cross purpose (unless upon such a broad scale as to make its intention obvious independently of context) is commonly regarded as an exception—these are restrictions peculiar to the orchestra, where individuality is principally a question of timbre.   But it is individuality of the parts themselves which is the life and soul of chamber music, the ensemble of which is not produced by word of command but by a mutual sympathy.   Obedience to a leader there may be, but it is precisely because of its being purely deferential that it results in a greater delicacy of expression than is consistent with subordination.   Hence, the road lying open for rhythmical refinements of quite a special order, chamber music acquires a sort of confidential character altogether opposed to that of the music of pageantry which has to attract the crowd.

15. This digression was necessary in order to dispose once for all of objections to the prominence here accorded to the study of rhythm, and we return to our ten opening bars the rhythm of which is allowed to occur three times in succession. This at once introduces us to a leading trait of Brahms's chamber-music, which consists of pursuing a phrase-formation long enough to give a *cachet* to the movement but not long enough to result in a mechanical outline.   The genus being thus fixed

we proceed by induction for the next twelve bars (2 × 4 + 4)
which, though they continue to breathe an atmosphere of first
subject, gradually prepare us for the second; as the student
may perceive by comparing the latter with the figure now
adopted.

Ex. 88, Op. 18, Allegro, Figure in preparation for Second Subject.

etc.

16. That there should be room for this proceeding between the
first and second subjects is proof in itself of a broad outline,
but much more happens before the second subject appears, observation of which is calculated to open our eyes considerably
as to Brahms's method of composition. We afterwards discover that in all this he is not merely bridging from first to
second subject but collecting materials for his Durchführung;
and something of the pains displayed in this endeavour is revealed by the fact that the counterpoint used to accompany the
first subject rhythm (bar 47) in this portion reappears later as
an accompaniment to the third subject. No one knew better

Ex. 89. Op. 18, Allegro, Counterpoint upon rhythm of First Subject.

than he that the sympathy between counterpoints and subjects,
when these are each employed independently, is too subtle to
court any but scientific observation. This counterpoint does not
recur until practically the middle of the Durchführung; so that
he must have had considerable faith in thus casting his bread
upon the waters. Unity was ever a first consideration with him,
however, and no expenditure of pains too great to secure it.

17. This working abuts upon an intermediate motive of such
importance that some have regarded it as a second subject, and
it certainly must be confessed to have greater independence

than is usually associated with an auxiliary.　Moreover, though fully instrumented, it is preceded by an episode very lightly scored, so that here is an instance of dissection in which the

Ex 90. Op. 18, Allegro, Intermediate motive.

student is free to make his own choice.　This motive also affords an instance of instrumentation of orchestral character in which small combinations are treated as units (see par. 5).

18. The boldness of this auxiliary secures a contrast for the second subject, which is delivered by the 'cello to an accompaniment in triplet quaver motion.　This brings us to mention

Ex. 91. Op. 18. Allegro, Second Subject.

the feature of graduated increase of motion as a Brahms characteristic, represented in this instance by normal quaver accompaniment of the first subject, triplet quaver accompaniment of the second and semiquaver bar-subdivision at climax of the Durchführung.

19. A short bridge passage at close of the second subject introduces us to the third; which is of disjointed and agitato character, as was rendered inevitable by the cantabile style of the opening theme.　The student will notice from the table that the first period of this subject concludes with a *minus* quantity

Ex. 92. Op. 18, Allegro, Third Subject.

to indicate the overlapping of two phrases. Cases of this kind are generally liable to different modes of dissection; what is important being that the student should intelligently select his own.

20. From this point the motion gradually subsides both in order to favour the repeat and to offer a placid point of departure for the Durchführung, which naturally opens with reminiscences of the first subject. After this almost the first manifestation we meet is the counterpoint already quoted as serving for accompaniment to the first-subject rhythm now doing the same duty for the third subject, and showing (to use a colloquial expression) that Brahms must have been keeping this up his sleeve during the first section. Now also the student

Ex 93. Op. 18, Allegro, Treatment of third subject in Durchführung.

will be able to contrast the instrumentation with that of the intermediate motive and to see clearly the difference between treating combinations as units, and handling each part individually.

21. The material just quoted figures largely in the Durch-führung and leads to the climax in semiquaver-motion already mentioned, when the score exhibits three degrees of motion simultaneously; the approach to the return groups being effected

Ex. 94. Op. 18, Allegro, Three degrees of motion.

etc.

very much in the same gradual manner as the climax was reached.

22. The rhythm of the remainder of the movement offers no new feature beyond a shortening of the treatment of first sub-ject, which is usual. The actual moment of return is rendered

RHYTHMICAL TABLE.

Ex. 95. Op. 18, Allegro, Return and Coda.

PORTION	MATERIAL	BARS	CONSISTING OF	EXTEND-ING TO
Return	1st subject	17	$2 \times 8 + 1$	250
	,, ,,	18	2×9	268
	,, ,,	18	$4 \times 4 + 2$	286
	Int. motive	8	$2 \times 2 + 4$	294
	,, ,,	8	2×4	302
	,, ,,	8	4×2	310
	2nd subject	18	$\left\{ \begin{array}{c} 2 \times 2 \\ 4 + 1 \end{array} \right\} 2$	328
	Bridge	5	5	333
	3rd subject	15	$4 \times 4 - 1$	348
	,, ,,	14	$4 \times 3 + 2$	362
Totals.		129		362
Coda	1st subject.	8	2×4	370
	,, ,,	16	4×4	386
	3rd subject	12	4×3	398
Totals.		36		398

very effective by the use of powerful syncopations in three parts against unison delivery of the theme by the other three, thus giving a highly agitato character to the original quaver motion. This new treatment of the first subject goes hand in hand with shortening of the space allotted to it, and really amounts to avoidance of literal repetition until the second subject is reached.   The conclusion is in *diminuendo* until the "poco piu

Ex. 96.   Op. 18, Allegro, Treatment of First Subject at return.

etc.

moderato" of the last twelve bars, these being given to the third subject.   Altogether, it is a bright movement, of perfect form, with every desirable contrast of material.   It is not so polyphonic as Brahms is usually, but from the popular stand-point this is far from being a defect.   To us the monophonic feature seems to have been the cause of the instrumentation being here and there not quite of chamber character, though this may also have been partly due to a want of sufficient habit in writing for strings alone.   None of the points mentioned for the reader's instruction are sufficiently serious to be counted as defects, and we may quite sincerely echo the words of Florence May :

This is a work to which neither *if* nor *but* can be applied, for it is without a flaw.

23. Epitome.
(a) Subjects.   See Ex. 87, 90, 92.
(b) Key, B flat, no recognised change.
(c) Time, ¾, no change.
(d) Length, 398 bars, or 538 with repeat of first section.

Ex. 97. Op. 18, Allegro. Outline.

FIRST SECTION	DURCHFÜHRUNG	RETURN	CODA
140 I II III 84 23 33	93	129 I II III 77 23 29	36

II. ANDANTE MA MODERATO.

24. This movement is a theme with variations, the sixteen-bar theme of which is formed of twice 2 × 4, extended however to 32 bars by repeat of each period. Similar repeats occur in each variation except the last, where an equivalent is provided by sixteen-bar Coda. They are all indicated by double-bar, except in the theme and Var. 4, where the periods are re-scored. The whole movement is thus outlined as 112 two-bar phrases or 28 eight-bar periods. Extremes surely meet when a master so identified with rhythmic flexibility writes under such rigid conditions.

25. The theme manifests that abiding love of folk-song which, as part of the composer's character, powerfully influenced his mode of expression. The result was that when he chose professedly to write in Volkslied style his melodies strike us as traditional. They produce upon us the singular effect of appearing original without being new—of being too fresh not to be new and too natural not to be old. It is not so much the phrases as their happy conjunction which does this—a proof that originality does not lie in eccentricity of note succession, as so many suppose.

26. It is difficult to convey an adequate idea of this movement on account of its extremely simple outline. Fuller-Maitland's wish for "some means by which exact quality can be conveyed short of a performance by ideal musicians" can be brought nearer to fulfilment when sonata traits help to vivify the account than when nothing appears but an interminable series of two-bar phrases. The reason why there is no monotony is that the phrases are all individually satisfactory when lending themselves to transient modulation, because of the

theme-structure allowing this to be done without involving any
melodic change.   It would be different if this proceeded by con-
demning the melody to the diatonics of a single key.   Quite
contrary to that, the melody itself modulates without any external aid.   If sung it would convey an expression evidently
susceptible of enrichment by various harmonies, but just as
evidently independent of any of them.

27. Harmony when thus employed is at its best; having to
do with a melody which gives it every opportunity, as we shall
see, opportunity not only of responding to melodic suggestion
but of itself making suggestions which the melody appears to
fulfil.   Thus it is not the melody which suggests the transient
modulations through A and D majors; but their use is a gain
to it at the cadence, though these are but two instances out of

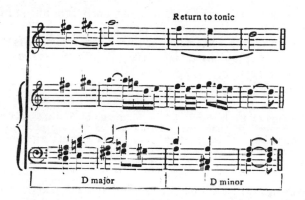

many. The fact is, as the student can see from the example, that each two-bar phrase takes us into a different key, such is the solidity of build of this truly remarkable theme. Whence comes its peculiar quality? In the answer to this question lies a most useful lesson, for the answer is—"the scale." The crude material of the two periods which form this melody is as under :

First period. Six bars tonic scale-ascent, two bars grade-ascent to dominant.

Second period. Six bars dominant scale-ascent, two bars grade-descent to tonic.

Ex 99. Op. 18, Andante. Material of theme.

28. This leads us perforce to consideration of the variation-"*form*," as it is called, in spite of the best variations merely repeating their themes's outline. Under the head of variations we do not include those which merely elaborate the actual theme-notes. These are not variations at all in the musicianly sense; but figurations, generally of the most paltry kind. The first

business of a variation is to *vary*, but such ignoble stuff varies nothing. It is no argument to say that some celebrated men have been caught by the fashion of giving schoolgirls material for a cheap display, as it is simply a human weakness to be influenced by custom. Wagner in allusion to the fact that none are exempt makes the following observation:

> The language of Bach stands to the language of Mozart, and finally to that of Beethoven in the same relation as did the Egyptian Sphinx to Grecian sculpture; and in the same way as the Sphinx with human face seems to strive to quit its animal body, so does the noble human figure of Bach seem to strive to quit its ancient periwig.*

Thus, even in spite of custom, the old writers sought to infuse some plan into their variation-scheme, and recourse to the old five orders of counterpoint was specially favoured. Brahms has here done precisely the same. Up to Variation 3 he proceeds by subdividing the original pulsation just as Albrechtsberger, Cherubini and other theorists of that school proceed after "note against note" to *so many* and then *so many more* "notes against one." Moreover, and as if to prevent our making any mistake, he comes to a lull with his fourth variation just as the old contrapuntists came to a lull with their fourth order, where they used nothing but syncopations. Finally, his fifth variation may be fairly taken as representing their fifth order of "florid" counterpoint.

29. What Brahms has done and what the old pedants could not do is to make each variation represent the theme in a different mood. His increase of motion attains to absolute wildness by the third variation followed by a calm in the lovely cantabile of Variation 4. His fifth or florid variations seems to make merry at the thought of nearing home, by indulging in a dance in which first and second violas take melody and musette respectively, with other instruments gambolling round about them. We are helped to feel that rest-time is now at hand when the theme reappears with a new and gentle instrumentation and seems to linger at its own cadence as if in loving reluctance to depart. Truly these are beautiful effects—produced too by the exercise of qualities for which Brahms is often held to blame.

---

* " Judaism in Music," p. 36 of present author's translation.

Ex. 100. Op. 18, Andante. Variations 1 to 6 (openings).

30. Epitome.
(a) Theme. Ex. 98. Variation openings. Ex. 100.

(b) Key D minor, except variations four and five which are major.

(c) Time $\frac{2}{4}$, no change.

(d) Length 160 bars, or with repeats 224.*

* III. SCHERZO.

31. The ardour and frolic of this movement are due, not as might appear to its freedom of modulation or gaiety of melody but to its rhythmic outline. Had this been of square-cut order nothing could have saved it from being commonplace; but, as it is, an evergrowing vivacity and excitement is successfully coupled with refinement. It is with rhythm as with those melodies which Wagner tells us we catch we know not why and continue to "tra-la" without knowing in the least why. We do not know that the outline charms us and would certainly, if questioned, give it no credit for our pleasure. But let us inquire.

32. A persistent feature is two-bar extension of the four-bar phrase; not happening capriciously but receiving identical treatment at corresponding points of the two sections. For example:

RHYTHMICAL TABLE.

Ex. 101. Op. 18, Scherzo

PORTION	MATERIAL	BARS	COMPOSED OF	EXTEND-ING TO
1st section	Subject	12	$2 \times 4 + 4$	12
	Development and return	30	$4 \times 6 + 2$ $\left.\right\}$ 4	43†
Trio	Subject	10	$4 \times 2 + 2$	54†
	Development and return	30	$4 \times 6 + 2$ $\left.\right\}$ 4	85†
D.C.	Repetition of 1st section	—	—	—
Coda	Trio subject	24	4 $\left.\right\}$ 2×4 4×3	109

* The Coda though of fifteen bars is really sixteen taking the final pause into account, the missing bar being made good by the alternative ending to Variation 5. The 160 bars mentioned above may therefore be taken as 8 × 20, the 20 periods being 4 for theme and Variation 4, and 2 for each of the others.

† Extra bar for 2da Volta.

seven four-bar phrases (with two-bar extension of the penulti-
mate) comprise the development and return alike of first section
and trio.

33. But why this identity for only the second parts of the
sections? Because, in the first place, the general design of the
movement is an ever growing *animato*, excluding the use of a
placid trio-contrast. Such continuity in a lyric movement is unusual and at variance with demarcation of the sections, leaving
only change of rhythm available for the latter purpose. The
change is therefore well accounted for in any event, but if we
examine it we shall find that it reveals another trait of symmetry. Compare for example the two opening rhythms:

First section: 2 × 4 + 4.
Trio: 4 × 2 + 2.

and the relation is at once perceivable. A strong build of this
description has a marvellous influence upon the life of a composition precisely because, like the melodies which Wagner mentions, it has an attraction for which we cannot account.

Ex. 102. Op. 18, Scherzo Subjects.

34. Epitome.
(*a*) Subjects. See Ex. 102.
(*b*) Key F, no change.
(*c*) Time ¾, no change.
(*d*) Length 109 bars, or 230 with repeats.

Ex. 103. Op. 18, Scherzo. Outline.

FIRST SECTION	TRIO	D.C.	CODA
|: 12 :|: 30 :|	|: 10 :|: 30 :|	12, 30	24

IV. RONDO.

Poco allegretto e grazioso.

35.   The opening subject of this rondo gives it a Haydnish character which Brahms's consistency confirms, but the working is so essentially his own that in spite of reminders the effects are new.

Ex. 104. Op. 18. Rondo. First Subject.

etc.

36.   There are two subjects, to each of which an intermediate motive is attached.   As usual these motives have the dual object of amplifying their themes and of providing development material, the latter being much required in a lengthy movement approximating to sonata-form.   The ingenuity of this method is in the possibility it offers of elevating motives to the rank of subjects and giving them auxiliaries in their turn; and its effect is not confined to mere increase of material, because this increase, being in a sort of chain, is far more suitable than any other for rondo purposes.

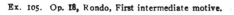

Ex. 105. Op. 18, Rondo, First intermediate motive.

etc.

37.   The first subject opens with twice sixteen bars of three-part harmony; melody of the first sixteen being given by 'cello, and of the second by violin.   We have then the first intermediate motive, return of first subject and an episode in faintly marked three-bar phrases as preparation for the second subject

Ex. 106. Op. 18, Rondo, Second Subject.

which is in that rhythm. Here also the rhythm is not marked with the strength we should expect at introduction of the three-bar phrase, but the composer's intention is rendered evident by a sequence formed from this theme, in which the rhythm is unmistakable (bar 90).

Ex. 107. Op. 18. Rondo, Second Subject—development.

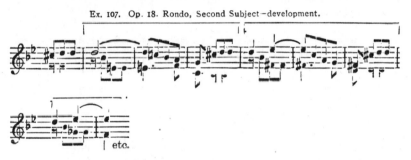

etc.

38. The three-bar rhythm of the second subject is not shared by its intermediate motive, which is duple. This causes the second subject groups to be duple and triple alternately, whereas first subject development as well as Durchführung and coda are all duple exclusively. For the former the first inter-

Ex. 108. Op. 18, Rondo, Second intermediate motive.

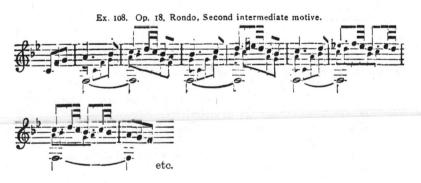

etc.

mediate motive is utilised as material, but as mentioned (paragraph 36) it is now provided with its own auxiliary.

Ex. 109, Op. 18, Rondo, Third intermediate motive.

etc.

RHYTHMICAL TABLE.

Ex. 110. Op. 18, Scherzo (opening section).

PORTION	MATERIAL	BARS	PHRASES	EXTEND-ING TO
1st section	1st subject	32	(4 × 4) 2	32
	Int. motive 1	8	4 × 2	40
	1st subject	16	4 × 4	56
	Bridge	15	3 × 5	71
Totals.		71		71
Sub-section	2nd subject	6	3 × 2	77
	Int. motive 2	12	4 × 3	89
	2nd subject	12	3 × 4	101
	Int. motive 2	13	4 × 3 + 1	114
	2nd subject	6	3 × 2	120
	Bridge	{ 17	4 + 1	125
			4 × 3	137
Totals.		66		137
2nd section	1st subject	16	4 × 4	153
	Int. motive 1	10	4 × 2 + 2	163
	1st subject	16	4 × 4	179
Totals.		42		179

The bridge passages are always in the rhythm of the section they approach, as may be observed from the rhythmical tables. The practical student is also invited to observe:

1. The diminished extent of statement given to the principal subject at all returns except the last; when just before the Coda, it is allowed free expansion.
2. The close similarity in outline of the two sub-sections, notwithstanding that in other respects they widely differ.
3. Use of the first intermediate motive in diminution to promote the animato of the Coda.

RHYTHMICAL TABLE.

Ex. 111. Op. 18, Rondo (concluding sections).

PORTION	MATERIAL	BARS	PHRASES	EXTEND-ING TO
Durchführung	Int. motive (a)	12	4 × 3	191
	,, ,, (c)	16	4 × 4	207
	,, ,, (a)	28	4 × 7	235
	,, ,, (c)	8	4 × 2	243
	,, ,, (a)	22	4 × 5 + 2	265
	Bridge	12	4 × 3	277
Totals.		98		277
3rd section	1st subject	16	4 × 4	293
	Int. motive (a)	10	4 × 4 + 2	303
	1st subject	4	4	307
	Bridge	15	3 × 5	322
Totals.		45		322
Sub-section	Int. motive (b)	12	4 × 3	334
	2nd subject	12	3 × 4	340
	Int. motive (b)	13	4 × 3 + 1	359
	2nd subject	6	3 × 2	365
	Bridge	23	4 + 1	370
			4 × 4 + 2	388
Totals.		66		388
4th section	1st subject	16	4 × 4	404
	Int. motive (a)	10	4 × 2 + 2	414
	1st subject	36	4 × 9	450
	Int. motive (a)	17	4 × 4 + 1	467
Coda, piu animato	,, ,, ,,	40	4 × 10	508
		1	Pause bar	
Totals.		120		508

39. Epitome.

(a) Subjects. See Exs. 104-6 and 108-9.

(b) Key B flat, no change.

(c) Time $\frac{2}{4}$, no change.

Ex. 112. Op. 18, Rondo Outline.

56	15	49	17	42	98	30	15	43	23	79	41
I	Bridge	II	Bridge	1	Durch-führung	I	Bridge	II	Bridge	I	Coda

OP. 25. FIRST PIANO QUARTET IN G MINOR.

(For Piano, Violin, Viola and Violoncello.)

Dedicated to Baron Reinhard von Dalwigk.

I. ALLEGRO.
II. INTERMEZZO. ALLEGRO MA NON TROPPO.
III. ANDANTE CON MOTO.
IV. RONDO ALLA ZINGARESE. PRESTO.

Arrangement for Piano (four hands) by the Composer.
Published by N. Simrock in 1863.

I. ALLEGRO.

1. THIS work is supposed to have been composed long before the date of its publication, but it is probably only to the present movement that this view applies. At all events it is this one which contains most evidence of an early origin, though not sufficient to justify its being classed with the early works. Besides that, the mere act of publication in 1863, and therefore at thirty years of age, when Brahms was already established in Vienna and had every reason to desire to make a good impression, is sufficient to show that he claimed no indulgence on its behalf.

2. The allegro's freedom of outline contrasts strangely with the symmetry of the corresponding movement of Op. 18, and even Brahms's intimate friends were reluctant to include it in the praise given to the whole work. Thus, Deiters:

We frequently hear Brahms with whom thought and fancy ever worked together in active union accused of being obscure. Such an accusation can only come from those who are ignorant of such works as this quartet —*above all of its middle movements.*

Elsewhere the same writer specially alludes to the allegro's "redundance of melodic contents," which means of course that there is too much thematic material for the structure. Joachim, whose intimacy with Brahms enabled him to express himself with entire candour, expressly says that the movement gives the impression of the composer having exercised later powers upon early material;* and he then goes on to describe the five-bar and six-bar extension of the first idea as an irregularity. But although he is right the same dimensions might have been regular enough had the music itself not lacked evidence of its own phrasing.

3. Thus we find Joachim considering as two five-bar phrases that which we feel unable to construe otherwise than as 4 × 2 + 2; and the important question is not as to "who is right?" but as to "why should there be a difference of view?" It is not as if these phrases occurred during the Durchführung where the phrasing is likely to become vague in consequence of a continuous flow, and where it may be therefore permissible to count mechanically by the prevailing phrase-length.

4. But Joachim also finds the broad four-bar phrasing of the first subject unsymmetrical as compared with the rhythm of the first idea. We, on the other hand, regard the entire opening as introductory and the real movement as commencing at bar 27; because it is only in this way that the outcome of an analysis becomes satisfactory.

5. To construe otherwise would be to admit an almost absurd disproportion between the first statement and the return groups; besides which, even after allowing this deduction we have to suppose that the composer intended his return groups and coda combined as a counterpoise to his first statement.

---

* In a letter to Brahms written from Hanover and dated October 15, 1861, Joachim says: "Am wenigsten lieb bleibt mir der erste Satz des G moll-Quartetts. Es scheint mir in der Erfindung unverhältnismässig weit den kommenden Sätzen nachzustehen, und manche Unregelmässigkeit in dem rhythmischen Bau kommt mir nicht durch characteristik geboten vor, die sie allein rechtfertigen könnte." And so on, at considerable length (see Vol. I of the Brahms-Joachim Correspondence, p. 306). From other passages in the Joachim Correspondence it is also discernible that Joachim's opinion, although agreeing completely with our own, was arrived at by an entirely different process—a concordance which goes to prove the relation between beauty as demonstrated by analysis and as affecting the emotions.

Unfortunately, however, the return groups, instead of artistically reducing the entire first statement's material, omit the important first intermediate motive altogether; so that our best efforts to bring the whole into line are only partially successful.

RHYTHMICAL TABLE.

Ex. 113. Op. 25, Allegro. First section.

PORTION	MATERIAL	BARS	CONSISTING OF	EXTENDING TO
Introduction	{ 1st subject	20	(4 × 2) 2 + 2	20
	{ ,, ,,	6	4 + 2	6
	1st subject	14	4 × 3 + 2	40
	,, ,,	9	4 × 2 + 1	49
	Int. motive 1	29	{ 4 × 2 + 1 } { 4 × 5 }	78
1st section	,, ,, 2nd subject	14	4 × 3 + 2	92
	Int. motive 2	8	4 + 2	100
	3rd subject	13	{ 4 + 2 } { 4 + 3 }	113
	Int. motive 3	17	(4 + 3) 2 + 3	130
Totals.		130		130

6. The Durchführung is given entirely to material deduced from the first subject; and, in common with the coda, is in strictly duple rhythm. Special solidity of construction for these departments is an almost constant feature with Brahms, and one in respect of which he differs from most composers; who display a more servile strictness during their first statements and seem to avenge it by taking extra licence during what is called the "working out."

7. The thematic material consists of three subjects with their attendant motives. The latter are not however on this occasion for use as Durchführung material, and do not even fuse with their principals sufficiently to enable us to pass subconsciously from one to the other; being on the contrary so defined that the first intermediate motive resembles a second subject—and is no doubt so accepted by most listeners on a first hearing.

RHYTHMICAL TABLE.

Ex. 114. Op. 25, Allegro, Durchführung to Coda.

PORTION	MATERIAL	BARS	COMPOSED OF	EXTEND-ING TO
Durchführung	1st subject	22	(4 × 2 + 3) 2	152
,, ,,	18	4 × 4 + 2	170
,, ,,	9	4 × 2 + 1	179
,, ,,	17	4 × 4 + 1	196
,, ,,	26	4 × 6 + 2	222
,, ,,	14	4 × 3 + 2	236
,, ,,	18	(4 + 2) 3	254
,, ,,	4	4	258
,, ,,	6	4 + 2	264
Totals.		134		264
Return	1st subject	16	4 × 4	280
	2nd subject	15	4 × 3 + 3	295
	Int. motive 2	8	4 × 2	303
	3rd subject	6	4 + 2 }	316
	,, ,,	7	4 + 3 }	
	Int. motive 3	16	3 × 4 + 4	332
Totals.		68		332
Coda	1st subject	10	4 × 2 + 2	342
	,, ,,	18	4 × 4 + 2	360
	,, ,,	12	4 × 3 }	373
		1	⌢ }	
Totals.		41		373

8. The first subject remains essentially the same whether we construe the first twenty-six bars as introductory or not. But

Ex. 115. Op. 25, Allegro, First Subject.

Str. (8ves)

Pf. (8ves)

obscurity results in either case; for if not introductory the first section is of unconscionable length, and if introductory the first idea is inadequately stated.

9. The first intermediate motive is not only an intrusion but has such a highly misleading rhythmical affinity with the second subject as to cause even some critics to insist upon its being the

real second subject and the latter merely a "tributary"; evidently thus overlooking the consequent absurdity of admitting

Ex. 116. Op. 25, Allegro. First intermediate motive.

two intermediates between first and second subjects. The inadvertence is useful however, as enabling composer-students to note how largely a successful use of dual subjects depends upon their members being so fused and collectively contrasted with companion themes as to leave no doubt of identity.

10. As against this the real second subject and its attendant motive are both very compact; and being treated at similar length and with one instrumentation for first section and return, contribute very greatly to cohesion of the movement.

Ex. 117. Op. 25, Allegro. Second Subject.

11. The same observation may be made respecting third subject and its attendant motive; but their instrumentation is so changed for the return that their contribution to unity is only saved by the keys being respectively dominant and tonic. This contrasts somewhat sharply with the return of second subject; which, being in E flat, or a semitone higher than its first statement, loses part of its structural significance.

Ex. 118. Op. 25, Allegro, Second intermediate motive.

12. The attendant motive of the third subject is rhythmically favourable to entry upon either Durchführung or coda; and these (especially the Durchführung) are the sections which cause us to forget the unfavourable outset. Fortunately the return is too compact to renew our perplexities, so that a happier outcome is secured than was augured by the opening.

Ex. 119. Op. 25, Allegro, Third Subject.

13.   A passing technical interest is offered by the written-out rallentando, and pause, leading to the use of bars which are not rhythmically integral.   The rallentando possesses no peculiarity

Ex. 120. Op. 25, Allegro, Third intermediate motive.

beyond that of being written out; but the pause presents that of a continued motion of subordinate parts. (See also Ex. 119 of Op. 8.)

Ex. 121. Op. 25, Allegro, Extension in lieu of rallentando.

Ex. 122. Op. 25, Allegro, Extension in lieu of pause.

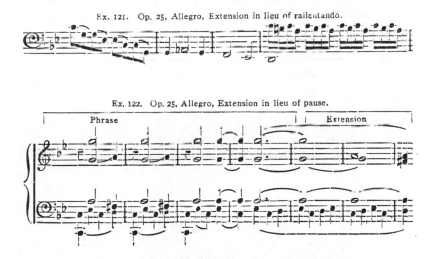

14. If we compare the first statement groups with those of the return, commencing at the point where they divide—the one to introduce the superfluous first intermediate motive and the other to pass on to the legitimate second subject we shall be struck by the coherence resulting to the latter by the same figur-

ation which had embellished the first subject forming an accompaniment to the second.

15. The enthusiasm thus improved upon in the return is spoiled in the first statement by introduction of the incongruous first intermediate motive; the general impression produced being that these two portions were written at different times and this motive probably only retained for the sake of old association. For actual research the student should take bars 39 and 277 as starting points from which to compare the first statement and return.

16. Epitome.

(a) Subjects. See Examples 115-20.

(b) Key, G minor; changing to D for second subject; returning to G minor; passing through A minor and G major during the Durchführung, and finally returning to G minor six bars before the return.

(c) Time, common; without change.

(d) Length, 373 bars. The first section is naturally unrepeated as it is already twice the length of the return groups.

Ex. 123. Outline of Op. 25, Allegro

FIRST SECTION	DURCHFÜHRUNG	RETURN	CODA
130	134	68	41
I II III		I II III	
78 22 30		16 23 29	

II. INTERMEZZO.

Allegro ma non troppo.

17. It is customary to describe in terms of ecstasy the lyric movements now to follow; but however aptly such glowing accounts may reflect the characteristics of the music they do not convey that information of the composer's methods which

it is our especial object to provide. To put it otherwise, we are not here to rhapsodise about beauty but to endeavour to explain how it results; and though, for example, it may be perfectly true that the note of the present movement is

yearning weakness, as of a wounded fairy,

it will be far better for the student to arrive at that conclusion independently, and still better for him to qualify for explaining to others how such effects are produced.

18. The student should here bear in mind the provision for non-counting of incomplete initial bars; the object of which is

RHYTHMICAL TABLE.

Ex. 124. Op. 25, Intermezzo.

PORTION	MATERIAL	BARS	COMPOSED OF	EXTEND-ING TO
1st section	1st subject (a)	17	$1 + (4 \times 4)$	17
	,, ,, ,,	17	$4 \times 4 + 1$	34
	2nd subject (a)	18	$4 \times 4 + 2$	52
	1st subject (a)	21	$4 \times 5 + 1$	73
	2nd subject (a)	31	$\left.\begin{matrix} 4 \times 5 + 1 \\ 4 \times 2 + 2 \end{matrix}\right\}$	104
	1st subject (a)	12	4×3	116
Totals.		116		116
Trio	1st subject (b)	15	$1 + (5 \times 2) + 4$	131
	,, ,, ,,	15	$1 + (5 \times 2) + 4$	146
	2nd subject (b)	21	$\left.\begin{matrix} (4 \times 1)\ 4 \\ 1 \end{matrix}\right\}$	167
	1st subject (b)	25	5×5	192
Totals.		76		192
Da Capo	Repetition of 1st $\left.\begin{matrix} \\ \end{matrix}\right\}$ section	116		308
Coda.	1st subject (b)	13	$\left\{\begin{matrix} 3 \\ 5 \times 2 \end{matrix}\right\}$	321
Totals.		129		321

to ensure commencing the rhythmic summary with the first strong pulsation of the opening phrase. Now in this case it curiously happens that the *whole* of the first bar forms an initial weak pulsation; which accounts for its standing alone in the table, at the beginning both of first section and trio. The opening of the Coda presents a still more exceptional case, for there no less than three bars transpire before we encounter the first strong rhythmic pulsation. The feature however is merely a difference in appearance and not in essence from the customary incomplete initial bar. As a rule, to extend the initial may add a refinement to the working up of detail, by the faculty it gives of holding the integral phrase-commencement in suspense; but that is all. It is therefore interesting to observe what now happens.

Ex. 125. Op 25, Intermezzo, First subject.

19. Here the first five quavers of the 'cello part which precede the initial notes of the melody merely give the *tempo*; and the same may be said of the piano part in the trio initial bar, of which the Coda entry with its three weak bars is merely an amplification.

Ex. 126. Op. 25, Intermezzo. Trio, First Subject.

20. So elementary a matter would end here but for the Brahms habit of deriving inspiration from traits generally disregarded —one which prevents those accustomed to analyse his works from ever setting anything down as trifling without exact knowledge of the use to which it is put.   The plaintive dreaminess of this movement, for example, is principally due to this full initial bar; for, after having been lured into waiting for the rhythmic impetus of first subject we find it natural (at bars 34 and 73) to do the same for that of the second.   Besides this the

Ex. 127. Op. 25, Intermezzo. First section, second subject.

composer elsewhere avails himself of the same elasticity to create a feeling of suspense at will, and to prolong it according to the importance of what is to follow.   It is thus that, when the return of the first subject is due, we find homage paid to it in extra bars (51-2 and 103-4); and also that the trio-subject becomes one of five bars by simply drawing the extra bar into service as part of the phrase.   It is impossible not to extend admiration to works which not only bear this close scrutiny but which actually require it for their full appreciation.   A lyric movement is generally one of little technical pretension, its category being one from which we expect no novelty of feature; but here are novel features too numerous to permit us even to describe them all.

21. Another of these occurs in connection with the trio five-bar rhythm, which would have appeared mechanical if either had

Ex. 128. Op. 25, Intermezzo. Trio, First and Second Subjects.

108   HANDBOOK TO BRAHMS (ORCHESTRAL).

been persisted in or suddenly dropped. The second subject is
accordingly, though phrased in five, made to sympathise with
the duple rhythm to which it must return. This is done by using
a phrase-length of 2 + 2 + 1; instead of 2 + 3, as was the case
with the first subject—the fact of neither of these subjects possessing much attraction in themselves only serving to exalt the
power of good workmanship. Brahms's themes are not generally beautiful in the conventional sense, but become lovable by
the treatment they receive—a fact which sufficiently explains
why his works require such study for their full appreciation that
first hearings convey only first impressions.

22. Epitome.

(a) Subjects. See Ex. 125 to 128.

(b) Key, C minor. Trio, A flat major, Coda, C major.

(c) Time, $\frac{6}{8}$, no change.

(d) Length, 321 bars (including D.C. printed in full), no
repeats.

Ex. 129. Op. 25, Intermezzo. Outline.

FIRST SECTION	TRIO	D.C.	CODA
116	76	116	13

III. ANDANTE CON MOTO.

23. This movement consists of two song-groups divided by
an intermezzo, the three sections being approximately of equal
length. It might therefore be described as in "ternary form,"
but the expression is better avoided as not always interpreted in
the same sense. The frequency of extensions and overlappings
of the phrase results in a first idea of its outline being best
obtained by considering it apart from all modification. Thus
the full rhythmical summary presents a rather complicated appearance at first sight, but not when compared with a statement
of normal phrase-lengths.

RHYTHMICAL TABLE.

Ex. 130. Op. 25, Andante con moto.

PORTION	MATERIAL	BARS	CONSISTING OF	EXTENDING TO
1st section	1st subject	16	4 × 3 + 1 ⎱ 4 − 1 ⎰	16
	2nd subject	10	4 × 2 + 2	26
	1st subject	17	4 × 2 + 2 ⎱ 4 − 1 + 4 ⎰	43
	2nd subject	16	4 × 4	59
	Bridge	15	2 + (4 + 1) 2 + 3	74
Totals.		74		74
Middle section	Subject	33	2 × 16 + 1	107
	Bridge	11	4 × 2 ⎱ 4 − 1 ⎰	118
	Subject	15	2 × 7 + 1	133
	Bridge	18	4 × 3 + 6	151
Totals.		77		151
Return	Preliminary statement of 1st subject in C major	16	4 × 4	167
	1st subject	16	4 × 4	183
	2nd subject	10	4 × 2 + 2	193
	1st subject	24	4 × 2 + 2 ⎱ 4 4 × 2 + 2 ⎰	217
Coda	,, ,,	18	4 × 3 ⎱ 3 + 2 + 1 ⎰	235
Totals.		84		235

24. No one could divine from the placid opening theme of this movement the wealth of exuberance to follow. At entry

Ex. 131. Op. 25, Intermezzo. Normal phrase-lengths.

I 4 × 13	Bridge of 4 × 4	II 4 × 18	Bridge of 4 × 4	I 4 × 13	Coda of 4 × 4

of the second subject the crotchet pulsations divide into triplet quavers and the phrases overlap. The effect is analogous to

syncopation upon a broad scale; for, just as syncopation sup-
presses percussion of the beat, so does overlapping of the phrase

Ex. 132. Op. 25, Andante. First Subject.

suppress that of the bar; the effect in each case being to create
a temporary suspense. As a consequence of the third four-bar
phrase having been already extended by one bar, the overlapping, though evident, does not disturb the mere number of
bars; but although the increased ardour is thereby rendered less
perceptible to the many, it is even more significant to those who

Ex. 133. Op. 25, Andante. Second Subject.

recognise it as the commencement of a finely graduated rise in emotion.

25. A feature of this movement is that its second subject receives no development; in lieu of which apparently its recurrences are very variously instrumented.

26. This variety of instrumentation stands however for far more than its face-value, as it provides the incentive to new ideas. Thus the second scoring after leading to a triumphal outburst starts off upon the march (in the two bars 60 and 61 which are extra to the phrase) by giving us merely a tramping rhythm unassociated with melodic motive but which is sustained for thirteen bars more before the new departure is disclosed. During these our expectation increases, as doubtless the composer intended it should do; and, though the material of this "bridge" work is fairly indifferent, it would be hard to say that its lack of individual interest was not also a part of the composer's plan—as ardent expectancy naturally decreases our interest in what is actually passing.

27. The "middle section" thus introduced is in every sense remarkable. It forms a splendid climax to the uprise of the first section; it provides contrast both by its material and its brilliancy of instrumentation and it subsides with eloquence. Our special duty however is to dwell upon the important technical question involved—that of the *march in triple measure.*

Ex. 134, Op. 25, Andante, Subject of middle section.

† R.H. doubles with added octaves.

We have already* had occasion to deal with this subject in connection with the Funeral March of the German Requiem, where Brahms (instead of being obliged, like Beethoven, Handel and Chopin in their funeral marches, to harp upon one note in the melody for fear of disturbing that equality of foot-tread which is the essence of the rhythm in such a case) secured freedom for his upper part by employment of the three-beat bar; which compels the *strong tread* to come to the assistance of the *weak beat* twice out of three times. For (as, in marching each alternate beat is a strong or weak tread as the case may be) it is clear that if we take, say, six such triads or beats we shall have, in common time, the strong tread always corresponding with the musical accent; whereas in triple time we shall sometimes have the strong tread helping the weak beat and sometimes the strong beat helping the weak tread. Here, for ex-

Ex. 135.   March in triple time.

ample (strong treads being crotchets) we find in duple time (the upper accents) strong beats and treads coinciding; but in triple time (the lower accents) we have, at "4," the strong beat of the triple bar assisting the weak tread, and, at "3" and "5," the

---

* Vol. I, p. 172.

weak beats of the triple bar reducing the weight of the strong tread. These influences combined result in that "neutrality of beat" which is especially desirable for the purpose of a mournful procession, but which is in some degree a constant feature of the $\frac{3}{4}$ march at any *tempo*.

28. We are thus enabled to see why it is in this movement that the phrase-length for the middle section is suddenly cut down to two bars. March-tread being essentially duple, the triple measure is naturally a disturbing influence—too much so for practical purposes unless adjusted at frequent intervals. Hence the rise and fall of the melody constituting the phrase-length as mentioned.

29. The middle section, which is in C major, employs, in subsiding, a motive easily mistaken for a subject, but which is merely a bridge-passage. Being used (bars 107 to 118) to join two instrumentations of the subject and then (bars 133 to 151) for the return its resemblance to a formal subject is increased. As to the use made of this "bridge," it certainly gives effect to

Ex. 136. Op. 25, Andante. Intermediate motive of middle section.

the new instrumentation (from bar 119) and might have made a splendid return (from the *sforzando*, bar 144) but for the delay which, for some obscure reason, is allowed to take place. Although devoted to first subject, this intermezzo is not the return proper; for, not only is it in the key of C (instead of being in E flat), but the sixteen bars occupied are altogether

outside the scheme; which, without them, accurately corresponds
with that of the first statement.

30. The Coda is so gentle and unpretentious that the novelty
of what may be called its "rhythmical *diminuendo*" is generally
overlooked. After twelve bars given to four-bar phrases the
phrase-length is gradually reduced, becoming three and two

Ex. 137. Op 25, Conclusion of Andante.

before the final pause bar; which, being aided by falling parts,
forms a conclusion of exquisite refinement. This, by the way,
is one of the movements described by "Blätter für Theater,
Musik und Kunst," upon the occasion of the first performance
of this quartet at Vienna, as "gloomy, obscure and ill-
developed."

31. Epitome.
(*a*) Subjects. See Examples 132, 133 and 134.
(*b*) Key, E flat major, changing twice to C major.
(*c*) Time, ¾, without change.
(*d*) Length, 235 bars; no repeats.

Ex. 138. Op. 25, Outline of Andante.

FIRST SECTION	MIDDLE SECTION	RETURN AND CODA
74	77	84

IV. RONDO ALLA ZINGARESE.

(Presto.)

32. The rhythm of this movement is as rigid as that of the Op. 18 Andante, in reviewing which we sufficiently treated the matter. Both are also folk-tune movements; with the difference, however, that this is a dance, whereas the Andante was a song movement—besides which the present being a gipsy rondo is brought within the "national" category.

33. As gesture has the greater need of variety we have here five distinct melodies, the alternation of which the critic of the Vienna "Blätter" ventured to call an "offence against the laws of style." Let us glance, therefore, at the general arrangement. Out of a total of 463 bars, 238 are occupied by material which excludes the first three subjects. What is here called "middle section" is therefore eminently remindful of sonata form. As for any merely mechanical alternation, its effect is so entirely relieved by the portion here styled "Quasi Cadenza" as to render further explanation of the peculiarities of that section unnecessary. Either free and unbarred; or, if barred, unphrased; or, if phrased, of erratic character; its intention is too obvious for comment.

34. Furthermore, the portion here named "first section" is rounded off by its own Codetta, by means of which the free working which follows it acquires the character of a Durchführung—and this in spite of the dance-motion which is everywhere well sustained. The first sign of caprice to which the enthusiasm of the "middle-section" leads is an irregularity in the recurrence of subjects and consequent postponement of the first subject until after the climax of the "Quasi Cadenza." After the outburst of the latter has been expended, and therefore in entire accord with every recognised standard of formal beauty, the principal theme returns; being then moreover furnished with an exultant Codetta, than which there could be no more appropriate counterpoise to the placid ending of the first section. Truly, for his own sake, the Vienna critic should have been more discriminate.

35. The next feature is an almost exclusive adoption of three-bar rhythm, exception to which occurs during the free section only, where we have eight four-bar phrases (excluding repeats)

Ex. 139. Op. 25, Rondo. Order of subjects.

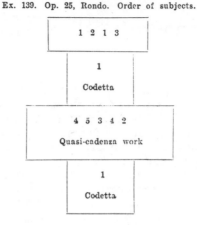

given to a new theme (No. 5) of cantabile character, and naturally heightening the effect; though, it must be confessed, more
by a timely appearance than by any individual merit. But it
would be hard to deny Brahms the privilege of being sometimes what the rhapsodical musician is always—an opportunist.

RHYTHMICAL TABLE.

Ex. 140. Op. 25, Finale. Rondo alla Zingarese.

PORTION	MATERIAL	BARS	CONSISTING OF	EXTEND-ING TO
1st section*	1st subject	30	3×10	30
	2nd ,,	36	3×12	66
	1st ,,	13	$3 \times 4 + 1$	79
	3rd ,,	12	$\|: 3 \times 4 :\|$	91
	,, ,,	24	3×8	115
	1st ,,	20	3×10	145
Codetta	,, ,,	9	3×3	154
Middle section*	4th ,,	18	$\|: 3 \times 2 :\|: 3 \times 4 :\|$	172
	5th ,,	16	4×4	188
	,, ,,	17	$\|: (4 \times 2) + 1 + (4 \times 2) :\|$	205
	3rd ,,	24	3×8	229
	,, ,,	8	$3 \times 2 + 2$	237
	4th ,,	18	3×6	255
	2nd ,,	37	$3 \times 12 + 1$	292
Quasi Cadenza	Subjects 3, 4, 5	69	See special Ex.	361
Return	1st subject	21	3×7	382
Coda	,, ,,	22	$3 \times 7 + \frown$	404

* Use of these terms is explained in the text.

36. The three subjects affording material for the first section have, in spite of their contrasts, a distinct affinity which, whether happening intentionally or otherwise, renders the variety of the middle section most welcome. The fourth subject, with which

Ex. 141. Op. 25, Finale, First Subject.

Ex. 142. Op. 25, Finale, Second Subject.

Ex. 143 Op. 25, Finale, Third Subject.

the middle section commences, is "meno presto," and still in three-bar rhythm; but with its phrases very pointedly marked off, as if to call attention to the rhythmic change about to follow. This accrues with the fifth subject, which later on provides material for the barred portion of the "quasi Cadenza," but that is all. Its formal recognition is therefore but slight.

Ex. 144. Op. 25, Finale, Fourth Subject

Str. (Piano doubles)

Ex. 145. Op. 25, Finale, Fifth Subject.

'Cello (upper notes) and Viola

Pf.

37. The "quasi Cadenza" is distinguished by boldness, originality and freedom. It is bold in emulating for a quartet the
kind of cadenza usually written out for a concerto; it is original
in choosing a rondo, of all movements, for such a strange experiment; and it is free by reserving for this section specialities
of the piano part, new counterpoints and new rhythms. The
preponderance of duple rhythm (coupled with total exclusion
of subjects 1 and 2) considerably helps the contrast of the
return besides contributing to the separate unity of this section
and making its object clear.

38. Epitome.

(*a*) Subjects. See Ex. 141-144.

(*b*) Key, G minor, changing to G major for bars 155 to 255
(subjects 4, 5, 3, 4).

(*c*) Time, $\frac{2}{4}$, without change—the bar being practically of
merely beat-value within the three-bar phrase. Note that the
bar subdivisions which are duple during the triple phrase become
triple during the duple phrase (bars 173 to 205).

RHYTHMICAL TABLE.

Ex. 146. Op. 25, Quasi-cadenza section of Rondo. Dissection of this item in Ex. 140.

MATERIAL	BARS	RHYTHM	EXTEND-ING TO
Pause on dominant chord of minor 9th; with sequence of short falling scale passages ending with ⌢ on dom.	1	free	293
" Meno presto " on motive taken from 5th subject modulating to B major (overlap).	8	3 × 3 − 1	301
" Poco piu presto " on 3rd subject, concluding with falling scale of F sharp minor ending on dom.	11	2 × 5 + 1	312
On subject 4.	21	{ 3 2 × 3 4 × 3	333
On subject 3.	20	4 × 5	353
Sequence of short rising scale passages ending with 1st subject.	8	4 × 2	361
	69		

(d) Length, 404 bars; or 463 with repeats.

Ex. 147. Op. 25, Rondo. Outline.

I	II	I	III	I	CODETTA	MIDDLE SECTION	QUASI CADENZA	I	CODA
30	36	13	36	30	9	138	69	21	22

OP. 26. SECOND PIANO QUARTET IN A MAJOR.

(For Piano, Violin, Viola and Violoncello. Dedicated to Dr. Elisabeth Rösing.)

I. Allegro non troppo.
II. Poco Adagio.
III. Scherzo (Poco Allegro).
IV. Finale (Allegro).

Published by N. Simrock in 1863.

Arrangement for Piano (four hands) by the Composer.

I. ALLEGRO NON TROPPO.

1. On this occasion we begin with a problem. Cases of phrase-extension or overlapping are extremely few in this movement. The extra bar* is necessitated by the repeat and the four bars† merely an alternative ending for first section. Such rhythmic peculiarities as do occur are therefore within the phrase—or even within the bar; which is the same thing as saying that they relate merely to subdivisions. Yet the rhythmic interest is of absorbing character. Why is this?

2. Something of the answer appears in the very first phrase, with the classic trait of foreshadowing the character of an entire movement by its opening bars. The plan is to evolve the desired characteristics by cultivation of the rhythmic basis of this phrase, which in spite of simplicity, becomes therefore an object of interest. Brahms is often supposed to have gone out of his way to make rhythm a speciality, but all his extravagance consisted of recognising its natural claims. A composer who does this finds rhythmic refinements easy precisely as a student who

RHYTHMICAL TABLE.

Ex. 148. Op. 26, Allegro non troppo.

PORTION	MATERIAL.	BARS	CONSISTING OF	EXTENDING TO
First Section	1st subject	36	(2, 2, 4) 4 + 4	36
	1st int. motive	16	4 × 4	52
	2nd subject	32	(4, 2, 2) 4	84
	,, ,,	10	2 × 5	94
	2nd int. motive	11	4 × 3 – 1	105
	3rd subject	18	(2, 2, 4) 2 + 1	} 124
	Extra bar*	1		
Totals		124		124
Durchführung	Extra bars†	4		128
	3rd subject	16	2 × 8	144
	1st subject	36	2 × 18	180
	,, ,,	10	2 × 5	190
	2nd int. motive	7	4 × 2 – 1	197
	3rd subject	16	(2, 2, 4) 2	213
Totals		89		213
Return	1st subject	37	(2, 2, 4) 4 + 5	250
	1st int. motive	16	4 × 4	266
	2nd subject	32	(4, 2, 2) 4	298
	,, ,,	10	2 × 5	308
	2nd int. motive	11	4 × 3 – 1	319
	3rd subject	25	4 × 6 + 1	344
Totals		131		344
Coda	1st subject	20	2 × 10	364
	,, ,,	16	(2, 2, 4) 2	380
Totals		36		380

does so finds their discovery and appreciation a pleasure. Thus
we see at once that at the introduction of the first intermediate

Ex. 149. Op. 25, Allegro, First Subject.

motive (bar 37) the original phrase-formation 2 + 2 + 4 yields
to a succession of four-bar phrases, but that these four-bar
phrases are sympathetically subdivided—that is to say they are
composed of 1 + 1 + 2, an exact reproduction of the rhythmic
proportions of the opening.

Ex. 150. Op. 26, Allegro. First intermediate motive.

3. This prepares us for a similar construction of the second
subject; and in each case although the four-bar phrase, as such,

Ex. 151 Op. 26, Allegro. Second Subject (first four bars).

is sufficiently assertive, its subdivision as stated remains clear.
This clearness is an essential; for without it not only the listener would miss the effect resulting from symmetry of design
but even the analyst would be impeded in his examination.
Such clearness, moreover, is absolutely necessary to give strength
to the new subject as basis for a new departure.

4. The new departure here is most interesting, but for its
right understanding we must first cast an eye to the Durchführung, in which free use of the two-bar phrase is in keeping
with the desired increase of excitement. Obviously the logical
introduction of this section requires that the listener should be
already initiated to a succession of these short phrases; but to
this the first phrase-formation (2 + 2 + 4) was unfavourable,
on account of ending with a four bar flow. The second phrase-
formation (1 + 1 + 2), by ending with a two-bar phrase, opens
the door for a succession of the latter; and accordingly we find
that, whereas the first eight bars of first subject consists of
2 + 2 + 4, those of second subject consist of 4 + 2 + 2. Fur-

Ex 152. Op. 26, Allegro. Second Subject (second four bars).

thermore, and as if to prevent all doubt as to the intention, the
statement of this theme is rounded off by a succession of two-
bar phrases (bars 81 to 94) previous to introduction of the
second intermediate motive.

5. Next, as to the reason why this induction of the listener
should have been confided to the second subject instead of to
the third; considering that to some it may appear that the
latter, occurring just before the Durchführung, would have been
the more appropriate intermediary. Had this course been
chosen not only the contrast offered by the Durchführung would
have necessarily suffered, but the approach to first subject, both
at return and Coda, would have been impeded by collision of
the two-bar with the four-bar phrase.

6. As to the construction of second intermediate motive little
need be said, such motives being generally in the rhythm of
the subjects which they introduce; but the third subject, beyond

Fx. 153. Op. 2ᶜ, Allegro. Second intermediate motive.

Str. alone

pizz.

performing the perfunctory duty of conducting us back to the original rhythm, is of practically no service. It adds nothing melodically to the movement by inflections which have already occurred, it contributes nothing of harmonic interest and even its instrumentation is the weakest feature of the movement. Whether, as in other cases, this lack of individual interest may have been designed to heighten effects to follow is of course a question, but even this intention is not well fulfilled; and the fulsomeness of statement which this poor subject receives at the return (bars 320-344) not only seems evidence of conscious weakness but impoverishes the Coda. The result is that the latter

Ex. 154. Op. 26, Allegro, Third Subject.

is merely normal. On the other hand, the Durchführung by turning the entire accumulation of material to good account is a retrieving feature.

7. Epitome.

(a) Subjects. See Ex. 149-154.

(b) Key, A major, changing to C major at entry of Durchführung, which during its course passes through C minor and returns to C major. The modulations involved provide some highly interesting progressions.

(c) Time, ¾, without change. The rhythm throughout is remarkably free from expansions and contractions, but at each introduction of third subject the phrases are overlapped.

(d) Length, 380 bars; or 499 with repeat of first section.

Ex. 155. Op. 26, Allegro. Outline.

FIRST SECTION	DURCHFÜHRUNG	RETURN	CODA
124	89	131	36
I II III 52 53 19		I II III 53 53 25	

III. POCO ADAGIO.

8. In his "Oper und Drama" Wagner tells us that Rossini, having arrived in Paris after writing "William Tell," knew very well why "he called upon Auber to make him an 'extra gracious compliment.'" Doubtless Brahms also knew very well why he made the structure of this piece of extra gracious simplicity. It was, in our view, that obviousness of general outline might atone for vagueness of phrase formation—might prevent us from losing our way whilst travelling along an otherwise misty road. Well might Huneker say* that Brahms's contribution to the technics of rhythm was enormous, for although he is always teaching us rhythm he rarely gives us the same lesson twice; and here, for the first time, we have it proved that material, the vagueness of which would otherwise have rendered it futile can, by being held within strong rhythmic delimitations, be made to convey a lesson of romantic tenderness.

9. Two sections; two subjects; the sections so far equal in length that a slight shortening of the second (even that taking place obviously in favour of the Coda) is the only cause of

---

* "Mezzotints in Modern Music," p. 7.

RHYTHMICAL TABLE.

Ex. 156. Op. 26, Poco Adagio.

PORTION	MATERIAL	BARS	CONSISTING OF	EXTENDING TO
1st section	1st subject	14	(3 + 2) 2 2 × 2	14
	,, ,,	9	3 + 2 − 1 3 + 2	23
	,, ,,	18	(3 + 2) 2 2 × 4	41
	2nd subject	16	4 × 2 2 × 2 + 4	57
Totals.		57		57
Free section forming counterpoise to Coda	Free working	28	4 × 7	85
Totals.		28		85
2nd section	1st subject	14	(3 + 2) 2 2 × 2	99
	,, ,,	9	3 + 2 − 1 3 + 2	108
	2nd subject	18	4 × 2 2 × 2 3 + 2 + 1	126
Totals.		41		126
Coda	1st subject	10	(3 + 2) 2	136
		8	2 × 2 + 4	144
		11	4 × 3 − 1	155
Totals.		29		155

difference; with a free section to balance the Coda and mark the half of our journey : this is the elementary plan the bracing effect of which is to enable us to confront rhythmic complication in detail with abiding knowledge of its relation to the whole.

10. With the strings muted the piano-part becomes governing factor of the first subject, and its sustained notes during the strings' anticipations of the next beat produce a pleasant and mysterious effect. The rise of the piano above the strings helps us to decide the subdivision of the phrase, besides preparing us for the two-bar phrases leading to the nine-bar episode marked in the summary. After this episode we are to have the first subject again with a new instrumentation; so that its duple rhythm serves not only to divide the two   settings but also as

Ex. 157. Op. 26, Poco Adagio, First Subject.

a trait of unity—the coming second subject being entirely duple. In the latter the figure which most characterises the first

Ex. 158. Op. 26, Poco Adagio, Second Subject.

subject not only reappears as counterpoint but is also combined with the new accompaniment thus originating the combination of normal with triplet quavers which is so largely used throughout the movement.

11. Undivided five-bar phrases are rare at any *tempo* and are almost inconceivable in extremely slow measure. In the same degree as the movement is slow, the demarcation into 3 + 2 or 2 + 3, as the case may be, becomes vague; until, in an Adagio, it may almost be said to be effaced. The result is

that there would be equal authority for construing in either way, but for the fact that the free section is duple. This shows the intended subdivision to have been 3 + 2—the duple sub-division being placed last as preparation for the new departure, and the refined expression of the movement thus resting upon the faintness of phrase-demarcation, justified by firmness of the general bearings.

12. Rhythmic vagueness however is not all which strength of outline is called upon to make good, as varieties of instru-mentation and figuration given to recurrences of the same theme would be altogether excessive in the absence of any compen-sating feature. There is the distinction between Brahms's colouring and ordinary changes of the kind; as the tints do not appear to have been arbitrarily chosen, but necessitated. The result of insufficient attention to this difference is that he is often praised and blamed with equal injustice. Here, for example, the piano passages are elaborate without there being any act or purpose of the kind; the elaboration being absolutely re-quired in order to continue what the 'cello has just delivered. The other strings are silent whilst the 'cello's individuality is asserted by contraction of the interval used in the first figure and have, as it were, no right to appear, otherwise than to assist its expansion. This is "instrumentation" in the true sense of obedience to the demands of material, and the two nine-bar episodes upon this first subject must always stand as illustra-tions of the use of colour in entire subservience to the require-ments of thought.

13. Epitome.

(*a*) Subjects. See Ex. 157 and 158.

(*b*) Key, E, with change to F minor on return of second subject, E being resumed for Coda.

(*c*) Time, common, no change.

(*d*) Length, 155 bars, no repeats.

Ex. 159. Op. 26, Poco Adagio. Outline.

FIRST SECTION		FREE SECTION	SECOND SECTION		CODA
57		28	41		29
I	II		I	II	
41	16		23	18	

III. SCHERZO.

(Poco Allegro.)

14. This is a highly matter-of-fact movement as the following description will testify. It has two subjects each of which opens with four-bar and closes with two-bar phrases. There is only one intermediate motive; and this, being in two-bar phrases, enables us to see the reason for diminishing the phrase-length for close of the first subject statement, viz., in order to provide a connecting link between these two items of material. Thus towards end of the section when a connecting link is no longer required the two-bar phrase entirely disappears.

RHYTHMICAL TABLE.

Ex. 160. Op. 26, Scherzo (first section).

PORTION	MATERIAL	BARS	CONSISTING OF	EXTEND-ING TO
1st section (1st part)	1st subject	24	4 × 5 2 × 2	24
	Int. motive	9	2 × 4 + 1	33
	2nd subject	21	4 × 4 2 × 2 + 1	
		1	Extra for " 2nd time "	55
1st section (2nd part)	1st subject	18	4 × 2 2 × 5	73
	Int. motive	8	2 × 2 + 4	81
	,, ,,	19	2 × 9 + 1	100
	1st subject (approach to)	9	4 × 2 + 1	109
	,, ,,	10	4 × 2 + 2	119
Return	1st subject	20	4 × 4 2 × 2	139
	Int. motive	9	2 × 4 + 1	148
	2nd subject	17	4 × 4 + 1	165
	1st subject	26	4 × 6 + 2	191
	,, ,,	21	4 × 5 + 1	212
		1	Extra	213
Totals.		213		213

15. The close of the second subject in shortened phrase is due to a different cause. This is partly revealed by the final one-bar extension shown in the table as preceding the repeat of first part of the section.

16. The general scheme may be described as one in which the phrasing of the first subject shortens as it concludes, thus

Ex. 161. Op. 26, Scherzo. First Subject.

leading to an intermediate motive conceived in the spirit of the shortened phrases and therefore of more agitated character. In the composer's plan this motive becomes an auxiliary of the first subject exclusively, following it at every recurrence; and,

Ex. 162. Op. 26, Scherzo. Intermediate motive.

after the repeat furnishing principal material for a free section. The second subject being of the conventional cantabile order does nothing to add to the interest of this simple plan, which,

Ex. 163. Op. 26, Scherzo. Second Subject.

considering the length of the movement, may therefore be considered as somewhat overworked. This would certainly be the result in the majority of such cases; but here we feel, on the one hand, that the working is too coherent to allow anything to be spared, and, on the other, that more compactness would have added to the charm.

17. The trio-section opens with twenty-one bars of canon, unworthy of the rest of the movement. The second trio-subject

Ex. 164. Op. 26, Scherzo. Trio, First subject.

approximates in character to the opening subject; and this, moreover, by no means adds to the general effect. The fact is evident that Brahms, having in the first section succumbed to the often-felt temptation of over-working light material, was not unwilling to compensate for this by dispensing with Coda.

Ex. 165. Op. 26, Scherzo   Trio, Second subject.

It is of course natural for a composer to think that, because his own labour is lightened by this omission, strain upon the listener's attention will be correspondingly eased; but weariness is only increased by repeating the first section D.C. without abridgement, whereas a shortened form of it rounded off by a good Coda is the best means of justifying any excess of previous dimension.

18. The second trio-subject differs from the first-section opening in proceeding more largely by grades; thus giving rise to the motive bracketed above, which is made a feature. A rhythmic vagueness here (as in Op. 16, see par. 20) results from

the use of a duple motive in triple time; and the phrase-formation 3 × 3 + 2, elsewhere described as a "rhythmic *diminuendo*," may be traced to the same cause.

RHYTHMICAL TABLE.

Ex. 166. Op. 26, Scherzo (Trio).

PORTION	MATERIAL	BARS	CONSISTING OF	EXTEND-ING TO
Trio (1st part)	1st subject	13	4 × 3 + 1	234
	,, ,,	8	4 × 2	
	2nd subject	12	4 × 2	246
			2 × 2	
		2	Extra	248
Trio (2nd part	2nd subject	24	4 × 6	272
	,, ,,	11	3 × 3 + 2	283
,, return	1st subject	13	4 × 3 + 1	296
	,, ,,	14	4 × 3 + 2	310
	2nd subject	8	4 × 2	318
	,, ,,	11	3 × 3 + 2	329
Totals.		116		329

19. Epitome.

(*a*) Subjects. See Ex. 161-165.

(*b*) Key, A major. Trio in D minor—passing to D major at last entry of first subject. Extensive transient modulations in middle portion of both sections.

(*c*) Time, $\frac{3}{4}$, without change.

(*d*) Length, 329 bars, or 628 with repeats and D.C.

Ex. 167. Op. 26, Scherzo. Outline.

FIRST SECTION	TRIO	D.C.
213	116	
]: 54 :] 159	1]: 32 :] 83	213

IV. FINALE (ALLEGRO).

20. The critical listener to this movement is liable to appear ungrateful for the pleasure he receives; for after enjoying it he proceeds to the discovery that joviality expressed in hundreds of two-bar phrases, though exhilarating while it lasts, is scarcely entitled to a lasting praise. It does not take him long more-

RHYTHMICAL TABLE.

Ex. 168. Op. 26, Finale.

PORTION	MATERIAL	BARS	CONSISTING OF	EXTENDING TO
1st section	1st subject	32	2 × 16	32
	1st Int. motive	16	2 × 8 ⎫	52
	,, ,, ,,	4	2 × 2 ⎭	
	1st subject	8	2 × 4 ⎫	84
	2nd Int. motive	24	2 × 12 ⎭	
	2nd subject	21	2 × 10 + 1 ⎫	105
	,, ,,	10	2 × 5 ⎭	115
	3rd Int. motive	26	2 × 13	141
	general pause	1	Extra ⎫	204
	3rd subject	62	2 × 31 ⎭	
Totals.		204		204
2nd section	1st subject	16	2 × 8	220
	1st Int. motive	16	2 × 8 ⎫	236
	,, ,, ,,	6	2 × 3 ⎭	242
	1st subject	40	2 × 20	262
	,, ,,	9	3 × 3	291
	1st Int. motive	27	2 × 13 + 1 ⎫	324
	,, ,, ,,	6	2 × 3 ⎭	
	2nd subject	21	2 × 10 + 1 ⎫	355
	,, ,,	10	2 × 5 ⎭	
	3rd Int. motive	26	2 × 13	381
	general pause	1	Extra ⎫	442
	3rd subject	60	2 × 30 ⎭	
Totals.		238		442
Coda	Free	24	2 × 12	466
	1st subject	52	2 × 26 ⎫	510
	,, ,,	1	⌢ ⎭	
Totals.		77		519

over to find out that recurrences of the principal theme are purposely kept far apart in order that painful obsession by the two-bar phrase may be diminished, and that this is done only too well; the distance being such that we become indifferent as to whether the theme return or no. We thus lose the rondo sense by forfeiting pleasurable expectation of the theme's return. But that is not all; for, as one fault invariably makes many,

Ex. 169. Op. 26, Finale. First subject.

Ex. 170. Op. 26, Finale. Second subject.

relief from the terrible persistency of the two-bar phrase has been also sought in the multiplication of intermediate motives. These motives, as in reality so many subjects, not only tend to a distracting redundancy of material but are not always of appropriate character.

21. This is true not only of immediate motives but also of principal subjects; of which the second, for instance, seems to be in some sort a reflex of the paltry canon of the scherzo. Whether these considerations have influenced other judgments we are unaware; but they cause us to agree that "had Brahms revised this quartet in later years, as he did the first trio, he would have modified this last movement."*

Ex. 171. Op. 26, Finale, Third subject.

22. The third subject provides a welcome feeling of repose, but the intermediate motives one and all do nothing to relieve the incessant two-bar procession.

Ex. 172. Op. 26, Finale. First intermediate motive.

---

* Colles.—Brahms, "Music of the Masters" Series, p. 40.

Ex. 173. Op. 26, Finale, Second intermediate motive.

Ex. 174. Op. 26, Finale. Third Intermediate motive.

23. To this accumulation of material must be added several counterpoints which occur in course of the instrumentation and which are really counter-subjects. One of the principal of these occurs at the second entry of first subject in second section and leads, from C major as starting-point to transient modulations through flat keys, with enharmonic return.

Ex. 175. Op. 26, Finale. Countersubject.

Pf. in octaves

Strings in octaves

24. A feature of the movement is the curious selection of keys in which the subjects are set, the effect of which is to make it the principal business of the intermediate motives to revive interest in the parent tonality. Thus the second subject appears first in C, and then in F (bars 105 and 355), as does also the third subject (at bars 143 and 383); but the principal theme is always in A, with only one instance of use of the minor.

25. The entire movement being given to the material described, the only freshening influence is the Coda; by the *animato* of which new life is infused into the first subject, and an exuberant termination secured. This expedient, added to

those already referred to (such as the wide separation of first subjects, the variety of intermediate motives and contrapuntal counter-subjects), tends to show that the composer realised the necessity of relief from the mechanical effect of the constantly recurring two-bar phrase; relying upon his own powers to provide it. The task was one impossible of an absolute fulfilment; but the brilliancy of instrumentation, the interesting dialogue and the *entrain* of logical development combine to reduce objection to a minimum.

26. Epitome.

(*a*) Subjects, see Ex. 169 to 171. Intermediate motives, see Ex. 172 to 174. Counter-subject, see Ex. 175.

(*b*) Key, A major, changing to minor.

(*c*) Time, allabreve; without change.

(*d*) Length, 519 bars; no repeats.

Ex. 176. Op. 26, Finale. Outline.

FIRST SECTION			SECOND SECTION			CODA
	204			238		I
I	II	III	I	II	III	
84	58	62	120	58	60	77

OP. 34. PIANO QUINTET IN F MINOR.

(For Piano, two Violins, Viola and Violoncello.)

Dedicated to Princess Anna, of Hesse.

I. ALLEGRO NON TROPPO.
II. ANDANTE, UN POCO ADAGIO.
III. SCHERZO ALLEGRO.
IV FINALE (A) POCO SOSTENUTO; (B) ALLEGRO NON TROPPO.

Published by O. Rieter-Biedermann in 1865.
Arrangement for Two Pianos, by the Composer, published (as Op. 34 *bis*) by O. Rieter-Biedermann in 1872.

I. ALLEGRO NON TROPPO.

1. IN the last movement discussed our hearing-sense was directly addressed: in this it is but the bearer of a message to our inner perceptions. It was expressly the lack of what he called "sound-charm"* which at first prevented Joachim from enjoying this fine work, and in view of others probably experiencing the same feeling we shall give his comments close attention.

2. He begins by instancing the "rhythmical displacements" following the opening; the instrumentation of which, he says, is too thin, and not sufficiently energetic to support the idea. From the "sound-charm" point of view this criticism is undoubtedly correct; and, as it will hence appear conclusive to the majority—who are either unaware of, or at all events rarely employ any other—an illustration may be useful.

3. The high value of Joachim's criticism as a rule converts this into a good instance of the kind of error which is due to

---

* "Klangreiz." Joachim Correspondence, II, p. 9.

force of habit. It was, for example, the mere habit of relying upon a normal bar-value which caused these innocent broadenings of the phrase to appear as serious "rhythmical displacements"; whereas they are in fact nothing of the kind, and only wear the appearance because of Brahms not having chosen to recognise them in the notation. The case might be compared to that of a man who, saying that he is angry, fails to convey his idea for want of gesticulation; Brahms, in broadening his phrase, having appeared vague only through neglecting to change his bar-value.

4. In order to illustrate this, if Joachim's "rhythmical displacements" had been conventionally barred the result would have been simply two bars of $\frac{3}{2}$ instead of three of common time. They merely amount therefore to a momentary expansion of the phrase—and one which happens most appropriately immedi-

Ex. 177. Broadening of C into $\frac{3}{2}$. Original passage.

ately after introduction of the first subject because of the clear warning thus given of something important to follow.

5. A disadvantage much suffered by works of extreme importance is that their intention is rarely realised at first, and often has very long to wait for its appreciations. Joachim's

Ex. 178. The same, with notation in $\frac{3}{2}$.

first and unfavourable impressions of this work date from 1863, but those of 1867 show his view to have completely changed; for he then speaks with rapture of his quartet party having played the work with Dietrich; whilst, of the very movement with which he had previously found such serious fault, he exclaims:

How lovely it is! It belongs to the most beautiful and full of meaning of any that I know.*

6. It may be inferred from this that the subjects do not in themselves present much melodic attraction; nor can they be expected to do so if we admit their invention to have been principally dependent upon design. To revert to Joachim's own expression, Brahms did not value a subject by its "sound-charm" but by its suitability for the treatment to which he destined it—a standard of judgment which incidentally helps us to understand his apparent indifference to timbre. The work moreover displays this indifference in another way, for it was first a quintet for strings alone and then a sonata for two pianos, in which form it still holds rank as an original work.

* "Wie herrlich ist der erste Satz, zu dem schönsten, tiefsten gehört er, das ich kenne."—Correspondence II, p. 40.

7. The subjects must be examined by the light thrown upon their mutual relation in the rhythmical table, as this largely helps to explain their individual traits.   Thus, the first subject by the nature of its announcement has been likened to the opening of Beethoven's C minor Symphony; which however it out-

RHYTHMICAL TABLE.

Ex. 179. Op. 34, Allegro non troppo.

PORTION	MATERIAL	BARS	CONSISTING OF	EXTEND-ING TO
1st section	1st subject	4	2×2	4
	,, ,,	3	$1\frac{1}{2} \times 2*$	7
	,, ,,	4	2×2	11
	,, ,,	7	$2 \times 2 + 3$	18
	,, ,,	4	2×2	22
	Int. motive	10	2×5	32
	2nd subject	24	2×12	56
	,, ,,	17	$2 \times 8 + 1$	73
	3rd subject	22	2×11	95
	,, ,,	5	Extra for 2da Volta	100
Totals.		100		100
Durchführung	1st subject	26	2×13	126
	free	13	$2 \times 5 + 1 + 2$	139
	2nd subject	15	$2 \times 7 + 1$	154
	,, ,,	16	2×8	170
Totals.		70		170
Return	1st subject	3	$1\frac{1}{2} \times 2*$	173
	,, ,,	4	2×2	177
	,, ,,	7	$2 \times 2 + 3$	184
	,, .	4	2×2	188
	Int. motive	10	2×5	198
	2nd subject	14	2×7	212
	free	10	2×5	222
	2nd subject	17	$2 \times 8 + 1$	239
	3rd subject	26	2×13	265
Totals.		95		265
Coda poco sostenuto	1st subject	22	$4 + (3 \times 2)$ $2 + 3$ $(2 \times 2) + 3$	287
Tempo I	,, ,,	17	$1\frac{1}{2} \times 2*$ $2 \times 3 + 1$ $(2 + 1) 2 + 1 \frown$	304
Totals.		39		304

* Virtually two bars of $\frac{3}{2}$ as mentioned in par. 4.

wardly resembles only by a bold unison, the prophetic inner
meaning being the real feature of affinity. By comparing the
rhythmical statement of the opening with that of the return the
student will moreover perceive the first four bars to be really an
introduction. That its vigour is of the restless kind is quickly

Ex. 180. Op. 34. Allegro non troppo. First subject.

shown by the broadenings of Ex. 177 and 178, and further on
by the hasty entry of the intermediate motive which occupies
the very bar (23) normally due to cadence of the first theme;
whilst the intermediate motive itself, by hovering round the
dominant, also tells of the weightiness of the coming work. In

Ex. 181. Op. 34. Allegro non troppo. Intermediate motive.

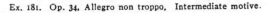

this motive we have the logical precursor of the real second subject (bar 33), which is stated in C sharp minor—a choice of key
giving ground for remark on account of some exaggerated
notions as to its irregularity. The student is invited to reflect
that the rise of a semitone, if considered as a mere expression of
earnestness, allows of C sharp being here regarded integrally as
C, and therefore as the dominant of the parent key. Moreover,
even if a literal acceptance of C sharp be insisted on, the relation
is far from remote, seeing that the dominant of that key is the
enharmonic equivalent of our relative major. The opinion that
both of these considerations were in Brahms's mind will receive
support from our examination of second and third subjects.

8. The second is a dual subject, the first member of which
features the notes of its chord (C sharp minor) very much in
the same way as the intermediate motive did the dominant of
the key. It is, however, the second member which goes to show

Ex. 182. Op. 34. Allegro non troppo. Second subject (a).

that Brahms had the semitonic upraising of his theme in mind;
for, having stated it in C sharp, he immediately proceeds to

Ex. 183. Op. 34, Allegro non troppo. Second subject (b).

repeat it practically in D.   And the view that he had also enharmonic equivalents in mind is supported by his third subject;
which by adopting the enharmonic key of D flat (bar 74) renders
the conclusion of his first section with natural return to the
opening announcement quite an easy matter.

Ex. 184. Op. 34, Allegro non troppo. Third subject.

9. We are aware of the danger of ascribing to composers intentions of which there is no direct intimation, but this is liable

to be reduced almost to vanishing point in cases where minute examination brings corroborative features to light. It may be mentioned therefore that in this case the following Durch-führung gives ample evidence that Brahms had set out to use what may be called the "frontier position" of the F minor key for all that it was worth. Thus, at the very outset, C flat, as seventh of D flat dominant chord, becomes third in G major (B), the relative minor of which (E) becomes seventh of F sharp dominant chord. This F sharp speedily becomes third in E flat minor (G flat), giving access to the relative major, G flat, which as F sharp acts in turn as dominant to B minor. The sojourn in this key is very transient, however, and the third of its dominant (A sharp) has now to serve as tonic in B flat minor. Considering that all this takes place within about forty bars, or little more than half of this short Durchführung (the remainder being of like nature), the student should easily form his opinion. He will probably find, as we do, that the principal beauty of this section, and certainly its special charm for the cultivated musician, lies in the wonderful grace with which the various keys are taken and left; the effect being not to weaken the consciousness of transition but to convert it into pleasure. Yet there is nothing showy or demonstrative about the whole process, the strong feature of which is that it admits no note without a meaning, in which respect it becomes a rather hard nut for those to crack who deny all intellectuality to the tonal language.

10. The extreme regularity of the return groups enables us to pass at once to the Coda, which, as usual, is entirely devoted to first subject. It opens "poco sostenuto" with a tonic pedal, and is of such purely contrapuntal character that but for the indications afforded by percussions of the pedal-note and by the various thematic entries its phrasing must have remained a mystery. How far this neutral effect may have been the composer's intention the student must judge for himself; bearing in mind that at all events the suspension of rhythmic demarcation during the "poco sostenuto" adds considerably to the effect of the outburst at the "Tempo primo" with which the movement concludes.

11. Epitome.

(a) Subjects. See Ex. 180 to 184.

(b) Key, F minor, changing to C sharp and F sharp minor.

(c) Time, common, without recognised change; for description of $\frac{3}{2}$ effects see par. 4 and Ex. 177 and 178.

(d) Length, 304 bars, or 394 with repeat of first section.

Ex. 185. Op. 34, Allegro non troppo. Outline.

FIRST SECTION			DURCHFÜHRUNG	RETURN			CODA
	100		70		95		29
I	II	III		I	II	III	
32	41	27		28	41	26	

II. ANDANTE, UN POCO ADAGIO.

12. This lyric movement is built upon a single subject—one which must for ever stand as model for the combination of melodic with rhythmic interest. Here the principal rhythm is

Ex. 186. Op. 34, Andante. Subject.

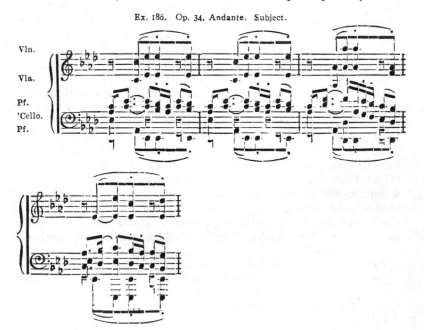

shown in the upper pianoforte part, in following which the closing modification for phrasing purposes must be observed; the opening rhythm being permanent but the divergence at the fourth bar of the phrase taking various forms throughout the piece with much effect.

13. The theme, by being systematically delivered in double notes, carries with it its own harmonisation; and is thus sufficiently independent of help to allow the other instruments to pursue their own rhythm. The characteristic of the latter is that it differs from and sympathises with the theme so equally that it has a double influence and therefore a power of suggestion capable of being variously and aptly applied. It is represented in Ex. 186 by the violin,* viola and piano-bass parts, the 'cello being held in reserve for the broader demarcations. That so simple a plan should result in this exquisite movement shows once more the marvellous power of consistency in design, but there are also other reasons for Brahms's success.

14. Though upon a single theme the piece contains no less than three intermediate motives; very different from one another in detail and pursuing very different vocations but all subordin-

RHYTHMICAL TABLE.

Ex. 187. Op. 34, Andante, un poco Adagio.

PORTION	MATERIAL	BARS	CONSISTING OF	EXTENDING TO
1st statement	Subject	16	4 × 4	16
	"	6	4 + 2	22
	1st motive	12	4 × 3	34
Middle section	2nd motive	20	4 × 5	54
	Subject (Subordinate rhythm only)	12	(4 + 2) 2	66
	" " "	8	4 × 2	74
	Subject	16	4 × 4	90
Return	"	14	4 × 3 + 2	104
	3rd motive	13	4 × 3 + 1	117
Coda	1st motive	8	4 × 2	125
	Cadence	1	1	126
Totals.		126		126

ate to the main theme in the same graceful sense. That they are not all equally prominent goes without saying and it is the first of these motives which figures most largely in the composition on

* The second violin is "tacet" for the time being, and is least active of all the parts, being principally used for amplification.

account of reappearing for Coda (at bar 118). This being in

Ex. 188. Op. 34, Andante. First intermediate motive.

diminuendo partly, but not wholly, accounts for its gentle character. Evidently the reason for the placidity of this motive is
that to the second is assigned, if not the vocation of Durchführung proper, at all events the maximum of motion and of
variety in bar-subdivisions. This second motive is therefore that

Ex. 189. Op. 34, Andante. Second intermediate motive.

which takes us most away from the key and for a moment seems
to hazard a sacrifice of the beautiful "oneness" of the movement.
Then it is, however, that the subordinate rhythm of the theme is
put to one of the uses mentioned in par. 13; for, appearing without its melody (at the "tempo primo," bar 55) it induces our
first mood by sheer power of suggestion. Had the subject itself
at once appeared the effect must have been rankly inartistic, but
the result of our being lulled by its subordinate rhythm for
twenty bars (in only two of which even the faintest suggestion

of the coming melody can be said to occur) makes the reappearance of the theme so different a matter that in the whole range of the classics it would be difficult to find a return made with greater grace—even leaving the refreshing novelty of means out of account.

15. The point for the student is that whilst the various auxiliary motives in no wise interfere with the prominence of the subject the vocation of each is well defined. Those of the first and second have already been pointed out, whilst that of the third may be said to be to play the same part to the return group as the first did to the main statement; and, as it thus

Ex. 190. Op. 34, Andante. Third motive.

naturally delays the return of the first motive for Coda, it partakes of the same gentle character.

16. Epitome.

(a) Subject. See Ex. 186.   Intermediate motives Ex. 188 to 190.

(b) Key, A flat, changing to E.

(c) Time ¾, without change.

(d) Length, 126 bars, no repeats.

Ex. 191. Op. 34, Andante. Outline.

STATEMENT	MIDDLE SECTION	RETURN	CODA
34	40	43*	9

III. SCHERZO, ALLEGRO.

17. A feature of this Scherzo is the frequent employment of the two-bar phrase in the dual capacity of being either an independent phrase or a component of one of four bars. A peculiar

* The " third intermediate motive " increases this Return by 13 bars. It would also be feasible, however, to account this motive part of the Coda, in which case the figures for Return and Coda would be 30 and 22 respectively.

vivacity would result from this under any circumstances; but the vivacity in this case receives considerable increase, due to the whimsical character thus given to overlappings of the phrase.

18. Another fantastic element is the frequency of change from $\frac{6}{8}$ to $\frac{2}{4}$; which, happening without any disturbance of the rhythmic pulsations, affects only the inner distribution of the bar-value. The piquancy of this effect has apparently been cultivated; because, happening occasionally at moments when only one two-bar component of the four-bar phrase has yet transpired, we should otherwise have to believe in a very remarkable coincidence. During the Trio, moreover, it even takes place at the fourth bar; where of course it is unexpected. Now, to make all this clear.

RHYTHMICAL TABLE.

Ex. 192. Op. 34, Scherzo. First section.

MATERIAL	BARS	CONSISTING OF	EXTEND-ING TO
Initial	2	2	2
1st subject	10	2 × 5 in 6/8	12
2nd subject	10	2 × 5 ,, 2/4	22
3rd subject	16	2 × 8 ,, 6/8	38
1st subject	18	2 × 9 ,, 6/8	56
2nd subject	10	2 × 5 ,, 2/4	66
Fugato on do.	9	2 × 4 + 1 in 2/4 ⎫	109
,, ,,	34	2 × 17 in 2/4 ⎭	
3rd subject	16	2 × 8 ,, 6/8	125
1st subject	32	2 × 16 ,, 6/8	157
2nd subject	36	2 × 18 ,, 2/4	193
	193		193

19. The first section is unusually rich in thematic material; having no less than three distinct subjects, two of which are fairly developed—one moreover giving rise to an interesting fugato. But the third subject is an exception to this treatment, for reasons soon to appear. No. 1, being highly syncopated, relies at its first pp appearance upon 'cello pizz. to provide the beat, and does not proceed far before giving us an instance of both the overlapping and change of *tempo* above mentioned. It may be well to exhibit these somewhat vividly in juxtaposi-

Ex. 193. Op. 34. Scherzo. First subject.

tion in order that the frolic of the second subject's premature
entry as well as the identity of rhythmic pulsation between $\frac{6}{8}$
and $\frac{4}{4}$ may be the better understood.

Ex. 194. Op. 34. Second subject.

20. In both first and second subjects the two-bar element is
stronger than the four, but in the third subject the four-bar demarcation is of the two the more distinctly assertive. The vocation of this third subject is evidently to approach the Trio in
style and thus give unity to the entire movement by avoiding all
Trio-contrast except that of comparative calm. By admitting
this view we also account for the two-fold appearance of this
theme during the first section. Each of its appearances is with

Ex. 195. Op. 34. Third subject.

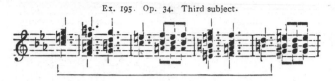

the full boldness of march character and each is confined to the
barest statement; both of these features being at all events consistent with the above suggestion.

21. Although the Trio has only one subject it manages by
introducing an intermediate motive to provide opportunity for
a change to $\frac{2}{4}$ in imitation of the first section. In the subject

RHYTHMICAL TABLE.

Ex. 196. Op. 34, Trio.

MATERIAL	BARS	CONSISTING OF	EXTEND-ING TO
Initial	1	1	194
Subject	28	4 × 7 in 6/8	222
,,	4	3 ., 6/8 1 ,, 2/4	226
Intermediate ⎰ Motive ⎱	16	4 × 3 ,, 2/4 3 ,, 2/4 1 ,, 6/8	242
Subject	16	4 × 4	258
Neutral bars joining by D.C. to initial	3	3	261
Totals.	68		261

itself however it is natural to find the four-bar influence pre-
ponderating, as broadening of the rhythmic outline is constantly in evidence where calmness is the object in view.

Ex. 197 Op 34. Trio-subject

Piano

'Cello.

The intermediate motive, having only a formal vocation need

Ex. 198. Op. 34, Trio. Intermediate motive.

only be quoted in brief; and the high development of the first section justifies the D.C. by rendering Coda unnecessary.

22. Epitome.

(*a*) Subjects. See Ex. 193-5, 197 and 198.

(*b*) Key, C minor. Trio in C major. During first section the third subject (for relation of which to Trio see text) is also stated in C major; though without recognised change of key.

(*c*) Time, $\frac{6}{8}$, with frequent changes to $\frac{2}{4}$ (see par. 18).

(*d*) Length, 261 bars. No repeats except D.C., including which the length is 454 bars.

Ex. 199. Op. 34, Scherzo. Outline.

FIRST SECTION			TRIO	DA CAPO
I 12	I 18	I 32	68	193
II 10	II 53*	II 36		
III 16	III 16			
—	—	—		
38	87	68		

The above exhibits the reason for there being no repeat of first section. It also shows the Trio-subject as taking the turn in rotation, which would otherwise have been occupied by third subject (to which it is related), and as exactly balancing the two previous subjects in point of length.

---

* Including the Fugato. See par. 19: also the Rhythmical Table, Ex. 192.

IV. FINALE.

Poco sostenuto (Introduction).

Allegro non troppo.

Presto non troppo.

23. This extraordinary movement seems to have so far eluded analysis that no one seems inclined to name its form.   This is not to say that there is any lack of information about it, but merely that none venture to say exactly what it is.   " It is Schumannesque" in regard to its opening; it is "better than a rondo" for a finale; it has a " Coda recalling the Scherzo"; it has "no Coda"; and its final presto "combines the functions both of Coda and development."   These are only a few criticisms, but they will serve to show that although the movement begets admiration on all sides it receives no baptism.

24. There is good reason for this.   A piece which hovers between forms, partly fulfilling the conditions of each, identifies itself with none.   From the opening of the Allegro we might fairly expect a lyric form; for it is a dual subject, both members of which are twice given; the whole being rounded off with a cadence-like working on tonic pedal.   But then an intermediate motive supervenes, leading to a second subject which shows no sign of close.   Surely this must be intended for a sonata movement, therefore.   Yet, if that be so, what can be the meaning of a third subject with such extraordinary development?   If the matter of this development were not so new and so totally devoid of relation to all the foregoing we might still perhaps cling to the old landmarks; but with the appearance of a fourth subject in capricious vein all thought of that must go.   At last, however, there is a ray of light in the reappearance of the theme; though it seems like catching at a straw to indulge the idea of such a gigantic rondo.   Still, forlorn as it is, this hope is quickly forbidden us; for the subordinate subjects are now developed at even greater length than in the first statement—to so great length in fact that return is out of question.   And to crown our

embarrassment a placid intermezzo now ushers in a presto of highly strenuous order—one to which all the glories of the Durchführung which ought to have been seem suddenly to have shifted.

25. It is the merest common-sense to conclude that had not such features been successful they would have been condemned as hazardous experiments. But success has hardened the ground upon which they stand, and through them we learn more of the real nature of form than would be possible from a composition in which traditions were precisely observed. The task of probing this matter being difficult we shall have to utilise every means of simplification.

26. The first of these will be the reduction of the rhythm to its lowest common denominator, the two-bar phrase. Not only is its flow rarely disturbed by extension or otherwise, but here, as in the scherzo, it is for the most part a component of larger phrases. The two-bar phrase therefore figures in our rhythmic summary as multiplicand, and in this case it will accordingly be from the multiplier that the larger rhythm must be sought. Thus an item such as 2 × 4 sufficiently indicates the eight-bar phrase made up of four times 2; whilst 2 × 2 + 2 as safely describes six bars consisting of a composite four-bar phrase extended by two.

27. The semitonic rise to which we referred in the opening movement (par. 8) now reappears in full demonstration of the neutrality of the semitone to which we could then but faintly allude, and as causing the key to remain vague until entry of

Ex 200. Op. 34. Finale. Introduction.

the dominant minor ninth on C at bar 13. From this point, and with a slight agitato resulting from triplet crotchets of accompaniment, we are borne on to bar 29, where the grade-rise is resumed. That the rise should now be sometimes of a full tone

indicates that caution is about to be renounced, and thus, at
bar 41, with our triplet motion faintly preserved, we cadence
dim. on the dominant *p.* The expression may appear strange,

RHYTHMICAL TABLE.

Ex. 201. Op. 34, Finale, Introduction.

MATERIAL	BARS	CONSISTING OF	EXTEND-ING TO
Semitonic progression	12	(2 + 2) 3	12
Cantabile	16	2 × 8	28
Diatonic progression	13	2 × 6 + 1	41
Totals	41		41

but the very blankness of this introduction is its perfection; in
that it attempts no statement, while showing a demeanour
betokening great things to come.

Ex. 202. Op. 34, Finale. First subject (*a*).

28. The first member of the Allegro opening-subject duly
accentuates chord notes, *à la* Brahms, and is accompanied in
semiquaver motion by piano. But the second member is of
totally different rhythmic character and is answerable for much
of the fulsomeness of treatment later on. It is the fondling of
this rhythm during the return which reduces the attention given
to the fourth subject in that section; and, even as it is, the return
(which is generally the shorter) exceeds the first statement by
sixteen bars. Whilst completely acknowledging success in this
instance however we must still hold that the custom of preferring
to expatiate in opening and abridge on return is the better.

Ex 203. Op. 34, Finale. First subject (b).

RHYTHMICAL TABLE.

Ex. 204. Op. 34, Finale. First section.

MATERIAL	BARS	CONSISTING OF	EXTEND-ING TO
1st subject (a)	8	2 × 4	49
,, (b)	4	2 × 2	53
,, (a)	12	2 × 6	65
,, (b)	6	2 × 3	71
,,	9	2 × 3 + 3	80
Int. motive	8	2 × 4	88
Bridge	6	2 × 2 + 2	94
2nd subject	14	2 × 6 + 2	108
,,	16	2 × 8	124
3rd subject	37	2 × 18 + 1	161
4th subject	22	2 × 10 + 2	183
Totals	142		183

29. It may now help to form the student's judgment if we contrast regular with irregular features. The former are presented by the second and third subjects as well as by the intermediate motive, all of which are treated in the usual way. On the other side we have the treatment of fragments of the first

Ex. 205. Op. 34. Second subject.

'Cello 8ve lower. Piano G pedal sustains.

Ex. 205. Op. 34. Third subject.

etc.

Ex. 207. Op. 34, Intermediate motive.

etc.

subject following that of its second member, and particularly the amplification of this department in the return; the practical abandonment of fourth subject; and the introduction of a separate concluding movement. We can only hope to turn this enquiry to good account by an explanation of these facts; but that, fortunately, does not lie very far to seek. It seems, for instance, fairly clear that Brahms's abundance of material brought him to the return (bar 183) without need of Durchführung. This would render it natural to give some over-

RHYTHMICAL TABLE.
Ex. 208. Op. 34, Finale. Second section.

MATERIAL	BARS	CONSISTING OF	EXTENDING TO
1st subject (a)	8	2 × 4	191
,, (b)	20	2 × 10	211
,,	12	2 × 6	223
,,	6	2 × 3	229
4th subject	9	2 × 4 + 1	238
Int. motive	8	2 × 4	246
Bridge	6	2 × 2 + 2	252
2nd subject	14	2 × 6 + 2	266
,,	16	2 × 8	282
3rd subject	39	2 × 18 + 3	321
Intermezzo	16	2 × 8 ⎫	341
Cadence	4	2 × 2 ⎭	
Totals	158		341

weight to the return, and equally natural to be so far still sensible of the difference between Durchführung and mere development as to desire relief in a final outburst. Whether these formal modifications were in contemplation from the first we cannot know, though from them we easily learn that coherence is ever a form in itself.

30. The affinity between the first subject in $\frac{2}{4}$ and that of the final presto in $\frac{6}{8}$ is best shown by exhibiting the note succession on parallel lines, where the different accommodation required for the two bar-values may be seen at one glance. The spas-

Ex. 209. Op. 34, Subjects of Finale, Presto and Allegro compared.

modic quaver motion (being by grades and therefore of easy application as counterpoint to almost any theme) naturally tempts the composer to give reminders of former movements, after which the second subject appears in plain-form innocence, just as if we did not know that the same counterpoint was immediately to follow. How this second subject is battled with

RHYTHMICAL TABLE.

Ex. 210. Op. 32, Finale. Presto.

MATERIAL	BARS	CONSISTING OF	EXTENDING TO
1st subject	24	(2 × 4) 3	365
,,	6	2 × 3	371
,,	24	(2 × 4) 3	395
2nd subject	8	2 × 4	403
,,	20	2 × 10	423
,,	32	(2 × 4) 4	455
,,	12	2 × 6	467
Conclusion	23	2 × 11 + 1	490
,,	2	2	492
	151		492

and ultimately caressed is not for words to tell, but with the pause (bar 467) we feel the close to be at hand. A friend is tenderly reminding us again and again of the semitonic progression, of the scherzo first subject and of the march-theme; and finally pleads sincerity by a hearty hand-shake—given with all the gusto of the Presto opening. Beethoven is the only composer whose name can be mentioned in company with this; which, in the words of Florence May, is "unquestionably one of the greatest works for piano and strings ever written." Averse to eulogistic criticism we are nevertheless taken captive by the

Ex. 211. Op. 34. Final Cadence.

warmth of Florence May's epitome here added by way of atone-
ment for our cold manner of dissection.

The imaginative power which surges through the first movement recalls
the daring of the youthful Johannes, guided now by a master hand. This
movement dominates the whole work. Its contrasted tones of passionate
splendour and scarcely less passionate mystery are reflected in the rich
pathos of the Andante, in the weird fitfulness of the Scherzo with its
heart-gripping Trio, and in the doubtful tranquillity of the Finale, bursting in the Coda into a rushing impetuosity which carries the movement
to a triumphant conclusion.

31. Epitome.

(a) Subjects. See Ex. 202, 203, 205, 206, 207 and 209.

(b) Key, F minor, changing to C sharp minor for the first
26 bars of the final Presto.

(c) Time. Introduction in allabeve, allegro in $\frac{2}{4}$, presto in $\frac{6}{8}$.

(d) Length, 492 bars, no repeats.

Ex 212. Op. 34, Outline of Finale.

INTRO.	FIRST SECTION			SECOND SECTION			CODA	
41	142			158			151	
	I	II	III	I	II	III	I	II
	53	30	59	69	30	59	54	97

It has been necessary for this simple outline to ignore the
fourth subject (for reasons which appear from the text) and to
credit all workings to one subject until appearance of the next.

OP. 36 SECOND STRING SEXTET IN G.

(For two Violins, two Violas and two Violoncellos.)

I. ALLEGRO NON TROPPO.
II. SCHERZO, ALLEGRO NON TROPPO.
III. POCO ADAGIO.
IV. POCO ALLEGRO.

Arranged by the Composer for Piano Duet.

Published by N. Simrock in 1866.

PRELIMINARY NOTE.

1. THE reader is invited to refer to the general observations upon the sextet given at par. 5 and 6 of Op. 18, and to assist their application to the present work by perusing the following quotations of opinion.

Alluding to the first performance, which took place in Vienna in 1867, Hadow makes the following remarks:

It is no discredit either to composer or audience that the new work was received with more astonishment than delight. The extremely elaborate polyphony, which is one of its distinguishing attributes, is probably too intricate to be comprehended by anyone at a single presentation, and we may infer that the public did not actually hear the melodies for the simple reason of their abundance.

The complaint of tunelessness which has been brought against every great composer in turn usually emanates from a criticism that cannot see the wood for the trees, and on this occasion it may be noted that Vienna saved its repute by wisely reserving judgment; and that Brahms's only repartee was to publish forthwith a delightful set of four-hand waltzes in which the top part had the tune and the other parts had the accompaniments, and everybody was satisfied.

2. The above, though written of Vienna, quite gives the universal opinion of this work. For the view held in England

(where it was first produced at a Monday Popular in 1879) we
may quote Antcliffe, as follows:

This sextet is more elaborate than the first and requires a knowledge
of the score before the beautiful significance of the somewhat involved
polyphony can be fully grasped.

and for the German view Ivan Knorr, who thus practically echoes
the same view:

It is to some degree of forbidding character, and the treasure it contains is not to be found on the surface. Like other creations of the
master it reveals it full beauty and significance only if we deeply
study it.

Brahms wrote only the two sextets, Op. 18 and 36, the contrast between which is extremely marked in every sense. Had
the intention been to provide the student with works offering
abundance of opportunity for comparison, it could scarcely have
been more effectively carried out.

I. ALLEGRO NON TROPPO.

3. It is a common trait of composers instinctively to reillus-
trate new sources of fertility upon which they happen to alight
by further works conceived in the same vein. This gives rise to
the probability of an affinity between works emanating from the
same period. For this the critic must be prepared.

4. When treating Op. 34 we remarked upon Brahms's use of
the semitonic rise and upon the grand service extracted from
the semitone's neutrality.* It was practically certain therefore
that we should soon re-encounter the same means of action, so
that the nature of the first subject in this instance need cause no
surprise. Not only is the semitonic rise of the chord of D (into
becoming E flat) evident enough, but the reason why E flat is
chosen is also evident, as we shall see.

5. That the movement is frankly of pastoral character and
that the *bourdonnement* (principally of viola but partaken of
also by other instruments) is a deliberate feature may be safely
assumed; the viola's solo entry and the long continuation of its
figure being also thus accounted for. But a viola pedal, as a
middle part, does not lie under quite the same conditions as a

---

* Op. 34, pars. 8 and 28.

bass pedal; if only that the latter by virtue of its depth can afford to disregard features of the upper harmony which a viola pedal cannot.

The semitonic wave of the viola figure is bound therefore to represent, either by its upper or lower note, the first, third or fifth of the chord; and the fact of the composer having this choice enables him to depress either the tonic or subdominant harmony or to raise that of the dominant by a semitone. It is

Ex. 213. The semitonic rise and fall.

contended that he has the power to do this in virtue of the neutrality of the semitone alone, and without incurring any charge of having modulated; whatever may be the aspect of notation. Thus, at (a) of Ex. 213, the tonic is depressed; at (b) the subdominant is depressed; and at (c) the dominant is raised; these changes occurring by adopting either the upper or lower note of the wave as part of the chord.

6. The variety imparted by the semitonic rise will now be evident if we compare the first subject as Brahms gives it with what it would have been otherwise.

Ex. 214. Op. 36, First subject, illustrating effect of semitonic rise.

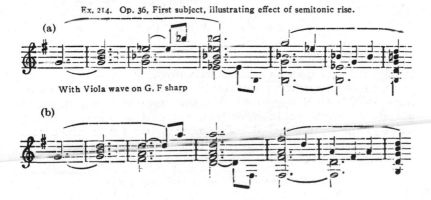

With Viola wave on G, F sharp

At *(a)* we have the Brahms outline and at *(b)* the same with the dominant unraised.

7. It goes without saying for those who know of Brahms's habitual consistency that the whole movement is characterised by a large use of this means, right up to the final cadence;

RHYTHMICAL TABLE.

Ex. 215.   Op. 36, Allegro non troppo.

PORTION	MATERIAL	BARS	CONSISTING OF	EXTEND-ING TO
1st section	Initial	2	2	2
	1st subject	6	4 + 2	8
	,, ,,	50	4 × 12 + 2	58
	,, ,,	36	4 × 9	94
	1st Int. motive	40	4 × 10	134
	2nd subject	28	4 × 7	162
	2nd Int. motive	50	4 × 12 + 2	212
	Bridge	18	4 × 4 + 2	230
Totals.		230		230
Durchführung	2da Volta	12	4 × 3	242
	1st subject	22	4 × 5 + 2	264
	,, ,,	76	4 × 19	340
	Bridge	16	4 × 4	356
Totals.		126		356
Return	1st subject	6	4 + 2	362
	,, ,,	50	4 × 12 + 2	412
	,, ,,	36	4 × 9	448
	1st Int. motive	34	4 × 8 + 2	482
	2nd subject	28	4 × 7	510
	2nd Int. motive	50	4 × 12 + 2	560
Totals.		204		560
Coda	1st subject	40	4 × 10	600
	Peroration	19	4 × 5 − 1	619
Totals.		59		619

though it is not quite in accordance with what we should expect to find him discarding the wave* on depression of the subdominant from C to B, apparently because, in order to use it, either a full-tone wave would have been required or removal of the wave to the semitone C B. The motive (bar 33) at which this occurs is also paltry, though it well enough serves its purpose of allowing the statement of first subject to be outdrawn.

---

* At bar 33 the viola wave suddenly ceases.

Ex. 216. Semitonic depression of sub-dominant,

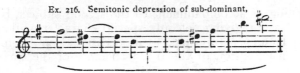

8. Very few words will suffice in mention of the rhythm, which is extremely simple. The phrases throughout the movement are of four-bar length, the only rhythmic interest consisting of the few shortenings or extensions which occur and emanate from one cause: viz., the vagueness created at the opening by the viola's two initial bars—compensated for by ingeniously shortening the second phrase to two bars (seven and eight). This may be readily perceived by comparing this phrase with bars 21-24 where it occurs without abridgement. All other deviations from the normal phrase-length are either traceable to the same cause or too obvious to require explanation.

The lack of rhythmic interest was however quite to be expected, as rhythmic and contrapuntal interests do not naturally combine, and the latter are present in a high degree.

9. The first intermediate motive serves to unite the first and second subjects, quaver-motion being preserved by repeated notes in one or other instrument. The apparent intention here

Ex. 217. First intermediate motive.

is to slacken the pulsation in view of the approach of second subject, but to do this without loss of actual motion. This view is strengthened by the semitonic wave appearing in augmentation in the same form; besides which the quaver-motion as such,

Ex. 218. Semitonic wave in augmentation, with repeated notes.

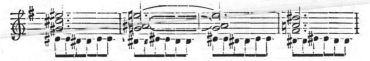

by continuing as accompaniment to the second subject, becomes
a leading feature, giving not only special character while it continues but lending significance to its occasional omission. This
occurs (with exception of the discontinuance of the wave men-

Ex. 219. Second subject.

1st 'Cello (2nd Viola and 2nd Violin have amplifying parts).

tioned in par. 7) only during the second intermediate motive—
or, as some would call it, third subject,* with the result of ren-

Ex. 220. Second Intermediate motive.

dering this theme more placid than the rest. This, of course, is
a perfectly conventional feature; as is also the gentle resumption
of the wave for the bridge-passages leading either to repeat or
Durchführung (bar 213).

Ex. 221. Bridge.

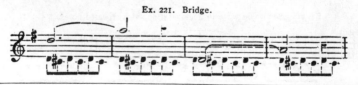

* It assumes the distinct character of a song group at bar 191.

10. An intermediate degree of motion is provided by syncopation simultaneously with crotchet-motion (bars 252-62) besides the two extreme degrees of semiquaver and triplet-quaver motion which occur just before the return (bars 337-56). Altogether there are therefore five degrees of motion, all so beautifully adapted to their situations as to leave no doubt of the objects severally in view.*

11. The Durchführung is rather short in comparison with the opening section, but it is full of interest—especially contrapuntal. A canon on the first subject in contrary motion makes its appearance during the bars (231 to 242) due for 2da volta and therefore before the real Durchführung begins; such marked character at the very parting of the ways being always a sign of serious business. It is curious that some should reproach the composer for having evidently had a contrapuntal scheme prepared beforehand and regard this as due to a lack of inspiration, forgetful of the fact that in the hands of an uninspired composer the same plan would have been of no avail. The scheme itself is in fact as nothing compared with the mastership displayed in carrying it out, which is of a nature completely to

Ex. 222. Canon.

defeat all attempt at description in words. How the semitonic wave is incessantly preserved (except when yielding for the sake of special effect to the other degrees of motion already mentioned); how at one time it is made to demonstrate the very climax of exultation of which the six instruments are capable and at another sinks to such a faint rustle that we can only just discern the rhythm of the first subject; how it modulates with

* Exception being made of the case mentioned in par. 7.

entire freedom returning with the utmost ease and bursts from all restraint only when within twenty bars of being called back into the fold of the return—all this must be studied in the score and heard in performance to be appreciated.

12. The return in spite of the new interest given to its material by the Durchführung does not, from the student point of view call for any remark but the coda (un poco sostenuto) is distinguished by its variety. After four placid bars it proceeds to broaden the interval of the wave passage in order to accommodate the depression of the sub-dominant,* after which we are

Ex. 223. Depression of Sub-dominant.

only held to the theme by inversions of it in the bass the working being otherwise free though purely in accordance with the general character of the movement. This unity of character is moreover happily illustrated by the final cadence; which, to the wise, is a lesson in itself.

Ex 224, Cadence.

With Viola wave G F♯ - - - - - - - - - - - - - -

13. Epitome.

(a) Subjects, see Ex. 214, 219. Intermediate motives, Ex. 217, 220.

(b) Key G, without recognised change.

(c) Time ¾, without change.

(d) Length, 619 bars or 833 with repeat of first section.

---

* See par. 5 to 7; Ex. 213 and 216.

Ex. 225. Op. 36, Outline of Allegro non troppo.

FIRST SECTION		DURCHFÜHRUNG	RETURN		CODA
230		126	204		59
I	II		I	II	
134	96		126	78	

II. SCHERZO, ALLEGRO NON TROPPO AND PRESTO GIOCOSO.

14. This movement is so completely lyric that its rhythmic summary presents no feature. This however only means that the special interest lies in other directions; for whenever Brahms's rhythm is ungarnished we may be sure that he has taken compensation for his self-denial. Such is the case here.

15. To begin with, the slightly Hungarian melody of the opening, by its grade series, bears promise of contrapuntal de-

Ex. 226. Op 36, Scherzo subject.

vice; and accordingly after the first sixteen bars (which it must be admitted are completed rather indifferently) the first violin and viola enter in octaves with a triplet-quaver melody—*tranquillo*, of course, as in keeping with that innocent demeanour to which we are accustomed whenever artful designs are afoot. Four bars take us from D minor to A minor, when the 'cello replies after the manner of a tonal fugue; which means that in four bars more the same melody, returned to D minor, is taken

RHYTHMICAL TABLE.
Ex. 227. Op. 36, Scherzo

PORTION	MATERIAL	BARS	CONSISTING OF	EXTEND- ING TO
1st section	Subject	16	4 × 4	16
	,,	12	4 × 3	28
	,,	5	4 + 1	33
	,,	1	2da Volta	34
	Episode	16	4 × 4	50
	,,	7	4 + 3	57
	,,	12	4 × 3	69
	Subject	14	4 × 3 + 2	83
	,,	12	4 × 3	95
	,,	14	4 × 3 + 2	109
	Codetta	12	4 × 3	121
Totals..		121		121
Trio	Subject	32	4 × 8	153
	Bridge	12	4 × 3	165
	Episode	16	4 × 4	181
	Bridge	12	4 × 3	193
	Subject	16	4 × 4	209
	,,	18	4 × 4 + 2	227
	Bridge	24	4 × 6	251
Totals.		251		251
Da Capo	As before	108	109 (less 1 for 1ma Volta)	359
	Codetta	13	12 (plus 1 for extension)	372
Totals.		372		372

up by second violin and viola. To this follows a little stretto formed out of a fragment of the same material—quite a miniature tonal fugue.

16. At first sight all this seems to have little to do with the opening—and all the less as the weakness of the second eight bars is due to the necessity of preparing for this triplet business. But the secret of the grade-theme and of the tonal-fughetta is easily found, and with it the reason of the composer having been able to indulge in inversions at will.

Ex. 228, Op. 36, Scherzo. Contrapuntal basis of Fughetta.

17. The student will readily recognise the above upper part as an inversion of the opening melody, but in the scherzo before us it is somewhat disguised—not only by syncopation but by the

Ex 229. Op. 36, Scherzo, continuation of subject.

combination of normal with triplet quavers. A highly important principle is here involved; for as much care has been taken to conceal relation to the theme as to secure it, and Brahms must therefore have been a believer in the latent influence of such traits, independently of their arousing direct attention. There will be no need to remind the student of similar perfections in the productions of nature, instances of which must at once occur to every reflective mind, and the question thus arises whether features only discoverable upon analysis have nevertheless an influence upon the listener.

18. By way of showing how this triplet subject was probably prepared we may mention that it is simply the inversion of a counterpoint the very simplicity of which would have been against it if used in its original form. The virtue of disguise is

Ex. 230. Op. 36, Scherzo. Evolution of Fughetta-subject.

therefore apparent, for by its aid puerility and vulgarity are avoided, whilst original connection is maintained. The same may be said of the episodial motive appearing shortly before the return (bar 51); which appears to be new, but is really nothing but the first bar of the theme followed by its own counterpoint.

Ex. 231. Op. 36, Scherzo. Composite episodial motive.

19. Before quitting this first section and in reference to the secret affinities mentioned in par. 17 we will draw attention to the episodial motive occurring after the repeat (bars 35-7) in order to be able to refer to it when treating the next movement,

Ex. 232. Op. 36, Scherzo. Affinity with coming movement.

the theme of which will explain the persistence of the intervals represented by these three opening notes.

20. The presto giocoso (which is really a trio though not so called) is thoroughly pastoral and of such delightful frankness as to soothe all suspicion of scientific guile : yet both the bridge

Ex. 233, Op. 36, Scherzo. Trio-subject.

which leads to its episodial motive and the motive itself are fraught with cunning. The former for example treats the sustained dominant with a counterpoint which though simple works up well in sequence. But after the episode and when the question is of returning to the subject the means employed is an inversion of the same counterpoint. Then again the episodial motive itself is nothing but the original subject in disguise

Ex. 234. Op. 36, Scherzo. Trio, contrapuntal bridge passage.

though it poses as being entirely new. But with mention of this
frolicsome diminution we must conclude; enough having now

Ex. 235. Op. 36, Scherzo. Trio. Intermediate motive.

etc.

been said. The return, though usually printed in full, is merely a
D.C.; with exception of the Codetta (" animato," bars 360 to 372)
which is an elaboration of bars 110 to 121.

21. Epitome.

(a) Subjects, see Exs. 226, 229, 231, 233 and 235.

(b) Key, G minor; presto giocoso (trio) in G major.

(c) Time, $\frac{2}{4}$; trio in $\frac{3}{4}$.

(d) Length, 372 bars or 404 with repeat of first part of first
section (first time).

Ex. 236. Op. 36, Scherzo. Outline.

FIRST SECTION AND CODA		TRIO	D.C. AND CODA	
121		130	121	
109*	12		108	13

III. POCO ADAGIO—PIU ANIMATO—ADAGIO.

22. In this case as in the corresponding section of Op. 18
Brahms has left the movement unnamed. It is therefore not
from him but by common consent that this adagio receives the
title of "Theme with Variations." Yet, though the earlier specimen may be said in this respect to admit of no doubt whatever,
the present seems to require the term to be applied with an eye
to the distinction between "variation" and "variation-form";
variations proper necessarily recalling their theme, whereas variation-form is a mere question of dimension. The present piece is
certainly in variation-form, the dimensional condition being well

* Add 32 for repeat of first part.

observed; but instead of each division harking back to the
theme for its cue it prefers for the most part to draw its inspiration from what has immediately gone before.

RHYTHMICAL TABLE.

Ex. 237. Op. 36, Poco Adagio.

MATERIAL	BARS	CONSISTING OF	EXTEND-ING TO
Theme	12	(2 × 2) 3	12
I	12	(2 × 2) 3	24
II	12	(2 × 2) 3	36
III	12	|:2 × 2:| |:2 × 4:|	48
IV	12	|:2 × 2:| |:2 × 4:|	60
Intermezzo	5	2 × 2 + 1	65
V	12	|:2 × 2:| |:4 × 2:|	77
Coda	10	2 × 5	87
Totals.	87		87

23. The merely occasional appearance of certain notes of the
theme in other sections does not give the latter the variation-
character, this feature being a mere expression of that unity to
which Brahms was so devoted. If, for example, the opening of

Ex 238. Op. 36, Poco Adagio Theme.

this theme discoverable as it is under all sorts of conditions were
to be held to confer the title of "variation" upon its surrounding we should have to consider whether this whole movement
were not a variation of the first allegro, which opens:

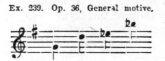

Ex. 239. Op. 36, General motive.

or, considering the passage quoted with Ex. 232, whether the
scherzo were not another. The fact is simply that Brahms has

used variation-form without variation character, by applying it to a movement which is perfectly continuous although set in divisions.

24. The first division (bar 13) opens with a chromatic melody, the first four notes of which actually repeat those just played by viola in the preceding cadence; besides exactly corresponding in character with the second violin part of the theme-accompaniment.* Vocations are here reversed therefore, for the 'cello accompaniment in this case is a diminution of the theme. But the great fact is that the whole proceeds with a new interest. It may

Ex. 240. Op. 36, Poco Adagio I.

be one begotten of the theme, but it leaves the theme behind; and will itself be left behind as soon as the form is filled and a new interest begotten in its stead.

25. This is precisely what happens. The diminutions seeming to create a desire for thematic quaver-motion we next find this motion applied to the material just quoted; whilst in the natural course of events we quickly pass on to triplet quavers in further satisfaction of the same desire. Obviously the triplet-

Ex. 241. Op. 36, Poco Adagio II.

* The same note-succession is also observable in Ex. 232.

quavers must now be made to furnish a new interest in due
order.   They might in fact be said to have appeared somewhat
prematurely as middle portion of the last division, and thus to
have almost compelled the adoption of semiquaver motion for
the next,* but this defect has been adroitly set aside by the
adoption of "piu animato" for No. 3; in addition to which a
further contrast is provided by the latter's martial character.
Naturally enough the semiquavers follow with No. 4, and, by

Ex. 242. Op. 36, Poco Adagio III.

way of logical continuation proceed to invert the last motive.
That the maximum of motion has now been reached however is
evident; for the middle portion of No. 4 opens calmly, and only
by a fine crescendo regains the enthusiasm of the march.   Not

Ex. 243. Op. 36, Poco Adagio IV.

only so, but a short intermezzo follows, the evident purpose of
which is to produce a slackening effect; for the leading notes of
the theme appear successively in crotchets and minims—and, as

---

* Compare this gradual increase of motion with par. 26 of Op. 18, in
reference to the old orders of counterpoint.

if for greater prominence, in the extreme parts.   In this way we
arrive at No. 5, the final Adagio in E major, which is practically
a semiquaver *moto perpetuo;* though it must be remembered that,
with incoming of the adagio, the note-value has been doubled.
Here all is gentleness; the part-writing full of interest and

Ex. 244. Op. 36, Poco Adagio **V.**

charm; allusions to the theme both frequent and of varied character—the whole concluding with a six-bar fall to the cadence,
pp.

   26. Epitome.

   (*a*) Theme. See Ex. 238; divisions I to V, see Ex. 240 to 244.

   (*b*) Key, E minor as to theme and divisions I to IV.   Division
V and Coda in E major.

   (*c*) Time, common.   Movement "poco adagio" as to theme
and divisions I, II.   Division III, IV "piu animato," division V
"adagio" ($\flat$ = $\flat$).

   (*d*) Length, eighty-seven bars, to which the following are to
be added for repeats :

Division III 4 + 8   12 ⎫
Division IV 4 + 8   12 ⎬ 36
Division V 4 + 8   12 ⎭

making 123 bars in all.

Ex. 245. Op. 36, Poco Adagio. Outline.

THEME	I	II	III	IV	INTERMEZZO	V	CODA
12	12	12	24	24	5	24	10

IV. POCO ALLEGRO.

27. This movement does not bear the same trace of painstaking, and has not the same finish as the others. Its construction, moreover, is somewhat erratic; the proportionate length of its sections being unusual without object, and some of its features being of undecided character. The opening for example, though occupying the place of first subject, is unable to sustain that character. Not only is its filigree out of keeping with what we expect from a main theme but it is turned to such subsidiary uses in course of the movement that we have felt compelled to regard it in our summary as a merely introductory motive.

Ex. 246. Finale. Poco Allegro, Introductory motive.

28. This motive interposes for a short time between the first and second subjects during the first statement but makes no such appearance on the return. It cannot be said to be missed, however, even by the keenest listener, as its figure is utilised in each case as accompaniment to second subject. It also appears during the short and inadequate Durchführung as accompaniment to a subject which returns later for the Coda "animato"; in addition to which it is somewhat in evidence during the bridge passages preceding the latter. Altogether therefore it may be said largely to characterise the movement notwithstanding the fact that it everywhere plays a subordinate part. Whatever may be said of a general utility motive in general its influence in this

case is equal to that of the special subject of Durchführung and Coda in imparting to the movement a marked individuality.

29. It is due to the influence of this filigree motive that little contrast is necessary between first and second subjects. The introduction or withdrawal of this busy semiquaver motion has in fact, and unfortunately, not only supplanted thematic contrasts but caused the Durchführung to be ill-developed and comparatively meaningless. As against all this it must be admitted

Ex. 247. Op. 36, Finale. Poco Allegro, first subject.

Ex. 248. Op. 36, Finale. Poco Allegro, second subject.

Ex. 249. Op. 36, Finale. Poco Allegro, Durchführung and Coda motive.

that it has abundance of what Joachim called "sound-charm," and that its lightness is specially suitable for the finale to a work of pastoral character. Upon the whole therefore it is perhaps wise not to regard this movement too seriously, for there is at least a possibility of its having been intended as a relief to the strained attention required for the previous movements.

30. Epitome.

(a) Subjects, see Ex. 246 to 249.

(b) Key, G; without change.

(c) Time, $\frac{9}{8}$; without change. The movement changes to "Animato" for Coda at bar 136.

(d) Length, 175 bars or 225 with repeat of first section.

RHYTHMICAL TABLE.
Ex. 250. Op. 36, Finale, Poco Allegro.

PORTION	MATERIAL	BARS	CONSISTING OF	EXTEND-ING TO
1st section	Int. motive	6	2×3	6
	1st subject	8	2×4	14
	,, ,,	8	2×4	22
	,, ,,	6	2×3	28
	Int. motive	5	$2 \times 2 + 1$	33
	2nd subject	10	2×5	43
	Bridge	8	2×4	51
		1	2da Volta	52
Totals.		52		52
Durchführung	Int. motive	18	2×9	70
	Bridge	10	2×5	80
Totals.		28		80
Return	1st subject	8	2×4	88
	,, ,,	8	2×4	96
	,, ,,	7	$2 \times 3 + 1$	103
	2nd subject	10	2×5	113
	Bridge	22	2×11	135
Totals.		55		135
Coda	Int. motive	24	2×12	159
		16	2×8	175
Totals.		40		175

Ex. 251. Op. 36, Finale, Poco Allegro. Outline.

*	FIRST SECTION	DURCHFÜHRUNG	RETURN	CODA
	52	28	55	40
	I II		I II	
6	27 19		23 32	

* Stands for Introductory Motive.

OP. 38. FIRST VIOLONCELLO SONATA IN E MINOR.

Dedicated to Dr. Joseph Gänsbacher.

I. Allegro non troppo.
II. Allegretto quasi menuetto.
III. Allegro.

Published by N. Simrock in 1866

I. ALLEGRO NON TROPPO.

THIS is the first of the works already mentioned as receiving only a concise account in order to allow of greater space being devoted to the more important scores. The reason for this special treatment is not that these works possess any less interest than others; but that in their case, on account either of the smallness of the score or the prominence of one instrument, the reader has less need of assistance.

1. Subjects.

Op. 38. Allegro non troppo.

Ex. 252. First subject.

Ex. 253. Second subject.

Ex. 254. Third subject.

2. Rhythmical tables.

Ex. 255. First Section and Durchführung.

PORTION	MATERIAL	BARS	CONSISTING OF	EXTEND-ING TO
1st section	1st subject	33	4 × 8 + 1	33
	,, ,,	24	4 × 6	57
	2nd subject	21	4 × 5 + 1	78
	3rd subject	12	4 × 3	90
		2	Extra for 2da Volta	92
Totals.		92		92
Durchführung	1st subject	23	4 × 5 + 3	115
	Free	12	4 × 3	127
	2nd subject	15	4 × 3 + 3	142
	3rd subject	21	4 × 5 + 1	163
Totals.		71		163

Ex. 256. Return and Coda.

PORTION	MATERIAL	BARS	CONSISTING OF	EXTEND-ING TO
Return	1st subject	33	4 × 8 + 1	196
	,, ,,	24	4 × 6	220
	2nd subject	21	4 × 5 + 1	241
	3rd subject	13	4 × 3 + 1	254
Totals.		91		254
Coda	1st subject	18	(3 × 4 + 2) 2	272
	Cadence	11	4 × 3 − 1	283
Totals.		29		283

3. Epitome.
(a) Subjects : Ex. 252 to 254.
(b) Key E minor, changing to B flat (bar 97) and F (bar 116) ;·

returning at bar 147. In E major from last entrance of third subject (bar 242) to the end.

(c) Time, common, without change. No change of movement.

(d) Length, 283 bars, or 371 with repeat of first section.

Ex. 257. Outline.

FIRST SECTION			DURCHFÜHRUNG	RETURN			CODA
92			71	91			29
I	II	III		I	II	III	
57	21	14		57	21	13	

4. Observations.

The general character is contrapuntal and to a certain extent heavy, relief however consisting of the marked contrast of subjects and of the lighter pianism introduced at bars 33, 143 and 197. The sadness of expression is intensified by the dominant minor being used for second subject, but somewhat modified by a third subject in the major. The executive work is equally divided, without particular display for either instrument.

II. ALLEGRETTO QUASI MENUETTO.

5. Subjects.

Ex. 258. First Section Subject.

Ex. 259. Trio-subject

6. Rhythmical tables.

Ex. 260. First Section.

MATERIAL	BARS	CONSISTING OF	EXTEND-ING TO
Initial	1	1	1
Subject	14	2 × 7	15
,,	14	2 × 7	29
,,	28	2 × 14	57
Initial	2	2	59
Subject	14	2 × 7	73
Cadence	2	2	75
Totals.	75		75

Ex. 261. Trio.

MATERIAL	BARS	CONSISTING OF	EXTEND-ING TO
Initial	2	2	77
Subject	11	2 × 5 + 1	88
,,	11	2 × 5 + 1	99
,,	8	2 × 4	107
,,	1	2da Volta	108
Bridge	6	2 × 3	114
Joining to opening initial for D.C.	1	1	115
Totals.	40		115

7. Epitome.
(a) Subjects. See Ex. 258, 259.
(b) Key, A minor. Trio in F sharp minor.
(c) Time, $\frac{3}{4}$.
(d) Length, 115 bars, or with repeats including D.C., 219 bars. No repeats in first section.

Ex. 262. Outline.

FIRST SECTION	TRIO	D.C.
75	40 + 29	75

8. Observations.
The interesting use made of initial bars is a feature of this movement. Also the canon-like dialogue between 'cello and

piano commencing at bar 38; and the almost incessant quaver-motion of the Trio. The plan is also to be noted of paraphrasing the first section in lieu of repeats, and of utilising the miniature Durchführung and Coda thus provided in lieu of an additional coda section.

III. ALLEGRO.

9. Subjects (placed in one key for simultaneous reading).

Ex. 263. First subject.

etc.

Ex. 264. Second subject.

etc.

Ex. 265. Third subject.

etc.

10. Rhythmical table.

The three subjects of this fugal movement form collectively a single contrapuntal scheme, and are therefore not introduced in ordinary rotation; but are mingled, and, generally speaking, capriciously combined; their suitability to which treatment may be at once ascertained by reading Examples 263-5 in score, as indicated by brace. The following table therefore must be taken as no more than an attempt to show that, notwithstanding this, an affinity with sonata form is traceable. The portions marked "free" are composed either of counterpoints previously employed or of expansions in the spirit of one or other of the subjects.

11. Epitome.

(a) Subjects. See Ex. 263-265.

(b) Key, E minor, without recognised change.

(c) Time, common, without change. Change to "piu presto" at bar 175.

(d) Length, 198 bars; no repeats.

12. Observations.

This is unquestionably the finest movement of the work, and one which displays Brahms to advantage in his special power to

RHYTHMICAL TABLE.

Ex. 266. Op. 28, Allegro (finale).

PORTION	MATERIAL	BARS	CONSISTING OF	EXTEND-ING TO
Entry	1st subject	8	4 × 2	8
1st section	All subjects	7	4 + 3	15
	,, ,,	15	4 × 3 + 3	30
	,, ,.	22	4 × 5 + 2	52
	3rd subject	12	(4 + 2) 2	64
	Free	11	4 × 2 + 3	75
Totals.		67		75
Durchführung	1st subject	11	4 × 2 + 3	86
	.. ,,	8	4 × 2	94
	2nd subject	10	4 × 2 + 2	104
	,, ,,	10	4 + 2 + 4	
	Free	21	4 × 4 + 1 + 4	135
Totals.		60		135
Return	1st subject	7	4 + 3	142
	,, ,,	15	4 × 3 + 3	157
	,, ,,	17	4 × 4 + 1	174
Totals.		39		174
Coda	Free	14	4 × 3 + ♮	188
	,,	8	4 × 2	196
	Cadence	2	2	198
Totals.		24		198

Ex. 267. Outline (on the tentative basis of the Rhythmical Table, Ex. 266).

ENTRY	FIRST SECTION			DURCHFÜHRUNG			RETURN AND CODA	
8	67			60			63	
	I (etc.)	III	free	I	II	free	Return	Coda
	44	12	11	19	20	21	39	24

compel mere contrapuntal device into artistic service. It is of
highly spirited and exciting character, and may be regarded as
ending the special mood under which this work and Op. 36 were
alike composed. Some have even traced the inspiration for the
present subject to the " piu animato " of the latter's third movement; regarding which the student can form his own opinion by
referring to Op. 36, Ex. 242.

OP. 40.   SECOND PIANO TRIO.

(For Piano, Violin and Horn.)*

I. ANDANTE.
II. SCHERZO, ALLEGRO.
III. ADAGIO MESTO.
IV. FINALE, ALLEGRO CON BRIO.

Published by N. Simrock in 1868.

PRELIMINARY NOTE.

1. THIS is one of the group of works composed after Brahms's resignation in 1864 of his post as director of the Vienna Choral Society. His own opinion of it as well as his decided preference for the wald-horn are conveyed by the following observations to Dietrich :

> For a quartet evening I can with a good conscience recommend my horn Trio, and your horn-player would do me a great favour if he would do like the Carlsruhe man and practise the French horn for some weeks beforehand, so as to be able to play it on that.

2. That Brahms was not only technically an expert in writing for the horn but that he thoroughly entered into the poetry of its utterance is here evident, and it therefore becomes the more remarkable that the transference of the horn-part to viola or violoncello should have had his approval. Nothing could more strongly show his concentration upon the sense of his music than this willingness to confide a part so beautifully adapted to one instrument to interpretation by another.

3. Excepting the Clarinet Trio, Quintet and Sonatas, Op. 114, 115 and 120 respectively, to the composition of which Brahms

---

* Or viola, or violoncello.

was induced by the excellence of Mühlfeld's playing, this is the
only chamber work in which a wind instrument figures. Even
this moreover may be partly accounted for by early associations,
so that it does not really infringe upon the composer's world, so
to speak, of chamber music for piano and strings. It is not surprising therefore to find such works preceded by some special
incentive to their production and Dietrich tells us that, one day,
when Brahms and he were wandering together on the wooded
heights above Baden-Baden, the composer showed him the spot
where the idea of this trio first came into his mind. The anec-
dote is interesting to those who know the Schwarzwald influence
even upon the generally unimpressionable traveller.

I. ANDANTE.

4. The form of this movement has been a puzzle to many.
Deiters thought that it might probably have been suggested by
that of Beethoven's Piano Sonata, Op. 54, commencing :

Ex. 268. Beethoven, Op. 54.

but this view is not supported by the result of a close examination. As usual, when Brahms seems for the moment to have
deserted the beaten track, we are first of all struck by the coherence of his work and set wondering how, in the face of what
seems to be entire caprice, this can have been attained. But it is
always open to those who are not content to remain mystified,
but who prefer to take the trouble to sift matters, to discover that
in every such case Brahms has practically made his own form;
and that the cohesion we remark is really no marvel whatever,
but simply the result of the studied symmetry of his new arrangement. It should not be forgotten that in such matters our
hearts are in advance of our heads and that we can at once feel
effects, to understand the reasons for which requires much pati-
ence and study.

5. It will repay the reader to consider the case of two contrasted subjects each expanded by the aid of its own intermediate motive, but the second also rounded off in dignified style.
Supposing that for convenience we call this rounding off a third
subject; then (adopting the abbreviations I, II, III, for subjects
and M1, M2 for motives) we have the form of this movement in
a nutshell.

Ex. 269.   Op. 40, Form of first movement.

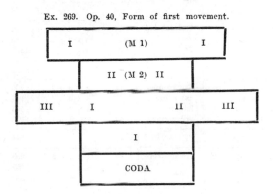

6. Substituting dimensions for description we have the same
result; which of course agrees with that shown by the rhythmical

Ex. 270.   Op. 40, First movement (dimensions).

Bars.

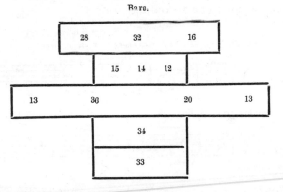

table.   The reader who possesses the score will at once identify
the subjects and motives alluded to, and no doubt come to a
conclusion as to the connection between the singularity of the

RHYTHMICAL TABLE.

Ex. 271. Op. 40, First movement.

PORTION	MATERIAL	BARS	CONSISTING OF	EXTEND-ING TO
1st section	1st subject	28	4 × 7	28
,, ,,	Motive 1	32	4 × 8	60
,, ,,	1st subject	16	4 × 4	76
Totals.		76		76
2nd section	2nd subject	15	4 × 3 + 3	91
,, ,,	Motive 2	14	4 × 3 + 2	105
,, ,,	2nd subject	12	4 × 3	117
Totals.		41		117
Bridge	3rd subject	13	4 × 3 + 1	130
3rd section	1st subject	36	4 × 9	166
,, .,	2nd subject	20	4 × 3	186
Bridge	3rd subject	13	4 × 3 + 1	199
Totals.		82		199
Return and Coda	1st subject	34	4 × 8 + 2	233
,, ,, ,,	Coda {	32	4 × 8	265
		1	1	266
Totals.		67		266

form adopted and the marked contrast between the two principal subjects. In Brahms nothing happens without a motive, and the fact of a second subject in a new time and degree of movement is one in any event to be accounted for.

Ex 272. Op. 40, First movement. (First subject.)

Andante

Ex. 273. Op. 40, First movement. (Second subject.)

poco più animato

6. What we have chosen to call a third subject is really a development of the second, to which however it is superior in dignity, besides otherwise possessing importance in the movement. In this respect it differs from the "motives," the distin-

Ex. 274. Op. 40, First movement. (Third subject.)

guishing feature of which is that they occur only once, and that generally for a more subordinate purpose. It is true that the first intermediate motive may be said to furnish material for the Coda, but the connection is vague, and the Coda equally traceable to first subject.

Ex. 275. Op. 40, First intermediate motive.

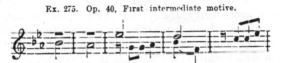

7. The great importance of the second subject in this movement is such that not only is the third subject an offshoot of its conclusion but the second intermediate motive a play upon its initial bar. This motive starts off (bar 92) with a pianoforte phrase; disregarding which (for brevity's sake) we find the rhythm of the second subject-opening converted into a sigh for the horn, sympathetic violin reply to which speedily develops into a glowing fervour. It is therefore scarcely to be wondered at that some critics have regarded the opening *andante* as a mere introduction; which however it is not.

Ex. 276. Op. 40, Second intermediate motive.

Pf. (both hands)

8. This completes our rigid survey of the movement; the full appreciation of which requires, however, that we should approach its detail even more closely. In the first place it is evident that this trio was, so to speak, written "round" the horn; for in no other way can the singular appropriateness of the material (not necessarily always as subject, but sometimes also as counter subject), be adequately accounted for. How far the exigencies of the same instrument may have influenced the form is a question which can be better judged after review of the other movements, but their influence upon the character and "atmosphere" is obvious from the very opening. It is by regard to these conditions that a less assertive factor, such as the horn, is enabled to hold its own with piano and violin and thus beget a special interest. The question of instrumentation should also not be lost sight of by those who are concerned to defend Brahms upon this point.

9. It follows that throughout the movement the violin and pianoforte parts are somewhat restrained; but herein lies also a charm, as neither of them suffer any loss of interest on that account. The piano though mostly subordinate is full of ingenious figurations, whilst the violin's melodic interest is continually increased by a perfect co-operation with the horn part. Only those who know of the numerous obligations devolving upon the composer of a work of this kind can sufficiently admire the masterly way in which they have been fulfilled.

10. Epitome.

(a) Subjects. See Ex. 272-276.

(b) Key, E flat; changing to G minor for second subject, returning to E flat for first subject, then passing to G flat for second subject and finally to E flat for coda.

(c) Time, $\frac{2}{4}$ for first subject and first intermediate motive. $\frac{9}{8}$

for second and third subjects and for second intermediate motive. Coda, being a development of first subject remains in $\frac{2}{4}$. *(d)* Length, 266 bars; no repeats.

Ex. 277. Op. 40, First movement. Outline.

FIRST SECTION	SECOND SECTION	THIRD SECTION	CODA
76	41	82	67

II. SCHERZO.

Allegro and Molto meno Allegro.

11. This movement introduces us to a rhythmic novelty of which no instance has yet occurred. Hitherto extensions of the phrase have been of less dimension than the phrase itself—a common example being the addition of one, or at most two, bars to the four-bar phrase. The conception of an addition of like time-value with the phrase itself would seem in most cases to be absurd, for the reason that such equality might very naturally entitle the addition to be considered as a new phrase. There is however no real conflict between the two views, for the added portion may easily be a new phrase in the mere time sense and still be a novel feature of the rhythmical scheme. If, for exam-

Ex. 278. Op. 40, Scherzo. First subject.

ple, we examine the opening four phrases in this case, we shall easily perceive that the fourth is really an addition, notwithstanding its time-equality with the other phrases. The distinc-

tion is important; as the speciality of the phrase in question is
to produce an effect of rhythmic variety (and with it a charming
pastoral tint) quite independently of any intrusion upon the
four-bar flow—the latter continuing throughout, with the single
exception of a two-bar extension immediately before the return
(bars 161-2).

12. Another rhythmic trait, co-operating with the one just
mentioned to impart to this movement an atmosphere of rural
gaiety, is the freedom with which the phrases are grouped. After
the four phrases above quoted six inseparable phrases go to complete the subject and to bring us to the motive acting as bridge

Ex. 279. Op. 40, Scherzo. First intermediate motive.

8ve lower - - - - - - - - - - - - - - -

to second subject. But here the grouping is 3, 2; or (if we construe the third phrase of the above as an addition) 2 + 1 + 2.
This accounts for bars 41 to 60; the point being to observe the
absence of the conventional four-phrase group, the conspicuous
rarity of which throughout the movement contributes so much to
its special character.

13. The second subject is a characteristic horn melody which
we only dignify as "subject" on account of its occurring twice

Ex. 280. Op. 40, Scherzo. Second subject.

within the movement. It cannot be said on either occasion to
receive any development; though it certainly supplies material
for the codetta with which the first section concludes.

14. A second intermediate motive (employed to introduce the miniature Durchführung commencing with bar 121) is principally remarkable for the pompousness with which it asserts the $\frac{2}{4}$ pulsation practically alone. It consists altogether of five phrases; of which one will suffice for quotation, by way of showing its identity with the extension of the opening subject.

Ex. 281. Op. 40, Second intermediate motive.

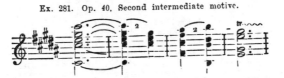

15. The symmetry of the first section, notwithstanding the apparent capriciousness of the phrase-groups, may be conveniently exhibited in number of phrases; which of course only require multiplication by four to arrive at the number of bars involved. This reduction of the rhythmical table to miniature proportions

Ex. 282. Op. 40, Scherzo. First section

1st subject	1st motive	2nd subject	1st subject	2nd motive	Quasi Durchführung"	1st subject	1st motive	1st subject	Bridge	Coda
	5	5	5	5		7	2	3	6	
10		20			10½		18			10¾

is an advisable course when, in consequence of the bars being short, they represent only the time-value of an ordinary beat. In such cases it is for the student to regard the phrase as a " bar of bars "—that is to say, as a large bar of which each beat is a smaller bar. But, for obvious reasons, we cannot repeat this mode of illustration, which is offered merely as a general guide to the student on such occasions.

16. The trio is approached by a bridge-passage, of which the first or initial bar is simply a replacement of that already deducted from the last phrase of the opening section; its contents being a perfunctory eight-bar E flat dominant arpeggio for

---

* The term is our own, used simply for purposes of explanation.

RHYTHMICAL TABLE.*

Ex. 283. Op. 40, Scherzo.

PORTION	MATERIAL	BARS	CONSISTING OF	EXTEND- ING TO
Opening	1st subject	16	4 × 3 + 4	16
	,, ,,	24	4 × 6	40
,,	1st motive	20	$\begin{cases} 4 \times 2 + 4 \\ 4 \times 2 \end{cases}$	60
	2nd subject	20	4 × 5	80
	1st subject	20	4 × 5	100
	2nd motive	20	4 × 5	120
Development		42	4 × 10 + 2	162
Return	1st subject	8	4 × 2	170
		20	4 × 5	190
		20	$\begin{cases} 4 \times 2 + 4 \\ 4 + 4 \end{cases}$	210
		24	$\begin{cases} 4 \times 4 \\ 4 \times 2 \end{cases}$	234
Coda	2nd subject	43	$\begin{cases} 4 \times 10 \\ 4 - 1 \end{cases}$	277
Trio	Initial	1	$\begin{cases} 1 \\ 4 + 2 \end{cases}$	286
	Bridge	8		
	Subject	32	4 × 8	318
	,,	32	4 × 8	350
	Bridge	12	4 × 3	362

piano with string holding-note—by the way, a woeful piece of emptiness for Brahms. The trio-subject is mournful and on that account of serviceable contrast with the main section, especially

Ex. 284. Op. 40, Scherzo. Trio-subject.

at the slower *tempo.* But another element of contrast is the rest-lessness due to an entire lack of full cadence throughout the whole seventy-six bars of which the trio consists. All we have to listen to is an uninterrupted succession of four-bar phrases, never arriving at any sort of rhythmical conclusion, and many of them ending upon light beats. The result is an expression of

---

* The totals are not drawn in this case, as (with the exception of the Trio) the divisions are more or less tentative.

timidity and indecision which may or may not be enjoyable but is certainly individualistic. Moreover, the subject being obviously one which lends itself to sequence the question arises whether such treatment of it may not have been carried too far. The sequences are interesting, no doubt; but there is so little difference of character between the horn and violin parts (which move together throughout) that only the shortness of the section saves it from becoming tedious.

17. Epitome.

(*a*) Subjects. See Ex. 278-81 and 284.

(*b*) Key, E flat, changing to B (bar 97) and returning to E flat. Trio in A flat minor, with D.C. and no coda. The recognised key-changes occur as convenient for notation and not at rhythmical divisions.

(*c*) Time, $\frac{3}{4}$, without change. For the practical admixture of $\frac{2}{4}$ in first section see text.

(*d*) Length, 362 bars, or 639 with D.C.

Ex. 285. Op. 40, Scherzo. Outline.

FIRST SECTION		TRIO	D.C.
277		85	277
40 80 42 72 43*		9 64 12	

III. ADAGIO MESTO.

18. Here we have another instance of Brahms's inventiveness in the matter of form. The whole movement consists of eighty-six bars, or eighty-four without the final chord; and there are two subjects, the treatment of which is so delightfully varied that unless we approach the matter unemotionally the framework upon which they depend is quite certain to escape our observation. Rhythmical summary shows the eighty-four bars to be cleanly cut into portions of eighteen, twenty-four and eighteen,

---

* For elucidation of these figures see Ex. 282.

RHYTHMICAL TABLE.

Ex. 286. Op. 40, Adagio mesto.

MATERIAL	BARS	CONSISTING OF	EXTEND-ING TO
1st subject	4	2 × 2	4
,, ,,	4	2 × 2	8
,, ,,	6	2 × 3	14
,, ,,	4	2 × 2	18
Totals.	18		18
2nd subject	8	2 × 4	26
,, ,,	5	2 × 2 + 1	31
,, ,,	11	2 × 5 + 1	42
Totals.	24		42
1st subject	4	2 × 2	46
,, ,,	4	2 × 2	50
,, ,,	6	2 × 3	56
,, ,,	4	2 × 2	60
Totals.	18		60
2nd subject	8	2 × 4	68
1st subject	5	2 × 2 + 1	73
,, ,,	11	$\begin{cases} 2+1 \\ 2 \times 3 \end{cases}$	84
Totals.	24		84
Close	2	2	86

twenty-four (devoted respectively to subjects one, two and one, two), the only deviation being one which we should naturally expect—viz., a reserve of the concluding space for return to first subject. That it should be possible to construct a movement on such purely mechanical lines, and yet by taking advantage of rhythmic subordinate features conceal the fact (save from the painstaking analyst), is a marvel in itself.

19. If we examine the two subjects simultaneously we shall find that although outwardly dissimilar they possess one important rhythmic feature in common; viz., that although in obvious two-bar phrases, these are alternately strong and weak. Thus, the movement might with equal correctness have been construed as in phrases of double length; though it is equally true that the single bars have a peculiar rhythmical completeness, enabling, for example, the first two and last two bars of the first subject to be practically repeated without interference with the phrase. The com-

Ex. 287. Op. 40, Adagio mesto. First subject.

Ex. 288. Op. 40, Adagio mesto. Second subject.

Horn 8ve lower   ⌣ Vln.   Pf. 8ves

bination of these two features amounts to a rhythmic pliability;
giving the composer a liberty which not only leaves no need to
adopt a less rigid outline but gives every reason to adhere to a
rectangular design—coherence being likely otherwise to become
imperilled. The inventiveness mentioned therefore consists in
the application of a rhapsodical style to a perfectly rigid design.

20. The term, "rhapsodical style," is used advisedly, and in
preference to "rhapsody"; with the intention of distinguishing
between emotion, the expression of which is kept within artistic
bounds, and that which, when subjected to analysis, seems rather
to betoken the emotion of the insane. The one is entitled to our
full respect, for it is an agitation associated with mental consciousness; whilst the other can at most claim but a sympathetic
indulgence. The wildness natural to rhapsody may impress the
crowd, but the beauty of a disciplined rhapsodical style appeals
more powerfully to the educated musician; and in this case, for
instance, the stringendo from bar 31—the second return at bar
69—the various extensions indicated in our table—the phrase
conclusions upon light beats—and the hushed entry (first return
bar 43) *quasi niente* of the theme after delay by a written out
rallentando converting one bar into two—all combine to bring
before us an emotion justified by truth in declamation. The
general effect is naturally sombre; and the piano part, though in
one sense elaborate, absolutely undemonstrative. The violin part
lies low; but this, being almost a consequence of the combination, need not be counted as a feature of the movement.

21.. Epitome.

(*a*) Subjects. See Ex. 287, 288.

(*b*) Key, E flat minor, without change.

(*c*) Time, $\frac{6}{8}$, with one bar (26) of $\frac{9}{8}$.

(*d*) Length, 86 bars, no repeats.

Ex. 289. Op. 40, Adagio mesto. Outline.

I	II	I	II	I	CLOSE
18	24	18	24		2

IV. FINALE.

Allegro con brio.

22. It is usual to consider this a Haydnish movement and there are here (as in the finale of Op. 18) some traits which undoubtedly and somewhat vividly recall "Papa." Foremost among these is fidelity to thematic material; though perhaps, to many, the jollity of the movement may be still more remindful. The general unpretentiousness and natural outflow of the contrasted melodies also help to remind us of the old master; and even to these might be added minor traits—if there were any utility in calling attention to such resemblances.

23. But, indeed, the contrary is really the case. Resemblances such as those mentioned must necessarily lie upon the surface, or they would not appeal to every one; and as we cannot suppose Brahms to have suddenly forsworn himself in this movement, the question is rather to note the *differences* between him and Haydn; which survive in spite of both masters working to a similar conception.

24. A very long story might be made of these differences if we were to include modernisms—either in harmonic or melodic inflection. But these can scarcely be said to form a Brahms subject at all, as they are more or less characteristic of all composition at the present day; besides which we are all so conscious of them that no benefit is to be derived from pointing them out. What we are not so conscious of is the difference between the phrase construction in the two cases; and how, notwithstanding close similarity in the broader rhythmic outline, there may be very considerable subordinate rhythmic distinctions.

25. A glance at the summary will show that nothing could be more orderly than the general scheme, but nothing more varied

RHYTHMICAL TABLE.

Ex. 290. Op. 40, Finale.

PORTION	MATERIAL	BARS	CONSISTING OF	EXTENDING TO
1st section	1st subject	16	$\begin{cases} (2+1+1)\,3 \\ 2+2 \end{cases}$	16
	1st. Int. motive	28	$\begin{cases} (1+1+2)\,5 \\ 2 \times 4 \end{cases}$	44
	2nd subject	16	$(2+2)\,4$	60
	Bridge	6	2×3	66
	2nd Int. motive	16	$\begin{cases} 2 \times 4 \\ 4 \times 2 \end{cases}$	82
	3rd subject	16	4×4	98
Totals.		98		98
Durchführung	2da Volta	8		106
	Bridge	6	2×3	112
	New subject	20	$(2 \times 4 + 2)\,2$	132
	,, ,,	12	$2 \times 5 + 2$	144
	,, ,,	24	$(2 \times 4)\,3$	168
Totals.		70		168
Return	1st subject	16	$\begin{cases} (2+1+1)\,3 \\ 2+2 \end{cases}$	184
	1st Int. motive	28	$\begin{cases} (1+1+2)\,5 \\ 2 \times 4 \end{cases}$	212
	2nd subject	16	$(2+2)\,4$	228
	Bridge	6	2×3	234
	2nd Int. motive	16	$\begin{cases} 2 \times 4 \\ 4 \times 2 \end{cases}$	250
	3rd subject	16	4×4	266
Totals.		98		266
Coda	Bridge	10	2×5	276
	1st subject	16	2×8	292
	,, ,,	3	$2 + 1 \frown$	295
Totals.		29		295

and capricious than the phrase construction. There is for example the strictest fidelity to the four-bar phrase; but a reference to the subjects themselves will convince the reader that he can scarcely do otherwise than construe them as sometimes a continuous four bars, sometimes a 2 + 2, sometimes a 2 + 1 + 1 and sometimes a 1 + 1 + 2, occasionally also the demarcation becomes so slight that two four-bar phrases show a disposition to join into one of eight; and that all this is intentional is clearly proved by the several features being each characteristic of its own ındividual theme. Thus the first subject is formed of 2 + 1 + 1 phrases :

Ex. 291. Op 40, Finale. First subject.

but the intermediate motive used in its development escapes monotony by reversing this arrangement. Moreover the future freshness of a return to first subject is safeguarded by the construction 1 + 1 + 2, once adopted, being retained.

Ex. 292. Op. 40, Finale First intermediate motive.

This therefore continues until introduction of the second subject; which, as requiring to be more sustained, is naturally in phrases of 2 + 2 The fact of the divisions being not even

Ex. 293. Op. 40, Finale. Second subject.

B flat

longer than two bars is, in itself, an indication that there is to be
a third subject, for which the full phrase-length is reserved.
Obviously therefore the 2 + 2 arrangement cannot be disturbed
by the intermediate motive which follows; as in whichever direction this might be done, the effect would be to spoil the incoming
of the third subject.

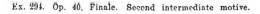

Ex. 294. Op. 40, Finale. Second intermediate motive.

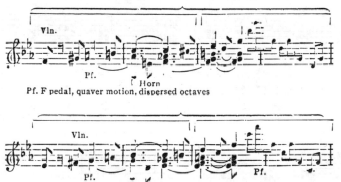

Pf. F pedal, quaver motion, dispersed octaves

26. Arrival at the third subject may now be utilised in order
to point out that changes, so far, have been in the direction of

Ex. 295. Op. 40, Finale. Third subject

lengthening the phrase-divisions   This does not, of course,
confer the least obligation upon the composer as to what he may
choose to do during his Durchführung; but we must admit
nevertheless that it was a very natural procedure for him to
employ his freedom in still increasing the continuity of phrase.
The Durchführung is somewhat short—this being one of the
movement's unpretentious features; and the sustained phrase is
also well in keeping with the desire for restraint.   At all events,
and whatever may have been the intention, the material of the
Durchführung is principally new, and in cantabile phrases which
may be easily construed as of eight-bar length.

Ex. 296. Op. 40, Finale. Durchführung.

27. The return groups are managed with such regularity as to
occupy precisely the same number of bars as the first statement
(1 to 98 as compared with 176 to 266); whilst the Coda though
effective is equally devoid of fresh feature.   As to the movement
generally its characteristic hunting phrases and frequent
employment of pedal basses, added to the rhythmic features
mentioned sufficiently stamp it as an appropriate finale to a
work of this kind; one of the principal merits of which is
restraint of the composer's exuberance to exact measure of the
combination chosen.

28. Epitome.

(*a*) Subjects, see Ex. 291 to 296.

(*b*) Key, E flat; copious modulations but no recognised change.

(*c*) Time $\frac{6}{8}$, without change.

(*d*) Length 295 bars, or 385 bars with repeat of first section.

Ex. 297. Op. 40, Finale. Outline.

FIRST SECTION	DURCHFÜHRUNG	RETURN	CODA
98	70	98	29
I II III		I II III	
44 98 10		44 38 16	

OP. 51 (No.1). FIRST STRING QUARTET IN C MINOR.

(For two Violins, Viola and Violoncello.)

Dedicated to his friend, Dr. Theodor Billroth, in Vienna.

I. ALLEGRO.
II. ROMANZE, POCO ADAGIO.
III. ALLEGRETTO MOLTO MODERATO E COMODO ; AND UN POCO PIU ANIMATO.
IV. ALLEGRO.

Arranged by the Composer for Piano Duet.
Published by N. Simrock in 1873.

PRELIMINARY NOTE.

1. THIS work, being commonly held to be representative of Brahms's austerity and asceticism, and to be so difficult that even with a previous knowledge of the score we are liable to fail in grasping its contents, presents us with a fitting opportunity to take stock of the advantages of analysis which we have so far acquired. The remarks upon Brahms's style of composition made by Maczewski in Grove's Dictionary will be an aid to this, as they so aptly epitomise the case in reminding us that the problem is always the same, and that the greater or less austerity of style or complication of detail of any particular work should never imperil the result of its analysis or hamper appreciation of its merit.

" Brahms," says Maczewski, " takes his stand upon systematic principles of musical form, upon which indeed his individual characteristics a good deal depend. In point of style and construction his music displays a power which is now quite unique. In all his works, from the greatest to the smallest, the hand of a master is manifest, and if we analyse them, we shall find the same unwearied energy and consistency throughout the movement as is used at the outset to express the leading idea.'

2. The thought, here expressed, of tracing the same methods and the same artistic finish in all works irrespective of the greater or less ambition of their design is one which levels all difficulty; and therefore requires only to be carried out in order to bring all compositions under one treatment. Such is the effect of our plan of rhythmical tables, which by a suggested explanation of every bar, by clear indication of outline and by the individualisation of all subjects and intermediate motives can scarcely fail to prepare the student to either read or listen with an intelligent interest.

I. ALLEGRO.

3. It is somewhat difficult to account for certain criticisms of this movement. Why, for instance, it should be regarded as having practically only one subject, would be a specially hard question to solve, considering that during its progress three subjects are, in turn, and each eloquently, appealing to us to be considered. Analysis in fact reveals so little ground either for this or for other hard things which have been said of the quartet generally that we prefer to dismiss its evil reputation as the work of some wicked fairy and to proceed to examination as if nothing had happened.

4. The normal character of this movement's construction will be evident from the merest glance at its rhythmical summary, and we therefore proceed at once to consider the subjects and their treatment. As to the latter we naturally expect it to be peculiar to the present work—and that to an extent reacting upon the form; for our labours hitherto must have been entirely without result if the student does not yet understand this to be the secret of so many practical varieties of form notwithstanding full adherence to the parent scheme. To master that idea is a condition of making Brahms's acquaintance; but when once thoroughly assimilated it affords an astonishing facility in the comprehension of his works.

RHYTHMICAL TABLE.

Ex. 298. Op. 51, No. 1, Allegro.

PORTION	MATERIAL	BARS	CONSISTING OF	EXTEND-ING TO
1st section	1st subject	10	2 × 5	10
	Int. motive 1	12	2 × 6	22
	1st subject	10	2 × 5	32
	2nd subject	20	2 × 10	52
	Int. motive 2	10	2 × 5	62
	3rd subject	12	2 × 6	74
	Bridge	8	2 × 4	82
Totals.		82		82
Durchführung	2da Volta	4	4	86
	1st subject	12	2 × 6	98
	2nd subject	12	2 × 6	110
	1st subject	17	2 × 8 + 1	127
	Bridge	12	$\left\{\begin{matrix} 2 \times 4 \\ 2 \times 2 \end{matrix}\right\}$	139
Totals.		57		139
Return	1st subject	14	2 × 7	153
	Int. motive 1	13	$\left\{\dfrac{2 \times 5 + 1}{2}\right\}$	166
	1st subject	10	2 × 5	176
	2nd subject	20	2 × 10	196
	Int. motive 2	10	2 × 5	206
	3rd subject	12	2 × 6	218
	Bridge	8	2 × 4	226
Totals.		87		226
Coda	Free	37	2 × 18 + 1	263

Ex. 299. Op. 51, No. 1, Allegro. First subject.

Cello 8ve lower   Vla. 3rd above for first 5 bars.   2nd Vln. reinforces first in 8ve below.

5. Here, for instance, it must be patent that ordinary treatment would involve the "echo" given by bars 9-10 being a *replica* of bars 7-8; with subsequent return to first subject. The fact therefore of these bars bending downwards and thus softening the clamour of the entry is a clear indication of an unusually early introduction of the motive which is to aid in development. These intermediate motives are as satellites of their subjects, with which for formal purposes, they are to be considered as one, and hence it is well within a composer's discretion to introduce one after the other in rapid succession should he so desire.

Ex. 300. Op. 51, No. 1, Allegro. First intermediate motive.

'Cello 8ve lower. Amplifying Vla. part omitted.

Moreover the motive of this attenuation of the first vigour is soon apparent in return of the first subject with every means of demonstration of which the string quartet is capable—melody in the bass and in octaves; clamorous double stoppings in quaver motion for second violin, and an excited figuration for the first.

6. The figuration alluded to may be easily observed as an accompaniment to the second subject which follows; and it may be safely surmised that the innocent procedure of so utilising it (and of thus promoting the unity of the movement) has proved a stumbling block to some, who have unwarily regarded it as a confounding of the two subjects. One would have thought that the rhythmical beauty of the new melody in depending upon the "Nachschläge"* for its assertion would have secured it recognition; but it must be admitted that the very richness of

---

* Literally—"after strokes."

Ex. 301. Op. 51, No. 1, Allegro. Second subject.

Vla. continues figure.

the subject—which is dual (see 'cello melody appearing at third bar) and, later on, the object of some intricate though splendid counterpoint—is apt to create a doubt.

7. The second intermediate motive is less interesting though well serving its own purpose of introducing the third subject,

Ex. 302. Op. 51, No. 1, Allegro. Second intermediate motive.

etc.

into the soft accompaniment of which it merges with an insurpassable grace; but this third subject, though exceedingly short, derives importance from the lovely bridge passage, or as some have it Codetta, which follows, and which, as concluding first section leads to the repeat.

Ex. 203. Op. 51, No. 1, Allegro. Third subject.

8. The bridge passage is not directly essential to our purpose of explaining the work, but claims quotation nevertheless.

Ex. 304. Op. 51, No. 1, Allegro. Conclusion of first section.

9. Strange to say the Durchführung does not in this case call for much remark; but, after the amount of exceptional resource displayed in the opening statements, its employment in support of the same material was almost a necessary course. It is, however, specially characterised by an extra vigour; by much modulation and by the peculiarity of its mode of effecting the return, which consists of gradually growing into the first subject and of then stating it with a novel harmonisation. The Coda, in allabreve, is a highly excited annexe to the movement; which it quite worthily concludes, though without presenting any feature to court attention from our point of view.

10. Epitome.

(a) Subjects, see Ex. 299 to 304.

(*b*) Key C minor, changing to A minor in leaving the first section and to C sharp minor during Durchführung, resuming C minor for the return and remaining in that key.

(*c*) Time $\frac{3}{2}$, changing to allabreve for Coda.

(*d*) Length 263 bars, or 342 with repeat of first section.

Ex. 305. Op. 51, No. 1, Allegro. Outline.

FIRST SECTION	DURCHFÜHRUNG	RETURN	CODA
82	57	87	37
I II III 32 30 20		I II III 37 30 20	

II   ROMANZE. Poco Adagio.

11. It would almost seem that Brahms had made it little short of exclusively his life-object to develop the technics of rhythm and to show what great things could be accomplished by rising superior to popular conventions. Thus, dactylic measures are generally supposed to lend themselves most readily to a cheerful motion; though if all that Bharms had done were to show their different application we should pass that by, on the ground that other masters had done the same. But other masters in venturing to use $\frac{3}{4}$ for a slow movement have been very careful to let it repose upon phrases of duple formation; by which means the dactylic influence has been infused only into the detail of their composition and has not affected its broad outline.

12. That is not the case here—so far as the first subject of this movement is concerned. We willingly admit that its phrase-formation may pass unobserved without the beauty of the theme being the less felt. To feel is good, but to both understand and feel is still better; and the romanticism in this case will be most keenly enjoyed by those who know its source. Let us note therefore that this movement is composed of two subjects, that these alternate, and consist of phrases of three-bars and two-bars respectively; that it is to the three-bar phrase that the special

tenderness of the movement is due; and that the rhythmic contrasts are the alternation mentioned and the conversion of the first subject into a two-bar motive for Coda. These various features (all observable from the summary) will now be more closely regarded.

RHYTHMICAL TABLE.

Ex. 306. Op. 51, No. 1, Romanze.

PORTION	MATERIAL	BARS	CONSISTING OF	EXTEND-ING TO
1st section	1st subject	24	3 × 8	24
	2nd subject	18	2 × 9	42
Totals.		42		42
2nd section	1st subject	32	3 × 11 − 1	74
	2nd subject	11	2 × 4 + 3	85
Totals.		43		85
Coda	1st subject	11	2 × 6 − 1	96
Totals.		11		96

13. The first subject, which would be rendered in metre as

$$| - \cup \cup | - \cup \cup | - \cup \cup |$$

has such a decided aspect of triviality that we have first to note how that feature is avoided. Firstly, the sprightly tendency is allowed only as a sort of antidote to what would otherwise prove excessive lugubriousness—with the result of creating an effect between the two. Then, the expression of the phrase (in common with that of any corresponding poetical line) ends with a special lightness acting as a sort of barrier to prevent one phrase from

Ex. 307. Op. 51, No. 1, Romanze. First subject.

running into another except at moments of exuberance. Thus, in examining the score we find that, whenever marks of expression occur at all, it is always a *diminuendo* or *pp* at end of the phrase—the only exceptions being at bars 57 and 63 during second section, at an expansion which is really the climax of the movement.

14. The special value of the second subject lies in its contrasting features—its two-bar phrases, frequent omission of the natural accents, division of the beat into triplets and so forth—

Ex. 308. Op. 51, No. 1, Romanze. Second subject.

its individual interest being but slight. But at bar 43, when the moment has arrived to prepare for returning to first subject, the three-bar phrase is suddenly resumed. This is done in a short episode which has been universally admired without anyone (so

Ex. 309. Op. 51, No. 1, Romanze. Return to first subject.

far as we are aware) having alighted upon the special cause of its beauty.

15. The return of the first theme is specialised by an accompanying variation for first violin, whilst the remaining parts are more or less paraphrased for its accommodation. As a variant this is fairly refreshing, whilst it certainly provides a much needed climax. The first and second subjects follow on orthodox lines, the rhythm of the latter being maintained for coda. The instrumentation is very delicate and tactful—too much so, in fact, for a first quartet. This view is fully corroborated by Brahms having told Kalbeck that he had written as many as twenty before finding one good enough to publish.

16. Epitome.

(*a*) Subjects. See Ex. 307 and 308.

(*b*) Key, A flat, without recognised change.

(*c*) Time, $\frac{3}{4}$; no change.

(*d*) Length, 96 bars; no repeats.

Ex 310. Op. 51, No. 1, Romanze. Outline.

FIRST SECTION	SECOND SECTION	CODA
42	43	11

III. ALLEGRETTO MOLTO MODERATO E COMODO.

With "Trio" section, Un poco piu animato.

16. This is in every respect a model movement of its kind; for, whilst everything proceeds with such an airy grace as to conceal art, it not only contains within the smallest limits several successful examples of scientific device, but these are so artistically assorted and combined—so mutually contributive of effect that interest in the contents seems out of proportion with the dimensions.

17. Beginning as usual with the rhythm, nothing could be more simple than the bare outline of this piece, the crude survey of which reveals but little. To those who penetrate no further it can only appear as a succession of four-bar phrases relieved occasionally by an extension; but of which the most that can be said is that, in point of grouping, they do not follow any set duple arrangement. Under cover of that simple outline however lies a detail of phrase-formation greatly in need of an explana-

RHYTHMICAL TABLE.

Ex. 311. Op. 51, No. 1, Allegretto.

PORTION	MATERIAL	BARS	CONSISTING OF	EXTEND-ING TO
1st section (1st part)	1st subject	14	4 × 3 + 2	14
	2nd subject	12	4 × 3	26
		2	2da Volta	28
		28		28
Development	1st subject	12	4 × 3	40
	Paraphrase	17	4 × 4 + 1	57
		29		57
Return	1st subject	10	4 × 2 + 2	67
	2nd subject	12	4 × 3	79
	Codetta	9	4 × 2 + 1	88
		31		88
Trio, 1st part	Subject	20	4 × 5	108
		1	2da Volta	109
		21		109
,, 2nd part	Subject	12	4 × 3	121
	,,	28	4 × 7	149
		40		149

tion—only to be given however under the reserve already men-tioned, and as serving not only for this movement but as a general indication of the nature of rhythmic refinements *within the phrase.*

18. The phrases of the first subject are of 1, 1 and 2* bars with an extension of two bars preceding second subject.

Those of the second subject are of 2, 1 and 1† with the extension of a continuous four before the repeat.

The 1, 1, 2 phrase is then resumed but shortly gives place to a form of 1, 1, 1, 1, followed by a continuous four‡ (from bar 41).

This being repeated and followed by an extension of one bar (extension of the last phrase is a favourite Brahms method of dividing subjects) the return ensues, and is naturally in the same rhythm as the opening statement.

19. The codetta of this portion is in 2, 2 phrases, with final extension of one bar dividing it from a section doing duty as "Trio," though not so called. Written in $\frac{3}{4}$, it is nevertheless a $\frac{6}{4}$ movement, as the reader will perceive who refers to the rhythmic repose presented by bars 97-8, 99-100, 101-2, 103-4,§ and in many other places. Independently of reference however the $\frac{6}{4}$ pulsation must be evident to every listener; so that the mere figures are apt to convey an incorrect idea in this case, the four-bar phrases counting only as two in æsthetic conception of the movement. It follows therefore that, when (as at bars 93-6)‖ the phrase-formation is in single bars apparently, it is really in half bars; and that the pulsation instead of being more languid, as is usual in a trio-section, is the reverse. But here, as in the last movement, Brahms shows his love for the association of contraries. The too lively pulsation is corrected by delightful undu-

Ex. 312. Op. 51, No. 1, Allegretto. First subject.

* See Ex. 312.   † See Ex. 313.
‡ See Ex. 314.   § See Ex. 315.
‖ See Ex. 315.

lations of the second violin and viola parts, which, between them, contrive to sustain a sort of humming sensation during the whole duration of the section.

19. All this becomes easily apparent ·on scrutiny of the subjects.

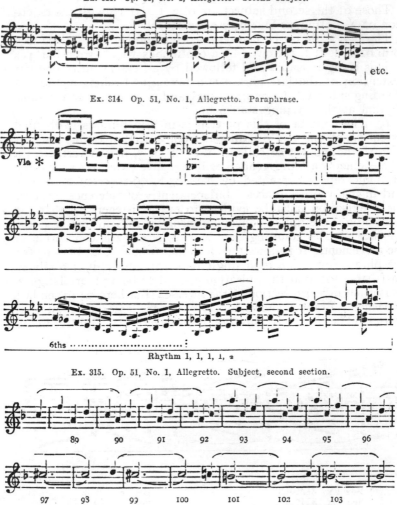

Ex. 313. Op. 51, No. 1, Allegretto. Second subject.

etc.

Ex. 314. Op. 51, No. 1, Allegretto. Paraphrase.

Vla *

6ths ....:

Rhythm 1, 1, 1, 1, ↓

Ex. 315. Op. 51, No. 1, Allegretto. Subject, second section.

89   90   91   92   93   94   95   96

97   98   99   100   101   102   103

* Elaboration of the original viola counter-subject should here be observed.

20. The devices to which reference has been made are :

1. Starting with two subjects of which one characterises the whole movement as figuration, while the other supplies thematic material.

2. Paraphrasing the counter-subject for a miniature Durchführung.

3. Treating the second subject in double counterpoint.*

4. Combining all the subject for codetta of first section.

21. Epitome.

(a) Subjects. See Ex. 312, 313 and 315.

(b) Key, F minor, with second section in major.

(c) Time, $\frac{2}{4}$, with second section in $\frac{3}{4}$.

(d) Length, 149 bars; or 268 with repeat of first part of each section and D.C.

Ex. 316. Op. 51, No. 1, Allegretto. Outline.

FIRST SECTION			SECOND SECTION		D.C.
	88			61	86
28	29	31	21	40	

IV. ALLEGRO.

22. As this extraordinary movement is well worth a special effort on the reader's part we shall, in view of its great difficulty, adopt a somewhat homely form of explanation. Let us therefore imagine the phrase which is first stated in unison but after-

Ex. 317. Op. 51, No. 1, Finale. First subject.

---

* The student will of course perceive that the parts in Ex. 313 are invertible.

wards treated variously standing as it were detached from the
movement. Let us expect it only to utter its cry and depart; to
be expatiated upon very rarely and never at length; and yet to
seem to inspire all the other subjects. Then let us try to picture
a sonata movement without any Durchführung, but with such a
multiplicity of subjects as to engender an intense agitation in the
mere statement of them—an agitation easily increased from any
desired point during development. By this time we shall probably have concluded that something quite revolutionary is at
hand. Not at all; for in spite of all this extensive outward
change every classic feature is preserved.

23. In such an exceptional case it would be idle to expect
agreement amongst critics, most of whom create their own embarrassment by insistence upon judging this movement in the
ordinary way. It cannot be so judged; for, to begin with, there
are no less than six subjects—real subjects, that is, and not mere
intermediate motives. Of these, the passage we have quoted is
naturally the first; and that Brahms himself must have regarded
the material of this movement very much in the same way as we
are doing would appear from the correspondence in the order of
these subjects during the two sections. Observation of this
enables us to take in the form at a glance.

Ex. 318. Op. 51, No. 1, Finale. Rotation of subjects.

First Section	1 2 1 2 1 3 4 5 4 1 6	
		and
		Coda.
Second Section	1 2 1 2 1 3 4 5 4 1 6	

24. The significance of this feature lies in the return being by
no means a repetition. It contains on the contrary so free a
treatment of the old material that there was positively no need
or inducement to adhere to the same order had it not strictly
appertained to the composer's scheme to do so. By aid of our
summary the reader will now be able to locate the subjects the

RHYTHMICAL TABLE.

Ex. 319. Op 51, No. 1. Allegro (finale).

SUBJECTS	FIRST PART			RETURN		
	BARS	CONSISTING OF	EXTEND-ING TO	BARS	CONSISTING OF	EXTEND-ING TO
I	2	2	2	2	2	95
II	10	2 × 5	12	6	2 × 3	101
I	2	2	14	2	2	103
II	6	2 × 3	20	6	2 × 3	109
I	12	2 × 6	32	14	2 × 7	123
III	9	4 × 2 + 1	41	9	4 × 2 + 1	132
IV	8	4 × 2	49	8	4 × 2	140
V	10	4 × 2 + 2	59	10	4 × 2 + 2	150
VI	8	4 × 2	67	8	4 × 2	158
I	3	2 + 1	70	3	2 + 1	161
VI	10	5 × 2	80	10	5 × 2	171
Bridge	13	2 × 6 + 1	93	22	2 × 11	193
Totals.	93		93	100		193

CODA

BARS	CONSISTING OF	EXTEND-ING TO
4	2 + 2	197
5	2 × 2 + 1	202
12	2 × 6	214
29	2 × 14 + 1	243
5	4 + 1	248
55		248

quotation of which in short form should enable him completely
to realise the character of the movement.

Ex. 320. Op. 51, No. 1, Finale. Subject 2.

Vlns.

'Cello 8ve lower.

etc.

* The viola has an amplifying part composed of this figure.

Ex. 321. Op. 51, No. 1, Finale. Subject 3

Ex. 322. Op. 51, No. 1, Finale. Subject 4

Ex. 323. Op. 51, No. 1, Finale. Subject 5.

Ex. 324. Op. 51, No. 1, Finale. Subject 6.

25. It is the individual subjects of the movement which most expose it to criticism. As Maczewski says (in the article to which we alluded in par. 1) after dwelling upon the beautiful cohesion and symmetry of Brahms's work:

The individual character of his ideas and the intellectual qualities of his nature stand in the way of his overcoming opposition and gaining the sympathies of the large mass of the musical public. His deep, brooding earnestness and his abstraction from external things absorb him so

---

† In small notes to indicate accompaniment. The subject is given by second violin.

‡ The three initial quavers give rise to many imitations during the development of this subject.

§ Continued in sequence, the subject being now taken up by first violin.

‖ With cello pedal bass on B flat, in syncopation to complete effect of crotchet pulsation.

¶ The five-bar rhythm of this subject should not escape notice.

completely in his idea that he sometimes loses his feeling for beauty of sound. With him beauty seems to hold a place subordinate to expression, and a certain harshness is occasionally met with in his harmony which must hinder the popularity of his works.

That the invention of his themes depended upon what he foresaw in the treatment of them is not to be doubted; and it easily accounts for any apparent lack of spontaneity and grace, these being traits liable to be considered by him as of lesser importance. Not the individual effect but the susceptibility of a theme was his measure of its beauty and our appreciation must therefore depend upon knowledge. It is the sheerest fiddle-faddle to accuse Brahms of strangeness. It is we who are devoted to conventions and resist their being set aside who are strange and unnatural. To quote Maczewski again:

There is an unapproachable asceticism about his genius which is opposed to all that is merely pleasing to the ear. He does not court the understanding; he rather demands from it arduous and unwearied service.

26. Epitome.

(a) Subjects. See Ex. 317 and 320 to 324.

(b) Key, C minor, changing to A minor (bar 102) and returning to C minor (bar 192).

(c) Time, allabreve; without change.

(d) Length, 248 bars, no repeats.

Ex. 325. Op. 51, No. 1, Finale. Outline.

FIRST STATEMENT	SECOND STATEMENT	CODA
93	100	55

OP. 51 (No. 2). SECOND STRING QUARTET IN A MINOR.

(For two Violins, Viola and Violoncello.)

Dedicated to his friend, Dr. Theodor Billroth, in Vienna.

I. Allegro non troppo.
II. Andante moderato.
III. Quasi minuetto, moderato; and Allegretto vivace.
IV. Finale, Allegro non assai.

Arranged by the Composer for Piano Duet.

Published by N. Simrock in 1873.

I. ALLEGRO NON TROPPO.

1. This quartet is said to be much easier of comprehension than No. 1; but it is doubtful whether the student who dissects it will find that to be the case—at all events so far as concerns the present movement. There is here perhaps a greater tunefulness upon the whole; but the student must beware of confounding this with the inner being of the quartet—to the understanding of which it is far more likely to be an obstacle than an assistance. There is also a somewhat fuller resonance, due to the greater mechanical facilities for strings in the present key, but this merely contributes to a better performance at the hands of average players. The constitution of the work is a totally different matter.

2. The first subject may, as has been said, have reference to Joachim's "F, A, E," motto—standing for "Frei, aber einsam," or "Free, but alone"—but is quite sufficiently explained by being in agreement with Brahms's habit of using chord-notes for his leading theme. We are thus led to expect matters to proceed in

the ordinary way; but far from this being the case, not only does the movement start upon the chord of D minor (for a movement in A minor, the tonic chord of which it merely touches in the second or weak bar), but it delays the strong rhythmical assertion of its key until the first two four-bar phrases are complete. This so far favours the motto notion that it isolates the first eight bars and thus accords with the composer's usual manner of working to what may be called a musical motto passage.* It is peculiar to this case however that it extends beyond the limits required by the motto itself; and, by postponing the tonic entry gives the opening something of a detached character.

3. The student will scarcely deem this trait to be one of great facility of comprehension, but there is much more to follow.

Ex. 326. Op. 51, No. 2, Allegro. First subject.

Ex. 327. Op. 51, No. 2, Allegro. Opening tonic statement.

'Cello 8ve lower. Viola in triplet crotchets

Here for instance and for the first time in Brahms's works until now, we have an example of extension *interior* to the phrase. Hitherto, extensions of the phrase have uniformly consisted of additions; similar in their nature to the additional clauses of a sentence. The extension of a musical period by an addition similar to the *parenthetical clause* in language has not yet occurred in such pronounced form. But, as we have now to make its acquaintance, we propose to characterise it by addition of the

---

* As, for instance, in the finale of the last quartet, the leading theme of which was also a motto-passage. (Refer to Op. 51, No. 1, par. 22, Ex. 317.)

word "interior"; whereby, for example, "4 + 3, interior" will be held to mean a four-bar phrase extended—not by the *addition* of three bars to its ending, but by the *insertion* of three bars before the ending takes place.

4. The first phrase of this kind follows immediately upon Ex. 327; in conjunction with which it should therefore be read, first

Ex. 328. Op. 51, No. 2, Interior extension of the phrase. (a) Phrase without extension.

without, and afterwards with, the parenthetical insertion.

Ex. 329. Op. 51, No. 2, Interior extension of the phrase. (b) Phrase with extension.

5. The "motto-subject"[*] (as we have seen in the finale of the last quartet), has a tendency to induce variety of material,[†] and therefore early introduction of intermediate motives. Illustration of the latter tendency has already appeared in the opening movement of Op. 51, No. 1; where the first intermediate motive occurs at the eleventh bar[‡] in consequence of traits in the leading theme similar to those which we are now treating. Immediately there-

---

[*] We are led to the use of this expression by want of a better term.

[†] Refer to Op. 51, No. 1, par. 23, where the disposition of *six* subjects of the finale of that work appears.

[‡] Refer to Op. 51, No. 1, par. 5, where the treatment is described and the scope of the intermediate motive defined.

Ex. 330. Op. 51, No. 2, Allegro. First intermediate motive.

fore after the above cadence the first intermediate motive here also appears, and is treated (as our experience must also lead us to expect) at greater length than the first subject itself. After an excessive amount of modulation, free indulgence in continuous quaver motion of middle parts, rapidly panting syncopations which at last subside by augmentation of their note lengths and a trivial first violin solo passage, we have the second subject; of which it has been remarked that it might easily pass for a *cantilena a due voci* in an opera by Rossini, Bellini or Donizetti.*

Ex. 331. Op. 51, No. 2, Allegro. Second subject.

Non-stem indication of basses. 'Cello crotchet motion pizz. viola triplet crotchets.

6. This subject is twice stated; four bars of its own intermediate motive appearing between the two occasions and exercising a binding influence on account of rhythmical affinity with the triplet-crotchet motion of the viola accompaniment to first subject. Now that the six-crotchet motion instead of being merely an

Ex. 332. Op. 51, No. 2, Allegro. Second intermediate motive.

Cello 8ve lower.

accompaniment has become a new and independent motive, the composer has a greater security for his cross rhythms which he is not slow to utilise.

7. But a still greater interest accrues to the treatment of this motive by interior extension of the phrase, as discussed in para-

* This is the expression of a Monday Popular programme critic.

RHYTHMICAL TABLE.

Ex. 333. Op. 51, No. 2, Allegro, First Section and Durchführung.

PORTION	MATERIAL	BARS	CONSISTING OF	EXTEND-ING TO
1st section	1st subject	12	4 × 3	12
	,, ,,	7	4 + 3 interior	19
	Int. motive 1	10	2 × 5	29
	, ,,	8	2 × 4	37
	,, .,	8	4 × 2	45
	2nd subject	12	4 × 3	57
	Int. motive 2	4	4	61
	2nd subject	16	4 × 4	77
	Int. motive 2	20	4 × 5	97
	,, ,,	6	4 + 2 interior	103
	3rd subject	16	$\begin{cases} 4+2 \\ 4 \\ 4+2 \end{cases}$	119
	Bridge to 1st subject	8	4 × 2	127
		3	$\begin{cases} 1 \text{ repeated} \\ 2 \text{ 2da Volta} \end{cases}$	130
Totals.		130		130
Durchführung		4	2 × 2	134
		12	1 × 12 (= 4 × 3)	146
		2	2	148
		14	4 × 3 + 2	162
		16	4 × 4	178
		6	2 × 3	184
		54		184

Ex. 334. Op. 51, No. 2, Allegro. Cross-rhythms on second intermediate motive.

graphs 3 and 4. The reader will have observed that, however dissimilar in exteriors, interior extension of the phrase is essentially one with the ordinary cadenza which, however long drawn or elaborate, is still but a prolongation of the closing phrase. That being so, there can be no surprise at finding that interior extension sometimes emulates cadenza freedom; which, as every one knows, shows itself in either barring capriciously or in dispensing with bars altogether. On the present occasion the exercise of this freedom gives rise to two bars of $\frac{3}{2}$; but why these bars should have ever been an object of mystery is itself a mystery—considering that they appear to have been cast in $\frac{3}{2}$ for the express purpose of preventing anyone from mistaking their mission. The parenthetical intent of these bars being too obvious to render more necessary, and the extension being followed by third subject, the two features may be read in conjunction, and occasion taken to observe that (as in literature) the sense of the phrase is not affected by omission of the parenthesis.

Ex. 335. Op. 51, No. 2, Allegro. Interior phrase extension with free bar length.

Ex. 336. Op. 51, No. 2, Allegro. Third subject.

RHYTHMICAL TABLE.

Ex. 337. Op. 51, No. 2, Allegro, Return and Coda.

PORTION	MATERIAL	BARS	CONSISTING OF	EXTEND-ING TO
Return	1st subject	12	4 × 3	196
	,, ,,	7	4 + 3 interior	203
	Int. motive 1	12	2 × 4 + 4	215
	2nd subject	12	4 × 3	227
	Int. motive 2	4	4	231
	2nd subject	16	4 × 4	247
	Int. motive 2	20	4 × 5	267
	,, ,,	6	4 + 2 interior	273
	3rd subject	6	4 + 2	279
Totals.		95		279
Coda	3rd subject	11	2 × 5 + 1	290
	Piu animato (free)	16	2 × 8	306
	,, ,,	10	4 × 2 + 2	316
	,, ,,	6	(2 + 1) 2	322
	1st subject	15	4 × 4 − 1	337
Totals.		58		337

8. Lengthy first statements being a luxury only to be enjoyed conveniently at expense of the Durchführung, the latter is here reduced to the smallest limits. The bounds allotted would have been insufficient for the display of fresh material, even had its introduction been desirable. This section is therefore merely an adroit play upon what has already occurred—interesting from every point of view, but contributing nothing to our stock. The only point in connection with it which promises to add to our knowledge is the manner of effecting the return; which obscures the re-entry of the motto-subject, whilst leaving the continuation of the leading theme intact. This does not look like paying much respect to the theme upon which the movement is supposed to have been founded, but it affords an instance of deferred settlement of the tonality of a first subject favouring a gradual growth into it of the Durchführung. By this means the listener, instead of having the opportunity to give a welcome to the return, finds to his surprise that it has been already made. Both sensations are pleasurable, though concealment of the actual moment of return is the greater novelty. The point is one for

the composer-student and lies closer to the nature of his subject
than to the exercise of his own will.

The coda requires no elucidation beyond that contained in the
rhythmic summary.

9. Epitome.

(a) Subjects. See Ex. 326, 330, 331, 332, 336.

(b) Key, A minor; change to A major for second subject on
return (bar 216), resuming A minor for coda (bar 280).

(c) Time, allabreve; change to $\frac{3}{2}$ for two bars during first section and return (at bars 98 and 268 respectively).

(d) Length, 337 bars, or 462 with repeat of first section.

Ex. 338. Op. 51, No. 2, Allegro. Outline.

FIRST SECTION	DURCHFÜHRUNG	RETURN	CODA
130	54	95	58
I II III		I II III	
45 58 27		31 58 6	

II. ANDANTE MODERATO.

10. This movement is of lyric character and of such simple
construction that its bearings are at once evident from observation of the summary. As usual with small movements of this
kind it is really a "one-subject" piece; the vocation of the
second subject being merely to provide contrast and divide the
two statements.

11. The broad leading theme has the air of proposing a more
important movement and the subsequent working therefore
creates a suspicion of original intentions not having been fully
carried out. A sign of weakness occurs immediately after the
first eight bars, where the 'cello continues the melody inanely for
three bars,* and is followed by a silly dialogue between extreme

* Or more properly for 2 + 1; as these bars consist of a two-bar phrase,
followed by one of no particular meaning.

RHYTHMICAL TABLE.

Ex. 339. Op. 51, No. 2, Andante moderato.

	MATERIAL	BARS	CONSISTING OF	EXTENDING TO
1st statement	1st subject	11	2 × 5 + 1	11
	,, ,,	6	2 × 3	17
	,, ,,	13	2 × 6 + 1	30
	Int. motive 1	7	2 × 3 + 1	37
	Bridge to 2nd subject	5	2 × 2 + 1	42
	Totals.	42		42
Middle	2nd subject	10	(2 × 2 + 1) 2	52
	,, ,,	7	2 × 3 + 1	59
	Int. motive 2	10	2 × 5	69
	Bridge to 1st subject	7	2 × 3 + 1	76
	Totals.	34		76
Return	1st subject	11	2 × 5 + 1	87
	,, ,,	7	2 × 3 + 1	94
	,, ,,	13	2 × 6 + 1	107
	Totals.	31		107
Coda	Int. motive 1	4	2 × 2	111
	Int. motive 2	9	2 × 4 + 1	120
	Cadence	4	2 × 2	124
	Totals.	17		124

parts for the next six, before the first subject reappears an octave higher to a new accompaniment. Another sign of unsettlement

Ex. 340. Op. 51, No. 2, Andante moderato. First subject.

1st Vln.

Viola ('Cello 8ve lower)

is that this formal reintroduction of the theme only lasts for four bars, the next four being employed to give the melody a tournure in the tonic direction. The two bars from which the force of this is derived (22 and 23) are especially devoid of finish, as they neither retain the new form of accompaniment nor the traits of the original melody. As for the tonic close it exists only for the analyst, the hearer having to be satisfied with an interrupted cadence and to wade through some bars of transient modulation before being allowed repose. No objection need here be taken to any of the means employed; the objection being simply that they fulfil nothing.

12. The passages which we have signalised "as first intermediate motive," only deserve that title in consequence of reappearing at the coda, which at all events saves them from being entirely incongruous to the movement; besides which the whole

Ex. 341. Op. 51 No. 2, Andante moderato. First intermediate motive.

construction right up to the second subject is so invertebrate that the rhythmisation here offered is merely one of many for each of which a plausible case could be made out.

13. Want of purpose is again displayed by the vagaries of the second subject, the melodramatic scoring of which creates an impression of the movement being intended for a different kind of audience to that which Brahms usually addressed. Inferior listeners are extremely exigent with regard to rhythmic regularity in matters of "tune," but this craving completely leaves them whenever the melodramatic shiver sets in. The composer addressing them would then be simply wasting his time to trouble about coherence—especially in view of the likelihood of the greatest incoherence being accepted as the most effective. We are naturally very far from applying the full force of these observations to the present movement, the misfortune being that they

Ex. 342. Op. 51, No. 2, Andante moderato. Second subject.

should be applicable at all. The extensions shown in the summary exhibit but faintly the irregularity of treatment of this subject, which, short as it is, includes an interpolated phrase at bars 55-6. The melodramatic feature which appeared so suddenly disappears quite in the same way (bar 60) in favour of the second intermediate motive. Having nothing in common with its own subject we should have deemed this a bridge to the return, but for the fact that, at bar 70, another motive appears for that purpose.

Ex. 343.   Op. 51, No. 2, Andante moderato.   Second intermediate motive.

14. The return is in F, modulating within sixteen bars to A; when the 'cello takes up the leading melody, the coda following with a *diminuendo* based upon the intermediate motives.

15. Epitome.

(*a*) Subjects. See Ex. 340 to 343.

(*b*) Key, A major, changing to F for sixteen bars at the return.

(*c*) Time, common, no change.

(*d*) Length, 124 bars, no repeats.

Ex. 344. Op. 51, No. 2, Andante moderato. Outline.

FIRST STATEMENT		MIDDLE		RETURN	CODA
42		34		31	17
30	12	17	17	* First subject	motives

* A feature consists of the return being given exclusively to first subject and the Coda entirely to the two intermediate motives. The total isolation of middle section is also remarkable.

III. QUASI MINUETTO AND ALLEGRETTO VIVACE.

16. We have already had the "Quasi-Minuetto" of Op. 16, some of our remarks upon which apply equally to the present movement. In each case the term "quasi" is the sign of a departure from custom; and in each the departure is rhythmical. But whereas the first more closely concerned the notation than the essence of the movement the present involves the correctness, or propriety as the case may be, of casting a minuet in three-bar phrases. To decide as to correctness is a matter for the ballet master: of the propriety, or rather impropriety, there can be no doubt. Custom has been so inveterately in favour of duple rhythm for this form that, however much licence may be allowed for "quasi," the adoption of three-bar phrasing is a renunciation of the character.

17. Taking the movement therefore independently of its peculiar name, we have to deal with two sections—practically with two short movements intertwined, each being of indisputable general interest. The allegretto section is in $\frac{2}{4}$ and of a character so completely opposed to all conception of the minuet that the attempt to wed the two styles by intermezzo (bars 73-8) can only be pronounced unsuccessful. Thus conditioned, the summary

RHYTHMICAL TABLE.

Ex. 345. Op. 51, No. 2, Quasi Minuetto.

PORTION	MATERIAL	BARS	CONSISTING OF	EXTENDING TO
1st statement 3/4	Subject	15	3 × 5	15
,, ,,	,,	24	3 × 8	39
Totals.		39		39
Middle 2/4	Subject	17	4 × 4 + 1	56
,,	,,	16	4 × 4	72
Middle 3/4	Intermezzo	6	2 × 3	78
Middle 2/4	Subject	44	4 × 11	122
Middle 3/4	Intermezzo	11	$\left\{ \begin{array}{c} 2 \times 4 \\ 3 \end{array} \right\}$	133
Totals.		94		133
2nd statement 3/4	Subject	15	3 × 5	148
,, ,,	,,	24	3 × 8	172
Totals.		39		172
Codetta	,,	6	3 × 2	178
Totals.		45		178

enables us to see how deceptive the mere calculation by number
of bars becomes where there are contrasted sections of different
degrees of movement. Here, for example, the 94 of "allegretto
vivace" are little more than the time equivalent of the 39 of
"moderato," the result being an almost perfect balance. It is
questionable whether Brahms's love of coherence is not here carried to a fault, for probably the allegretto would have been
better without having any reminder of the minuet—literally
thrown into its midst. Some have praised this six-bar insertion
for its counterpoint—a feature completely exposing it as a carefully prepared bit of "Machwerk" and shedding far too strong
a sniff of the composer's workshop to be welcome to those who
cherish his best interest. The reader will however form his own
opinion of this matter through the examples.

Ex. 346. Op. 51, No. 2, Quasi minuetto. First subject.

Ex. 347. Op. 51, No. 2, Quasi minuetto. Subject of middle section (allegretto vivace).

18. Firstly, he will notice that nothing could be more complete than the contrast between the subjects—which differ in
mode, in bar value, in phrase length, in degree of movement and
extent of bar subdivision; even the prevailing bowing being

staccato for the second, as against legato for the first section.
The impropriety of planting a six-bar intermezzo of first section
pattern right in the middle of the second section can only be explained therefore by supposing the composer to have had an
extra tender regard for this titbit of contrapuntal cleverness; in
which the upper part follows the note succession of the allegretto
subject (but is quite unrecognisable in that sense by the listener
on account of the altered rhythm), the viola canons with it at
bar distance (but gives us only one real bar of canon—this being
eked out by means of inversions for the rest of the intermezzo)
and in which simultaneously with all this the same sort of canon
goes on between second violin and 'cello. The latter canon is
constructed purely upon the first five notes of the opening subject; and the unfortunate listener (who naturally wonders what
it is all about) so gratefully accepts the return of the allegretto
that herein lies the only effect of the intrusion.

Ex. 348. Op. 51, No. 2, Quasi minuetto. Contrapuntal intermezzo.

19. Eliminating these matters as well as disregarding title, the
movement is not only a success on account of the sedateness of
the first movement being splendidly contrasted with the brilliancy of the second—but it gives us practically a new form of
middle division. It should be noticed however that the second
statement is merely a D.C. and that the coda is insignificant—

its shortness being an especial matter of regret; as, after so important a middle section, it becomes natural to expect something in the way of peroration.

20. Epitome.

(*a*) Subjects. See Ex. 346, 347.

(*b*) Key, A minor, for first statement and return; A major for middle section.

(*c*) Time, $\frac{3}{4}$ for "quasi minuetto moderato," and $\frac{2}{4}$ for "allegretto vivace." Six bars of $\frac{3}{4}$ as "intermezzo" within the latter (bars 73-8). Same intermezzo in A minor at resumption of $\frac{3}{4}$ (bar 123).

(*d*) Length, 178 bars, or 193 with repeat of first part of first section.

Ex. 349. Op. 51, No. 2, Quasi Minuetto. Outline.

FIRST STATEMENT	MIDDLE SECTION	SECOND STATEMENT.
Quasi minuetto 3/4 39	Allegretto vivace 2/4 ...... 77 } 94 Tempo di minuetto 17	Return .... 39 } 45 Codetta 6

IV. FINALE. ALLEGRO NON ASSAI.

21. Although the leading theme and features are here conspicuously unlike those generally associated with the rondo, this movement must be so considered—allowance being made of course for Brahms's usual freedom of outline. His, however, is a freedom full of method; for, though his work may appear to override certain traditions, it is usually found upon analysis to accentuate essential features. In the present case for example only the principal subject is in triple, whilst the second subject and the several attendant motives are all in duple, rhythm; an arrangement which naturally gives additional effect to each return. There are three statements (or four if the coda be also

counted as one); the middle section between each two of which
consists of the second subject, followed by suitable intermediate
motives.   Of such middle portions there are naturally three, of
which the first and last entirely correspond as to material, the
second being free and somewhat shorter than the others.   It is
therefore principally in the character of its leading theme that
the movement departs from customary rondo style.

Ex. 350. Op. 51, No. 2, Finale. First subject.

22. The ground covered by this subject will be evident from
the summary, but the figures in this case would be rather misleading were it not pointed out that (with exception of the
second) the intermediate motives are so grafted to their subjects
and to one another as to form one long continuous flow.   Their
recognition as separate motives is in fact mostly a question of
bar subdivision, or in other words of sudden change in the prevailing melody; and the result of exploring the ground in this
way is to show that the first subject has only one motive assigned to it—that being in its own rhythm and always followed
by change to duple rhythm for the bridge to next subject.   This
plan of giving the head theme a separate rhythm and only one
motive to aid its development seems in effect to ennoble it; and
its isolation by this ennoblement (instead of by detachment from
other material) is significant—in view of the fact that the detachment of the second subject from its first motive is very specially
marked.   The continuous quaver motion sustained by viola and
second violin not only suddenly subsides, but the two bar

RHYTHMICAL TABLE.

Ex. 351. Op. 51, No. 2, Finale.

PORTION	MATERIAL	BARS	CONSISTING OF	EXTENDING TO
Statement I	1st subject	24	3×8	24
	Int. motive 1	12	3×4	36
	Bridge	8	2×4	44
Totals.		44		44
Middle	2nd subject	14	2×7	58
	Int. motive 2	16	2×8	74
	,, ,, 3	8	2×4	82
	,, ,, ,,	17	$2 \times 8 + 1$	99
	Bridge	16	2×8	115
Totals.		71		115
Statement II	1st subject	8	$(3 + 1) 2$	123
		5	$3 + 2$	128
	Int. motive 1	15	$3 + (2 \times 6)$	143
Totals.		28		143
Middle	2nd subject	18	2×9	161
	Intermezzo	24	2×12	185
	Bridge	12	2×6	197
Totals.		54		197
Statement III	1st subject	24	3×8	221
	Int. motive 1	12	3×4	233
	Bridge	4	2×2	237
Totals.		40		237
Middle	2nd subject	14	2×7	251
	Int. motive 2	16	2×8	267
	,, ,, 3	8	2×4	275
	,, ,, ,,	17	$2 \times 8 + 1$	292
	Paraphrase of 1st	21	$2 \times 10 + 1$	313
Totals.		76		313
Coda	Bridge	20	2×10	333
	Piu vivace on 1st	26	2×13	359
Totals.		46		359

phrases are as suddenly left empty—except for the merest rhythmic pointing.

Ex. 352. Op. 51, No. 2, Finale. First intermediate motive.

Ex. 353. Op. 51, No. 2, Finale. Second subject.

Ex. 354. Op. 51, No. 2, Finale. Second intermediate motive.

23. This second intermediate motive is also the subject of the intermezzo commencing with bar 161, which for about a dozen bars is treated fugally. But it is remarkable that, whereas the first subject always relinquishes its triple rhythm well before entry of the next subject into which it accordingly merges, the duple rhythm is steadfastly maintained upon return, so as to make the first subject appear as if literally pounced upon;

whereby the effect of its reappearance is considerably heightened. The interest attaching to the remaining intermediate motive is therefore but slight, in spite of an inversion of its parts which

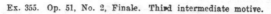

Ex. 355. Op. 51, No. 2, Finale. Third intermediate motive.

'Cello 8ve lower.....................

cannot fail to arrest attention, but which appeals to us princi-pally as being clever. In short, it may be confessed that, fine as is this movement in every detail, it is more a question of work-manship than of inspiration. The workmanship is too perfect to allow to inspiration any of that waywardness which is its con-genial atmosphere, and we consequently miss that delightful union of both qualities which constitutes the perfect work of art.

24. Epitome.

(a) Subjects. See Ex. 350 and 352-5.

(b) Key, A minor; changing to A major for last appearance of second subject, returning to A minor for "piu vivace" of coda.

(c) Time, $\frac{3}{4}$; without change.

(d) Length, 359 bars; no repeats.

Ex. 356. Op. 51, No. 2, Finale. Outline.

	FIRST	SECOND	THIRD	CODA
STATEMENT	44	28	40	
				46
MIDDLE	71	54	76	

OP. 56a. VARIATIONS FOR ORCHESTRA.

ON A HAYDN THEME IN B FLAT.

NOTE.—Op. 56b is the composer's arrangement of this work for Two Pianos.

Theme. Chorale St. Antonii. (Andante.)

VARIATIONS
- I. ANDANTE CON MOTO.
- II. VIVACE.
- III. CON MOTO.
- IV. ANDANTE.
- V. POCO PRESTO.
- VI. VIVACE.
- VII. GRAZIOSO.
- VIII. POCO PRESTO.

FINALE, ANDANTE.

Published by N. Simrock in 1874.

Score : Piccolo, 2 Flutes, 2 Oboes, 2 Clarinets, 2 Bassoons, Double-bassoon, 4 Horns, 2 Trumpets, Drums, Triangle, Strings.

PRELIMINARY NOTE.

1. THIS being the work for orchestra alone next following the Serenades, Op. 11 and 16, and therefore not only belonging to a much later period but being preceded by the " German Requiem," the cantata " Rinaldo," the " Rhapsodie " for alto solo and male choir, the " Schicksalslied " and the " Song of Triumph " in each of which the orchestra is extensively employed, it would be strange indeed if it did not represent a considerable advance. It does this so indisputably and with the result of creating such a chasm between the present and Brahms's early work that it is our intention in the following account to avoid all comparisons and to treat this Op. 56 as an entirely new departure in the orchestral sphere.

2. So considered it is the forerunner and in many respects the prototype of the whole of the seven works of which Brahms's output in the orchestral line consists. Objections to the scoring of these works are perfectly intelligible to those who treat the whole question of instrumentation dispassionately. What is wanted is to enable those who hold them to appraise their exact force as proceeding from the choice between two ideals.

3. The one conceives music for the orchestra as existing for the orchestra alone and therefore as not prejudiced if, on being transferred to some other means of interpretation its effect and interest should either disappear entirely or be so considerably lessened as to appear insignificant. Adherents of this school may even go so far as to admit their music to be partly a kaleidoscopic display of timbre differences; partly either a melodramatic collision of force-differences or a separate display of force-extremes, partly an appeal through the influence of timbre to our mental associations and partly a merely gorgeous habiliment of ideas not necessarily worthy in themselves. The effect of all these admissions is, however, neutralised by its being claimed that such objects and methods are not only legitimate but that their pursuit and employment (if not exclusively at all events without reserve) is the very *raison d'être* of orchestral music.

4. The other ideal, though perfectly admitting the value of all orchestral means of intensification claims that what is good must be appreciable as such apart from all splendour, that it must have an existence of its own no more dependent upon the orchestra than a literary classic is dependent upon an edition-de-luxe—that, in short, it must be music orchestrated and not orchestration musicalised.

5. We have no intention of persuading the reader in either of these two directions, the object of pointing them out being merely to show the real cause of most of the objection to Brahms's instrumentation. To put it plainly, his instrumentation is blamed for being instrumentation merely *of* the work—the prevalent idea nowadays being that, at all events to a large extent, instrumentation should *be* the work.

6. That this was not Brahms's conception of the use of the orchestra is manifest in a variety of ways, but perhaps the most convincing is his comparative indifference as to the substitution of instruments other than the originals in works where the latter had been characteristically employed to perfection; the

important fact with him being that behind mere colour-beauty stood *the work itself*. This is recognised in the following, from Grove :—

> As there can at no time have been any difficulty in finding publishers ready to issue his works in their proper form, we are entitled to assume that these arrangements and the issue of such things as the horn-trio and the clarinet trio and quintet with alternative string parts as substitutes for the wind instrument were undertaken with complete satisfaction to the composer ; and we may see here a sign of how very much more important the *matter* of his ideas was to him than the manner of their presentation ; what he had to say was always far more important than how it was to be said, in other words, he was, as has often been said, a draughtsman rather than a colorist in his treatment of the orchestra. Symmetry of form, originality of design, the logical development of his themes, these appeal to him far more strongly than the desire to elicit from the orchestra new combinations of tones.

Already sufficiently clear, these observations will acquire fresh force from our various reviews.

CHORALE, " S. ANTONII."

7. Having imitated the old *divertimento* form in Op. 11 and 16 Brahms now draws from the same source a theme for variations. No one knows whether the tune is really by Haydn, or what it has to do with St. Anthony; although Kalbeck thinks that the variations illustrate the temptation of that saint. However that may be, it is quite easy to see how the theme tempted Brahms to give it variations. We readily picture his welcome of the two-fold five-bar-phrase opening, four-bar-phrase continua-

Ex. 357. Op. 56, Theme.

tion and eccentric conclusion. Considering his appetite for rhythmical refinements we can feel no surprise at his resolution not to let such a *bonne-bouche* escape.

8. Although the five-bar phrases are quite obviously 3 + 2 it might easily escape observation that the four-bar phrases are mostly 3 + 1 and that the last three bars are single pulsations. Such an aggregate of rhythmic interest would be interesting in any case; but as variation basis it amounts to an ideal, and especially when the classic variation form in which Brahms so excelled is in view.

VAR. I (ANDANTE CON MOTO).

9. The single pulsations are here the chief point of interest,

Ex. 358. Op. 56, Var. 1.

the last three bars of the theme being taken as bass of the opening and transferred to the upper part for the second five-bar
phrase, when all the other parts are correspondingly inverted—
a result of double counterpoint. The middle section reiterates
the same pulsations upon the dominant, accompanied by figuration of the other parts similar to that of the first section; the
return being also upon the single pulsations—this time grandly
asserted at the onset, but gradually dying away.

VAR. II.   (PIU VIVACE).

10. The first three notes of the theme serve as the kernel of
this variation; the composer's intention that they shall be so
accepted being unmistakeably enforced by the opening phrase,
the *f* of which is delivered by the entire orchestra, the *p* being

Ex. 359. Op. 56, Var. 2.

for strings lightly scored with clarinets and bassoons. Allowance being made for difference of material the treatment of this
variation is very similar to that of the first; the motive appearing
on the dominant for second section and the sequel exhibiting
the same relation to the opening. The expression is, however,
widely different, the key being minor the movement more
energetic and the scoring responsive to the contrast shown by the
opening.

VAR. III. (CON MOTO.)

11. This is really a double variation—in the sense that the repetition of each section is a filigree version; the result being of course to give to this variation twice the usual number of bars. The process of what may be called "variation in the second degree" is one to which we may imagine Brahms in seclusion to have been somewhat accustomed, and even indebted for some of the subtlety of his variations' affinity with their theme.   The bass of the present sample for instance may have been first

Ex 360.   Op. 56, Var. 3.

* Groups by first and second flute and bassoon alternately (second time).
† First and second oboes, doubled by bassoons in lower octave (first time).
‡ Basses, doubled by 'cellos and violas in 8ve and super 8ve (both times).

written for the theme as it stands; its legato and sinuous
character being next accepted as characteristic, and in turn
adorned with the filigree aforesaid.

12. The violins are silent at first; being kept in reserve to
supply the parts relinquished afterwards in favour of the semiquaver figure, the instrumentation being thus extremely simple.
It is slightly more varied for the second section, however, which
is duly subjected to the same filigree process—the distribution of
the semiquaver figure being this time shared in by violas and
'cellos, oboes and clarinets.

VAR. IV. (ANDANTE CON MOTO.)

13. We have already had a variation in the minor, but in this
case we have also a three-quaver bar value; besides which, with
a sustained semiquaver motion we are about as far removed from
the theme in exteriors as it is possible to get. Add to that, that
this is a highly scientific variation; being nothing less than a
masterly exposition of double counterpoint in the twelfth (illus-
trative inversions serving as material for repetition of the sections)—that the melody is highly sympathetic—(being fully cap-

Ex. 361. Op. 56, Var. 4.

able of holding our attention on its own account) and that there is nevertheless so close a relation to the theme that we seem to hear the latter throughout. This is simultaneously enlightening upon three points—the value of affinity, the resources of counterpoint and the justification for Brahms's view of orchestration.

14. It should not be omitted that in each variation the treatment of the single pulsations at the close of the theme is a special feature for the student—and, it may be added, one affording amusement to the educated musician as an instance of apparently unconscious humour.

VAR. V. (POCO PRESTO.)

15. This is another case in which inversion is used on repetition—though only of the first section. We here also revert to the major, and to a rapid degree of motion; besides adopting a six-quaver bar. There is accordingly a remarkable freshness about it all, in spite of certain symptoms of this being a variation upon variation 2.

Ex. 362. Op. 56, Var. 5.

Upper parts doubled above and below by flutes and bassoons.
Violas and double basses silent after first four notes.

16. The general character of this section is humorous. But it is philosophic humour; and, like the brilliancy of the instrumentation, entirely springs from necessities of the idea. It is the breadth of the latter which makes it suitable for orchestra: otherwise the conception is of pure chamber character and is so worked out—not being scored in the ordinary sense.* If the orchestral effect is magnificent notwithstanding this shows that play upon tone-colour need not be the mere glamour to which we are painfully accustomed.

---

* Compare with the reviews of Op. 18 and Op. 26.

VAR. VI. (VIVACE.)

17. In this variation we return to the use of repeated sections of the ordinary kind, as well as to that of the two-crotchet bar. The degree of movement being rapid and the style martial, however, combine to remove us from the atmosphere of the theme; the affinity with which is also less than in the preceding variations. On the other hand the adherence to its rhythm is absolute and leads us to the conclusion that in this instance Brahms has principally relied upon that feature. The second section is

Ex. 363. Op. 56, Var. 6.

marked by such extreme freedom of modulation that, had not the original rhythm been faithfully preserved, we should have lost sight of the theme altogether. This variation is therefore an example of the saving force of identity of rhythm for variation purposes. Without it this description of heroic appassionato would certainly not have been possible.

VAR. VII. (GRAZIOSO.)

18. The position of this variation is undoubtedly well chosen —one of idyllic thus following one of martial character—but its inherent charm is such that in any position it would have been effective. The pastoral simplicity of the melody delivered

by violins and clarinets—the grace of the counter-melody given
by flute and violas (with completive interspersions by the basses)
—the amusing inversion of the parts in rounding off the section
and the sympathetic continuation pending the return—all combine to render this a specially favourite portion of the work.

Ex. 364. Op. 56, Var. 7.

VAR. VIII. (PRESTO NON TROPPO.)

19. This variation offers a large employment of imitation in
contrary motion—not as scientific display but in graceful elucidation of the theme. The strings are, besides being muted,
lightly distributed, except towards the close; and their dialogue
with the wood-wind, to which the piccolo is now added, produces
the novel effect of a *misterioso* in presto movement. The rhythm

Ex. 365. Op. 56, Var. 8.

(a) Dialogue in contrary motion—first section.

Vla 'Cello

Pico. Clar. Fag.

(b) Dialogue in contrary motion—second section.

of the theme is strictly maintained; the first section however being reinstrumented in lieu of repeat. The whole variation is of hushed effect and the syncopated elaboration of the single pulsations which close the theme form a fitting prelude to the dignified finale.

FINALE (ANDANTE).

20. The rhythm of each variation being a repeat of that of the theme no summary has until now been necessary. For the finale however it will be useful to adopt the ordinary course* in spite of the fact that to the eye this movement consists simply of seventeen repetitions of a five-bar ground-bass with a grandioso repetition of the theme to conclude; for although in this approach to Passacaglia there is no evidence of a desire to unite with sonata-form as in the Passacaglia of Op. 16, there is a method governing the settings which can only be effectively exhibited in tabular form.

21. The basso ostinato may be described as a bass version of the first five-bar phrase of the theme; and as there is no departure from it except for coda, it entirely determines the rhythm

* That is to say as from bar 363. The previous 362 bars are accounted for as follows: Theme and eight Variations, 29 bars each, 261. Variations 3 to 5 and 1st Section of Var. 8, doubled in notation, 29 × 3 + 10, 97. Cadences of 2nd Section, Var. 4, 2. Alternative endings, Theme and Var. 6, 2. Total, 262.

Ex. 366. Op. 56, Finale. Basso ostinato

of the superstructure. The whole seems to lend itself to classification into four groups of four settings each; the third and
fourth of these groups being divided by a transition setting
which enables the transfer of the theme to upper parts and its
change of mode to be effected without shock.

RHYTHMICAL TABLE.

Ex. 367. Op. 56, Finale.

GROUP	DESCRIPTION	SETTINGS	BARS	EXTEND-ING TO
I	Crotchet motion	1 to 4	20	382
II	Gradual increase of motion	4 to 8	20	402
III	Counter melody	9 to 12	20	422
Transition	Removal of sustained bass (figuration of same by str. pizz.)	13	5	427
IV	Minor settings con-cluding with one in major, and 2-bar phrase extension	14 to 17	22	449
Coda	Theme (consisting of 10 − 1 and 2 × 8 − 1		24	473
Totals.			111	473

22. The first group opens in organ style, its upper parts being
so legato as to appear incognisant of the rhythm of the *ostinato*.
Our suggested grouping of the settings is therefore confirmed
when, at the due moment, the strings and wind suddenly break
forth into a dialogue of vigorous chords.

Ex. 368. Op. 56, Finale. Opening of settings 1 and 5.

Bass 1 and 2 octaves lower

23. The incoming of the next group is equally well marked by first violin counter-melody (in octaves divisi) for the first setting; the remainder of the group being a continuation of the same by the wood-wind. This is preparatory to the transition-

Ex. 369. Op. 56, Finale. Opening of setting 9.

setting which serves as intermediary between the foregoing and delivery of the subject in an upper part (by the oboes) and in the minor. Gradually becoming more intense this group passes into

Ex. 370. Op. 56, Finale. Opening of setting 14.

the major mode for its last setting—the basses meantime resuming their rights. Two-bars extension of the phrase now herald the final proclamation of the theme (in the original harmonisation) by the entire orchestra; which is done in perfectly plain form, except that the wood-wind emphasises the rhythm by frantic scale-passages serving to indicate that the final cadence is approaching. A *diminuendo* succeeds to completion of the theme and seems to toy with the single pulsations which are its final trait; when, five bars before the close, the whole orchestra precipitately reiterates the tonic chord. Apart from the mere counterpoint of the movement the rise and fall of expression is so regulated as to cause the interest always to increase and thus present a proof of the power of the Passacaglia form when properly handled—a power Brahms was destined only once more to exercise, in the finale to the Fourth Symphony.

24. Epitome.

(*a*) Theme. See Ex. 357.

(*b*) Key, B flat major for Theme, Var. 1, 3, 5, 6, 7 and finale, B flat minor for Var. 2, 4, 8.

(*c*) Time, $\frac{2}{4}$ for Theme and Var. 1, 2, 3, 6; $\frac{3}{8}$ for Var. 4; $\frac{6}{8}$ for Var. 5 and 7; $\frac{3}{4}$ for Var. 8, and allabreve for finale.

(*d*) Length, 473 bars; or 635 with the following repeats: Theme 10 and 18. Var. 1, 10 and 19. Var. 2, 10 and 19. Var. 6, 9 and 19. Var. 7, 10 and 19. Var. 8, 19.

Ex. 371. Op. 56, Outline.

THEME	VARIATIONS	FINALE		
29	8 at 29 bars each (with sundry additions, see par. 20) 232	17 settings at 5 bars each: I—1 to 4; II —5 to 8; III—9 to 12. Transition, 13. IV—13 to 17. Extension 2 bars	87	CODA 24

OP. 60. THIRD PIANO QUARTET IN
C MINOR.

(For Piano, Violin, Viola and Violoncello.)

I. ALLEGRO NON TROPPO.
II. SCHERZO, ALLEGRO.
III. ANDANTE.
IV. FINALE, ALLEGRO COMODO.

Published by N. Simrock in 1875.

I. ALLEGRO NON TROPPO.

1. DEITERS tells us that although this quartet appeared very
much later than the others for the same combination, it really
belongs to the same period; and therefore that the tragic pathos
to which it rises, the technical treatment and invention which
it reveals and altogether the essentially riper development
which it displays are not to be attributed to any gradual increase of power. The work however bears traces of having
passed through an earlier condition; and even some crudities
remain, which can scarcely be other than the residue of numerous
points reserved by the composer for improvement.

2. We know for example that this quartet was originally
written in C sharp minor,* in which condition the present slow
movement (in E) stood to the parent key in a feasible relationship. But although the Scherzo which precedes it has now been
made to finish in C major (no doubt with a view to reconcile us
to the key of E which follows) nothing prepares us for the
finale; which being in C minor and immediately following upon
a sustained chord of E, can only have been passed by the
composer unwillingly.

---

*It is sufficient to mention, as to this, the Joachim letters on the sub-
ject (Joachim Correspondence, Vol. I, pp. 124-7), which are dated 1856,
and contain the quotation of passages in the original key.

3. The rhythmisation of the entire work presents rather extraordinary difficulty, if we insist upon differentiating the duple phrases of various lengths. But if, as in a former instance,* we are content with reduction to the lowest common denominator, the matter becomes much simplified, and the beautiful

RHYTHMICAL TABLE.

Ex. 272. Op. 60, Allegro non troppo.

PORTION	MATERIAL	BARS	CONSISTING OF	EXTENDING TO
Introductory	1st subject	10	$2 + (2 \times 4)$	10
,,	,, ,,	21	$2 + (2 \times 9 + 1)$	31
Totals.		31		31
1st statement	1st subject	10	2×5	41
	Motive 1	10	2×5	51
	Bridge	18	2×9	69
	2nd subject	16	$(2 \times 4)\,2$	85
	Motive 2	16	$(2 \times 4)\,2$	101
	2nd subject	8	2×4	109
	Bridge	12	2×6	121
Totals.		90		121
Durchführung	1st subject	12	$(2 \times 3)\,2$	133
	,, ,,	8	2×4	141
	,, ,,	18	$(2 \times 3)\,3$	159
	,, ,,	4	2×2	163
	Dominant pedal	18	$(2 \times 3)\,3$	181
	,, ,,	17	$2 \times 8 + 1$	198
Totals.		77		198
Return	1st subject	14	$(2 \times 5) + (2 \times 2)$	212
	Motive 1	4	2×2	216
	Bridge	11	$2 \times 5 + 1$	227
	,,	8	2×4	235
	2nd subject	24	$(2 \times 4)\,3$	259
	,, ,,	10	2×5	269
	Motive 2	8	2×4	277
	,,	10	2×5	287
Totals.		89		287
Coda	1st subject	20	2×10	307
	,, ,,	7	$2 \times 3 + 1$	314
	,, ,,	12	2×6	326
Totals.		39		326

* The finale of the piano quintet. See Op. 34, par. 26.

symmetry even more apparent than would otherwise be the case. There is an attendant disadvantage however against which the student should guard—that of obscuring the rhythmical refinement of subdivisions—as an example of which we may quote the view of the first ten bars as 2 × 5 instead of 2 + 4 + 4 which they really are. There is no conflict between the two

Ex. 373. Op. 60, Allegro. Introductory statement.

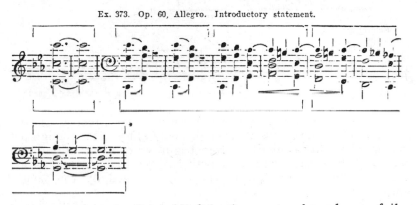

statements, but the flat rule of continuous two-bar phrases fails to show that the last eight bars are in two phrases of four bars each.

4. The first feature of this movement is its introductory statement, occupying thirty-one bars, and thus reminding us of the first piano quartet.† As a trait in the formal outline of a serious movement this is very highly to be commended and is far superior to the more usual introduction at a slower *tempo*; the latter being not only fragmentary but failing so effectually to prepare the mind of the listener for the opening subject. But whether, under cover of this introductory statement, a composer is justified in starting off with a variation of his first subject is quite another matter. In this case we have to wait for the return in order to hear the first subject in its entirety; and that the opening is really a variation upon it may easily be seen by comparison.

---

* Compare this phrase with that leading to the sixteenth bar of Beethoven's Sonata, Op. 10, No. 1. Also the principal subject of this movement with the song group of the first movement of the same sonata.

† See Op. 25, par. 5, and the attendant rhythmical table showing an introductory statement of 26 bars.

Ex. 374. Op. 60, Allegro. First subject, comparison of opening and return statements.

5. This, in our view, is one of the features which tend to show this quartet to have passed through many stages; for though a composer would assuredly never begin with a variation, he might as the result of many repetitions get to regard it as a natural statement, or at all events as justified by the same subject's introductory phase.

6. The first intermediate motive is of highly spirited char-

Ex. 375. Op. 60, Allegro. First intermediate motive.

acter though in a formation long since worn threadbare by contrapuntists. We spare the reader quotation of the inevitable working in thirds and the obvious sequences which supervene, in order to pass on to the interesting transient modulation (bars 56-69) introducing the second subject, and to instance this as further evidence that the work combines the younger with the maturer Brahms.

Ex. 376. Op. 60, Allegro. Second subject.

The second subject very strangely consists of five settings of the same eight bars; the first being delivered by piano alone, the second principally by viola (though to an elaborate accompaniment), the third and fourth being characterised by a new rhythmical figure of such importance as to constitute a new motive and the last forming a sort of "grandioso," preceding the codetta which closes the first section—of which latter there is no repeat. This is an entirely novel treatment of a second subject—one which we might easily be incautious enough to rule out as too complete within itself but for knowledge of the danger of so treating Brahms's apparently "hazardous experiments."* It is better to remember how foolish such arguments appear when confronted with success.

7. The reason why Brahms has succeeded in what all propriety would condemn is that at the third setting he has not only introduced the entirely new and highly important rhythmical second intermediate motive but he has so completely disguised his theme† (the opening strong bar of which is now represented by 'cello *p* and *pizz.*) that whilst no one but the analyst can know the real nature of what is going on even the uninstructed listener feels the effect of a strong cohesion.

The Durchführung is almost entirely devoted to the first subject, the treatment of which is extremely free and animated, with modulations involving passing recognition of the keys of B major and E minor. After fifty-four bars however (at bar 176, on resumption of the key of C minor) it introduces highly interesting canonic references to the second subject—

* See Op. 34, par. 25.

† By making the piano enter with apparently great importance at its *second* bar, thereby deceiving even some critics who have quite erroneously taken this for the commencement of a tributary subject.

Ex. 377. Op. 60, Allegro. Second intermediate motive.

upon a dominant pedal, lasting for twenty-two bars and leading directly to the return. The imitations occur firstly at three, then at two, and finally at one beat distance—the latter leading to the climax preceding the return and the whole being somewhat remindful of a fugal *stretto*.

Ex. 378. Op. 60, Allegro. Second subject in stretto on dominant pedal.

(a) At 3 beats' distance.

Ex 379.   (b) At 2 beats' distance.

Ex. 380.   (c) At 1 beat distance.

8. The laboured character of these imitations is a further reminder of the early origin of the work; but it does nothing to hinder the effect in view; which is efficiently protected by the gradual rise and *crescendo*, coupled with the systematic widening of the figuration of the pedal note.   This figuration reaches octave width at three bars before the actual return, when it is joined in by all the instruments in unison.   Then, with a semitone rise of the whole, the piano announces the return of the first subject while the violin and viola graft the sections by holding on to the figuration for two bars more.

9. The return contains nothing beyond what the student will naturally presuppose, but the coda is distinguished by several special features.   Some critics fix its commencement at bar 308 (twenty bars from the close), but this judgment is at variance with our analysis, confirmation of which rests with the coda style adopted, as from bar 288.   Here the first subject is finally resumed (a sure sign of the Brahms coda), the piano part assumes an unwonted elaboration, the modulations become even more free than those of the Durchführung, and the whole bespeaks an agitato expression.   The final " animato " is merely a cadence in the same spirit, and is appropriately followed by another cadence—this time of *diminuendo* character (bar 315 to end). A serious, fervent, dramatic, and upon the whole melancholy movement, of which it is said that the composer on showing it to Deiters told him to listen to it whilst thinking of a man just about to shoot himself because there was nothing left for him to do.

10. Epitome.

(a) Subjects.   See Ex. 373-377.

(b) Key, C minor; passing through B major and E minor during the Durchführung; returning to C minor for the dominant pedal of the latter.   Transition to E minor during the return (when preparing for return of second subject in G); final return to C minor (at bar 304) during Coda.

(c) Time, $\frac{3}{4}$; no change.

(d) Length, 326 bars, no repeats.

Ex. 381. Op. 60, Allegro. Outline.

INTRODUCTORY	FIRST SECTION		DURCHFÜHRUNG		RETURN		CODA
31	90		77		89		39
I	I	II	I	II	I	II	I
	38	52	54	23	37	52	

II. SCHERZO (ALLEGRO).

11. This movement may in respect of its form be described as midway between lyric and sonata. Thus, although it has no Trio so called it has a third subject doing duty as such; though the first two subjects do not form a section they are provided with a codetta which marks them off as one; though we must not speak of a Durchführung the thing is there to all intents and purposes; and the return, though only a written-out D.C., is rounded off with a developed Coda. These features make it an interesting sample for the student who is attracted by affinities in matters of form.

RHYTHMICAL TABLE.

Ex. 582. Op. 60, Scherzo.

PORTION	MATERIAL	BARS	CONSISTING OF	EXTEND-ING TO
1st section	Introductory	4	2 × 2	4
	1st subject	18	2 × 9	22
	2nd subject	11	2 × 5 + 1	33
	1st subject	14	2 × 7	47
	,, ,,	6	2 of 9/8, 4 of 6/8	53
Totals.		53		53
Codetta	1st subject	18	2 × 9	71
Totals.		18		71
In lieu of Trio	3rd subject	19	2 × 9 + 1	90
	,, ,,	24	2 × 12	114
	1st subject	21	2 × 10 + 1	135
	,, ,,	5	2 × 2 + 1	140
	3rd subject	14	2 × 7	154
Totals.		83		154
D.C.	Introductory	4	2 × 2	158
	1st subject	18	2 × 9	176
	2nd subject	11	2 × 5 + 1	187
	1st subject	14	2 × 7	201
	,, ,,	6	2 of 9/8, 4 of 6/8	207
Totals.		53		207
Coda	1st subject	16	2 × 8	223
	,, ,,	11	4 × 3 + 1	234
Totals.		27		234

12. The rhythmisation is subject to the conditions stated in par. 3, but is otherwise perfectly simple—except in respect of the expanded phrase preceding the Codetta mentioned in par. 11, and repeated before the final Coda. The phrase so expanded is one evolved from the first subject, appearing how-

Ex. 383. Op. 60, Scherzo. First subject.

ever only after the second subject has been stated, and then evidently taking the place of the ordinary phrase extension which Brahms was accustomed to employ for purposes of division. Its rhythmical vagueness is not only in keeping with, but is the natural counterpart of the phrase contraction of the second subject into three bars (bars 31-3); besides which it

Ex. 384. Op. 60, Scherzo. Second subject.

would appear as if some reliance in the production of scherzo effect had been placed upon a frequent confusion of strong and weak bars. The student having formed his own opinion of these matters, will be sure to recognise that the $\frac{9}{8}$ bars of the

Ex. 385. Contraction of second subject phrase.

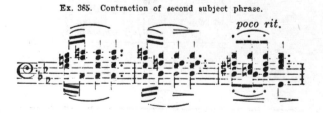

Ex. 386. Re-statement of first subject.

etc.

Harmonised as as in Ex. 383

expanded phrase are merely required to delay the attack of $\frac{6}{8}$ bar phrases similar to those immediately preceding and that the four following $\frac{6}{8}$ bars might more consistently have been presented as two of $\frac{12}{8}$ had the object of the notation been to present the rhythm to the eye. In short, this expanded phrase is one composed of four members which we are only prevented from calling "bars" by desire not to oppose the usual acceptance of the term.

13. This explanation is necessary in order to counteract the idea of Brahms's transient changes of bar value being ever due to caprice or of their betokening a careless style; for it is precisely because of the contrary that such instances have a special value—as may be at once perceived if we disregard the bars of the mere notation and recognise those indicative of phrase-members only.

Ex. 387. Op. 60, Scherzo. Gradual expansion of phrase (melody only).

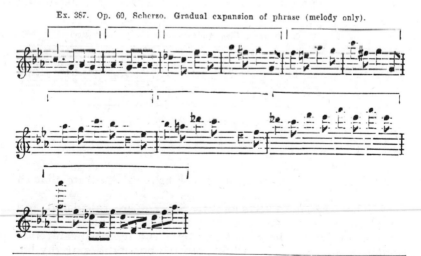

* Melody opening at second bar of the phrase; the second bar of the original version being now omitted.

14. After the Codetta now following the third subject appears; and that it is intended to serve as Trio is not only evidenced by its cantabile character but also by its being omitted from the return—which is a mere D.C. of two subjects. The

Ex. 388. Op 60, Scherzo. Third subject.

quaver motion, which at first is continued by the piano, is afterwards taken up by the strings—the parts being reversed—whereupon there follows a specially modulative and gradually more and more excited working up of the first subject which to all intents and purposes is a Durchführung in spite of its place here as a mere bridge to the D.C. This faintness of the line which divides it from sonata form is a charm of the movement—though all doubt of its lyric character is dispelled by the subjects being untransposed on return. The phrase expansion

Ex. 389. Op. 60, Scherzo. Final phrase expansion (melody only).

with which the Coda concludes will help to illustrate that of Ex. 387.

15. That the fine effects of this Scherzo are calculated and hence somewhat deserve to be called "musician's music" is true. But not even those who accept that term as a reproach can refuse Brahms honour for such insight into the possibilities of rhythm as a factor in musical composition as is here displayed.

16. Epitome.

(a) Subjects. See Ex. 383, 384 and 388.

(b) Key, C minor—no recognised change.

(c) Time, $\frac{6}{8}$; two bars of $\frac{9}{8}$ during first statement and again during the return.

(d) Length, 234 bars. The D.C. being written out, there are no repeats.

Ex. 390. Op. 60, Scherzo. Outline.

FIRST STATEMENT		CODETTA	MIDDLE	D.C.		CODA
53		18	83	53		27
I	II	1	III I III	1	11	1
22	31		43 26 14	22	31	

III. ANDANTE.

17. Beginning with a complete song for violoncello to a syncopated piano accompaniment this movement develops by another verse of the same, for which the violin is added and a new piano figure applied. The fact of the spirit as well as portions of the melody being retained serves to show an entire resemblance to a song "durchcomponirt." Every note of all this seems to carry with it an individual charm in addition to its contribution to the ensemble; and, the viola being added at the eleventh bar of the second "strophe," the expression continues to grow in intensity until the new verse (with a final two-bar extension in lieu of cadencing) welds itself to a second subject. The solo effect of the opening, the duet effect when the violin is added, the trio on completion of the strings and the quartet, when for the first time the piano's individuality is asserted by melodic progressions, form a graduation of intensity fit to be taken as a model.

18. As the express vocation of the subject which follows this is to provide contrast for the movement it will be well to note contributory features. These are, firstly, that the continuity of melody is not now confided to any one instrument, but results from various combinations, and that two forms of syncopation now proceed simultaneously—the key being that of the dom-

Ex. 391. Op. 60, Andante. First subject.

'Cello 8ve lower

inant—ample means for the eleven bars given to statement of second subject. The thirty-two then given to development

RHYTHMICAL TABLE.

Ex. 392. Op. 60, Andante.

PORTION	MATERIAL	BARS	CONSISTING OF	EXTENDING TO
1st section	1st subject	16	2 × 8	16
	,, ,,	18	2 × 9	34
Totals.		34		34
Middle	2nd subject	11	2 × 5 + 1	45
	Expansion of do.	17	2 × 8 + 1	62
	Bridge	15	5 × 3	77
Totals.		43		77
Return	1st subject	16	2 × 8	93
	,, ,,	17	2 × 8 + 1	110
Coda	2nd subject	12	2 × 6	122
Totals.		45		122

must for purposes of survey be divided into 17 and 15, the
first representing a more passionate continuation of the statement and the second a gradual return to the spirit of the first
subject.   The way in which the latter is effected is of special

Ex. 393. Op. 60, Andante. Second subject.

interest to the student of composition, as it consists of a dialogue of recitative between the combined strings and piano.
The necessary rhythmic freedom is secured by adoption of the
five-bar phrase; whilst freedom in expression proceeds from
giving the first of these phrases to the entire combination and
dividing the other two into portions of two and three bars for
piano and strings respectively—but uniting these portions by
an overlap.   It would be difficult to discover another instance
in which ingenuity and artistic conception co-operate so happily.

19. For the return the material is unchanged; so that although
the instrumentation is effectively varied (the distribution of the
parts being entirely new and the effect generally fuller than

Ex. 394. Op. 60, Andante. Recitative-like dialogue between piano and strings.

for the first statement) it does not seem to present any feature for special attention. The Codetta with which the movement concludes is simply twelve bars of reminiscence of second subject. On the question of key refer to paragraph 2.

20. Epitome.

(a) Subjects. See Ex. 391 and 393.

(b) Key, E major; no recognised change.

(c) Time, common; no change.

(d) Length, 122 bars; no repeats.

Ex. 395. Op. 60, Andante. Outline.

FIRST SUBJECT	SECOND SUBJECT	BRIDGE	RETURN	CODA
34	28	15	33	12

* 'Cello part octave lower and viola with double stoppings. Note the approach of 'cello part to melody of first subject.

† Note that these, being *normal quavers*, represent a graduation of approach to the pulsation of first subject, compared with the *triplet* quavers of the first bar of the example.

IV. FINALE (ALLEGRO COMODO).

21. This is too straightforward a movement to provoke much comment; even its rhythm offering no speciality, consisting as it does of one dull succession of phrases without a single extension or modification of any kind until the Coda. It is true that the third subject is in five-bar sets; but this promise of novelty remains unfulfilled by the chorale character of the theme converting each fifth bar into a mere written-out pause; and, whilst the piano *moto perpetuo* figure which always accompanies the first subject is admittedly interesting, the interest is not of the kind to be expected in the finale of so serious a work. Other traits pointing to the same conclusion might be cited; but they may be all summed up in the observation that this movement does not leave us with any such impression as that only Brahms could have written it.

RHYTHMICAL TABLE.

Ex. 396. Op. 60, Finale.

PORTION	MATERIAL	BARS	CONSISTING OF	EXTEND-ING TO
1st section	1st subject	42	2 × 21	42
	Motive	12	2 × 6	54
	2nd subject	20	2 × 10	74
	3rd subject	20	5 × 4	94
	Bridge	4	4	98
	2da Volta	1	1	99
Totals.		99		99
Durchführung	Bridge	4	4	103
	All subjects	48	2 × 24	151
	,, ,,	22	2 × 11	173
	,, ,,	44	2 × 22	217
Totals.		118		217
Return	1st subject	42	2 × 21	259
	Motive	12	2 × 6	271
	2nd subject	20	2 × 10	291
	3rd subject	25	5 × 5	316
Totals.		99		316
Coda	Bridge	12	3 × 4	328
	{ 1st subject	23	2 × 11 + 1	351
	{ and motive	29	2 × 15 + 1	380
Totals.		52		380

22. A glance at the summary of the movement suffices to show the painfully orthodox nature of its proportions and to create the suspicion that only the brilliant instrumentation is of later date. Treatment of *all* the subjects during Durchführung smacks also of youthful obedience to precept; besides which the Mendelssohnian handling of the piano figure suggests a period of comparative subjection to outer influences. In any case the movement remains a sample production of high-class musicianship—but nothing more.

Ex. 397. Op. 60, Finale. First subject.

p leggiero

etc.

23. Only one intermediate motive is employed, and that apparently with a view to the provision beforehand of a triplet-crotchet pulsation as formula for the accompaniment of second subject.

Ex. 398. Op. 60, Finale. Intermediate motive.

Ex. 399. Op. 60, Finale. Second subject.

24. The same formula provides material for the piano interludes with which the chorale phrases of the third subject are interspersed.

Ex. 400. Op. 60, Finale. Third subject.

25. The conventional character of the movement does not of course prevent its resonant effect from being superb, or, in many cases, the pleasure of a first hearing from surpassing that likely to be produced by work of greater originality. Every real student however knows that too favourable a first impression is a sure sign of that only having been stated for which the mind has already been prepared by previous experience; and, altogether, this finale leaves it to be regretted that Brahms never returned to the handling of the same combination of instruments.

26. Epitome.

(a) Subjects. See Ex. 397-400.

(b) Key, C minor; changing to C major for Durchführung and resuming C minor for Return. During the latter the major again enters at statement of intermediate motive and remains until the Coda which resumes the original key.

(c) Time, allabreve; no change.
(d) Length, 380 bars; or 477 with repeat of first section.

Ex. 401. Op. 60, Finale. Outline.

FIRST SECTION			DURCHFÜHRUNG	RETURN			CODA
99			118	99			52
I	II	III		I	II	III	
54	20	25		54	20	25	

OP. 67. THIRD STRING QUARTET IN B FLAT.

(For Two Violins, Viola and Violoncello.)

Dedicated to his friend, Prof. Th. W. Engelmann, in Utrecht.

I. VIVACE.
II. ANDANTE.
III. AGITATO (ALLEGRETTO NON TROPPO).
IV. (A) POCO ALLEGRETTO CON VARIAZIONI.
(B) DOPPIO MOVIMENTO.

Published by N. Simrock in 1876.

Arranged by the Composer for Piano Duet.

I. VIVACE.

1. As Brahms-music this movement is exceptional—principally for the importance laid by the composer upon securing effects pleasant to the ear. This is exhibited not only in the choice of subjects courting immediate if not enduring sympathy, but also by some almost humorous contrasts; besides which the scoring is more than usually conventional. A new feature is however presented by the introduction of what may be called the combined intermediate motive.

2. Hitherto Brahms's use of the intermediate motive had always been as an independent, though subordinate, subject. Here, however, it is combined with its theme, and might indeed be considered as mere counterpoint but for a separate individuality. That this procedure was adopted with a view to ear-pleasure is fairly certain—especially when considered in conjunction with frequent introduction of the hunting strain of the first subject—with which, by the way, we never part company for very long. There is furthermore the introduction of a jovial new subject for the Durchführung—one not very decidedly in

keeping with the composer's usually deep methods in that department—and finally, it must be confessed, a diminished regard for that symmetrical beauty which associations cause us to look for as a matter of right in a Brahms movement.

3. It is noticeable that Brahms in writing about this quartet to Joachim expressly hopes that it will "sound" well,* and

RHYTHMICAL TABLE.

Ex. 402. Op 67, Vivace.

PORTION	MATERIAL	BARS	CONSISTING OF	EXTENDING TO
1st section	1st subject	20	2×10	20
	Combined motive	12	2×6	32
	2nd subject	25	$\begin{cases} 2 \times 8 + 1 \\ 2 \times 4 \end{cases}$	57
	3rd subject	5	$2 \times 2 + 1$	62
	,, ,,	22	2×11	84
	Combined motive	16	2×8	100
	Bridge	3	$2 + 1$	103
Totals.		103		103
Durchführung	Bridge	4	2da Volta $1 + 3$	107
	Special subject	21	$2 \times 10 + 1$	128
	1st subject	21	$2 \times 10 + 1$	149
	2nd subject	36	$2 \times 17 + 2$	185
	Special subject	20	$2 \times 10 + \frown$	205
Totals.		102		205
Return	1st subject	21	$2 \times 10 + 1$	*226
	,, ,,	4	2×2	230
	Combined motive	10	2×5	240
	2nd subject	25	$\begin{cases} 2 \times 8 + 1 \\ 2 \times 4 \end{cases}$	265
	3rd subject	.5	$2 \times 2 + 1$	270
	,, ,,	22	2×11	292
	Combined motive	16	2×8	308
	Bridge	6	2×3	314
Totals.		109		314
Coda	3rd subject	10	2×5	324
	$\begin{cases} \text{1st subject with} \\ \text{combined motive} \end{cases}$	10	2×5	334
	1st subject	7	$2 \times 3 + 1$	341
Totals.		27		341

* "Recht schön und deutlich in den Ohren klingen." Joachim Correspondence II, p. 113

that round about the same period he seems to have been generally more mindful of Klangreiz* than formerly. It is therefore
pardonable to regard the traits mentioned as so many bids for
favour; but, as Fuller-Maitland observes, this quartet is not a
very general favourite in spite of the attractiveness of its
material.

4. The outline being commonplace deprives our summary of
the usual degree of instructiveness; but at all events the dis-
proportionate allotment to third subject is shown by it; this
subject being allowed for some not very appreciable reason to
disturb the form.† The different dispositions of first subject
and combined motive in first section and return respectively
(which is also visible in the summary) is another symptom of
the looser kind of writing adopted for this quartet—the divergence not being caused by any logical requirement of the theme,
but by quite avoidable necessities. Figures however completely
fail to show the frequent interspersions of fragments of the first
subject by which, in our view, the purity of themes is vitiated.
It may well be that these reminders facilitate the work for some
listeners. But they repel those of a keener sort, for whom—to
say the least—they are superfluous.

5. The fact of the hunting character of the first subject not
being sustained evidently counts for nothing in the composer's
intention. This first manifests itself at introduction of the

Ex. 403. Op. 67, Vivace. First subject.

intermediate motive, which, as mentioned, is now combined with, instead of following its subject. A purposeless modulation

Ex. 404. Op. 67, Vivace. Combined intermediate motive.

etc.

(commencement of which is shown in our quotation) here leads to the use of two redundant bars—obviously redundant as shown by their omission in the return group*—though their use is now compulsory. By their aid however we emerge from the desert in time to meet the second subject in the dominant.

6. A very natural misconception has occurred with regard to this subject; which some describe as episodial, or as a preamble

Ex. 405. Op. 67, Vivace Second subject.

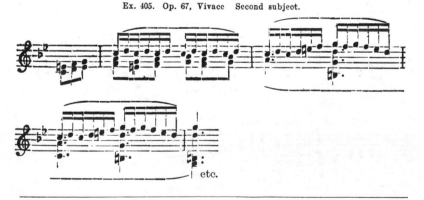

etc.

---

* The bars in question are 27, 28, which in the Return are omitted, causing (see Ex. 402) the combined motive to occupy only ten bars in the Return as against twelve in First Section.

to second subject—meaning by "second subject" that which we range as third.* The undue attention given to the latter however is of no influence in this case—beyond leading to deceptive appearances.

7. The second subject consists strictly of only eight bars, but these (by inversion of the quaver-motion) become converted into seventeen—the difference between this and the twenty-five shown in the summary being occupied by allusions to first subject. Stranger still, the third subject proceeds for only two bars before the first again appears.

Ex. 406. Op. 67, Vivace. Third subject (a).

etc.

8. The third subject is of dual character—its second member combining with the florid first-violin passages now evidently

Ex. 407. Op. 67, Vivace. Third subject (b).

steering toward repeat of first section. For this, however, the irrepressible first subject cannot wait; but, by entering six bars before the section is complete, diminishes the effect of its own return.

9. For the Durchführung allusions to all subjects are naturally appropriate, and it would not be wise to deem some pre-

---

* See par. 4.

ferable to others. Two things must, however, occur to every
student—firstly, that the Durchführung's natural point of departure is from the end of third subject—(bars facilitating the
repeat of first section being due to " 1ma Volta "); and secondly,
that the effect of the first subject's ultimate re-entry is best
promoted by abstention from it until due. At all events when,
as here, a special subject is given to the Durchführung there is
every reason for allowing it to remain pure, and so to attain its

Ex. 408. Op. 67, Vivace. Durchführung special subject.

etc.

object—that of affording the listener some relief. In this case,
moreover, the subject so incessantly repeated being of no particular interest prevents even the freshness of suggestion which
might have become an atoning feature. Moreover, its sudden
exclusion for the remainder of the Durchführung shows clearly
enough that the composer suspected its being somewhat overworked. Most pointed in the latter sense is the appearance of
the special Durchführung subject at bar 185 (just before the
return) where it shakes itself completely free.

10. It goes without saying that, with so much sacrificed for
"sound-charm," the scoring is brilliant, the ordinary listener
being well studied throughout. For his benefit even the artistic
traits of the work seem to have been carefully prepared—such,
for instance, as the semi-humorous change to $\frac{2}{4}$ for introduction
of third subject. The return groups and Coda contain only
what must necessarily happen in a movement of this kind.

11. Epitome.
(a) Subjects. See Ex. 403-408.

(b) Key, B flat major; changing to A and returning to B flat during Durchführung—otherwise no change.

(c) Time, $\frac{6}{8}$; occasional changes to $\frac{2}{4}$ for third subject. Exceptionally both times occur simultaneously when subjects combine.

(d) Length, 341 bars or 443 with repeat of first section.

Ex. 409. Op. 67, Vivace. Outline.

FIRST SECTION			DURCHFÜHRUNG	RETURN			CODA
	103		102		109		27
I	II	III		I	II	III	
32	25	46		35	25	49	

II. ANDANTE.

12. The summary of this movement at once shows its construction to be of the simplest, though two features call for

RHYTHMICAL TABLE.

Ex. 410. Op. 67, Andante.

PORTION	MATERIAL	BARS	CONSISTING OF	EXTENDING TO
1st statement	Prelude	2	2	2
	First Subject	28 { 16	2 × 8	18
	„ „	8	2 × 4	26
	Postlude	2	2	28
Middle	Second Subject	28 { 16	2 × 8	44
	Quasi Cadenza	12	undissected	56
Return	First Subject	28 { 16	2 × 8	72
	„ „	12	{ 2 × 4 } { 2 × 2 }	84
Coda	„ „	11	2 × 6 − 1	95
Totals.		95		95

special attention. The first is the little prelude and postlude (bars 1, 2, and 27, 28) each of two bars by which the first statement of the subject is, so to speak, enframed; and the second is the sub-section consisting of what is practically a "Quasi-Cadenza" of the same nature (though not of character) as that occurring in the finale of Op. 25.*

13. The prelude and postlude in question need not be quoted as the only point attaching to them is the idea of surrounding a theme and thus isolating it from the rest of the movement; but the first subject is a really beautiful melody readily lending itself to modulative treatment.

Ex. 411. Op. 67, Andante. First subject

14. The "postlude" by concluding with the chord of A prepares us for the second subject in D minor. This opens with two bars of rather martial character which are at all events useful in calling attention to its entry. The remaining six bars of the strain revert to the opening legato style, after which there

Ex. 412. Op. 67. Andante. Second subject.

follows a second and rather more demonstrative eight bars singularly tapering off upon the chord of C dominant without any attempt to cadence. This is where the episode here called "Quasi Cadenza" occurs, which, although barred, seems by every feature of its contents to be endeavouring to become free.

Ex. 413. Op. 67, Andante. " Quasi cadenza."

413

* See Op. 25, pars. 33 and 34.

It also carries its listlessness so far as to be careless of returning
to the original key. Taken in conjunction with the fact that
when the first subject returns it is not only in the key of D but
also in free elaboration, this portion of the movement gives us a
good glimpse of Brahms's liberty within form.

Ex. 414. Op. 67, Andante. Free form of first-subject return.

414   Cello (amplifying parts by 2nd Vln and Viola omitted)

15. The return to the original key being thus delayed for the
sixteen bars corresponding to bars 3 to 18 of first statement the
subsequent formal re-entry of the theme (bar 73) is all the more
imposing. In addition to this gain the rhapsodic freedom of
the "Quasi Cadenza" has been enjoyed for twenty-eight bars,
notwithstanding that unity has been entirely preserved. Unity
is still further favoured and Brahms's attachment to it rather
amusingly illustrated by the fact that the Coda concludes with
the substance of the little prelude-postlude which so fostered
the principal subject.

16. Epitome.

(a) Subjects. See Ex. 411 and 412.

(b) Key, F major; no recognised change.

(c) Time, common; with two bars of $\frac{5}{4}$ in free portion of
middle section.

(d) Length, 95 bars; no repeats.

Ex. 415. Op. 67, Andante. Outline.

FIRST STATEMEN2	MIDDLE	RETURN	CODA
28	28	28	11

III. AGITATO (ALLEGRETTO NON TROPPO).

17. The peculiar plaintiveness of this movement is due to the prominence of its viola melody—the viola alone of the four instruments being unmuted. This prominence is further increased by the rhythm of the accompaniment, which to a great extent allows the viola to be heard alone upon the strong beat.

Ex. 416. Op. 67, Agitato. First subject.

416   ＊ Viola *8ve higher, con espress.*

18. The broader rhythm opens with groups of three four-bar phrases; for the second of which the violin is allowed the melody, whilst the viola (in preparation for the new prominence it is about to assume in a new subject) changes to a florid accompaniment. The violin, however, in addition to being muted, is deprived of "first-beat" prominence; this remaining with the viola notwithstanding the altered character of its part. The movement thus remains a sort of viola solo with trio accompaniment; and, with the appearance of second subject, the rhythm

Ex. 417. Op. 67, Agitato. Free form of first subject.

1st Vln and Vla parts only.

417

becomes practically $\frac{6}{4}$. The disposition of the phrases is now no longer in groups of three, so that this portion of the movement is of somewhat more masculine effect. The new subject, moreover, is dual, with a second member gracefully preparing

RHYTHMICAL TABLE.

Ex. 418. Op. 67, Agitato.

PORTION	MATERIAL	BARS	CONSISTING OF	EXTEND-ING TO
1st section	1st subject	12	4 × 3	12
	,, ,,	12	4 × 3	24
	2nd subject	32	4 × 8	56
	3rd subject	20	4 × 5	76
	bridge	12	4 × 3	88
	1st subject	12	4 × 3	100
	{ parenthetical phrase }	9	4 × 2 + 1	109
	1st subject	12	4 × 3	121
	,, ,,	8	4 × 2	129
Totals		129		129
Trio	subject	16	4 × 4	145
	,,	16	4 × 4	161
	,,	16	4 × 4	177
	,,	8	4 × 2	185
Totals		56		185
Coda	cadence	18	1 + (4 × 4 + 1)	203
Totals		18		203

the way for the sostenuto passages intended later on for cadence and bridge purposes. These occur firstly as the fourth

Ex. 419. Op. 67, Agitato. Second subject.

419

set of eight bars in the second subject's development and rather unexpectedly introduce a third subject; which, fortunately for the outcome of this section, is of short duration. We incline to consider this subject *de trop*; and in any case the listener is

Ex. 420. Op. 67, Agitato. Third subject.

420

gratified when again greeted by the sostenuto work—this time
to introduce an elaborate organ point for violin and viola
serving as bridge for re-introduction of the first subject. From

Ex. 421. Op. 67, Agitato. Organ-point.

this point the treatment is new, but the novelty relates merely
to details of scoring as compared with the opening—with the
exception of a parenthetical phrase marked as such in the summary (Ex. 418). This interpolation makes it probable that
Brahms regarded the remainder of this section as Codetta.

19. The Trio opens quaintly with eight bars by the violins
and 'cello before the viola enters with the subject, the same
eight bars again serving as accompaniment to the opening of
the melody. The style continues the same during eight four-

Ex. 422. Op. 67, Agitato. Trio-subject.

bar phrases; when, for the rest of the section, the melody is given
to the first violin and the instrumentation gradually approaches
that of the opening. The perfection of this Trio prevents the
application to it of any kind of criticism, as from whatever
point of view we might regard it we could wish for neither a
note more nor one less. The few bars of Coda being in the
major are in fitting apposition to the trio-key, which is that of
the dominant minor.

20. Epitome.

(a) Subject. See Ex. 416, 419, 420 and 422.

(b) Key, D minor and A minor for first section and Trio respectively. The Coda is in D major.

(c) Time, $\frac{3}{4}$, without change.

(d) Length, 203 bars as printed. To this must be added 124 for D.C. as far as the Coda sign, making 327 in all.

Ex. 423. Op. 67, Agitato. Outline.

FIRST SECTION	TRIO	D.C.	CODA
129	50	124 (to coda-sign)	19
I II III T 24 32 32 41			

IV. POCO ALLEGRETTO CON VARIAZIONI.

21. Again we have a melody of Volkslied character—a melody which modulates independently of exterior aid* and suddenly returns to its burden. We have already seen how much of Brahms's success in variation-form was due to his theme-selection, and we are here reminded of how much his selection was guided by recognising that the equivalent of every augmented and diminished interval is contained in the ordinary diatonic scale. A wandering of the untutored voice is therefore happily represented by chromatics, and its natural endeavour to finish at the first pitch rightfully given as a sudden tonic cadence. It is easy to see how in the hands of a master a simple tune so treated acquires artistic interest; and this, once created, seems to forbid our tracing it back to its origin. The interest of the student however requires us to show how what we have described might feasibly happen by presenting side by side with the Brahms theme what may be supposed to have been its germ.

---

* See Op. 18, par. 22.

Ex. 424. Op. 67, Finale. Theme.*

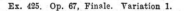

It may be remembered that a similar wandering of the voice took place in the theme of the Op. 18 Variations,† and that this was attended with each of the present results—viz., an unwonted modulation and sudden return to the key.

22. The Volkslied trait just mentioned is one not only very beautiful in view merely of the melody as such, but it also immeasurably enhances the latter's value as material for variations; and it is scarcely too much to affirm that the greater part of Brahms's success as a variationist depends upon this very fact. For, truth to tell, there is nothing specially wonderful in the workmanship of the present movement. We see the composer still haunted by the old "five-orders-of-counterpoint" tradition; and, just as in the slow movement of Op. 18, he starts his first variation with "two-notes against one." What saves it from being commonplace and whets our appetite for more

Ex. 425. Op. 67, Finale. Variation 1.

development is precisely the individuality due to its modulation and broken rhythm, by which we are always open to be called back to the theme in spite of all elaboration.

23. For the reasons stated these Variations do not otherwise possess much interest. Nos. 2 and 3 are of "two and three notes

---

* The large notes show the Brahms theme and the small the suggested origin. The supposition is that the voice having wandered at (a) continues involuntarily in the new key; and that (b) is the attempt to return, which succeeds at (c).

† See Op. 18, Ex. 98, third and fourth bars from the end.

against one" respectively, and carry on a simple process of elaboration without change of mood. The composer's plan seems to have also been to feature the viola in No. 1 with No. 2

Ex. 426. Op. 67, Finale. Variation 2.

Ex. 427. Op. 67, Finale. Variation 3.

"concertante"; then to feature the first violin in No. 3 with No. 4 "concertante"; then to feature the violoncello in No. 5 with No. 6 in the fourth order of counterpoint consisting of continued syncopation, and then to follow on with No. 7 as a florid or "fifth order" variation. A most orderly scheme in any event.

24. The fourth, being the first Concertante variation, is a point of new departure—the three variations 4, 5 and 6 forming a separate group, each member of which is in a new key.* The characteristic is the same for variations 4 and 5—except that in the latter the triplets given exclusively to the 'cello cause it to stand apart. The speciality of Var. 6 is that the syncopations of which it consists are accompanied *pizz.* by 'cello and viola, for the first and second sections respectively.

---

* The keys are B flat minor, D flat and G flat. For some strange reason the B flat minor of Variation 4 is represented completely by accidentals, but for the others the key-signatures are given.

Ex. 428. Op. 67, Finale. Variation 4.

428   Cello   Vla. enters with 2nd Vln.

Ex. 429. Op. 67, Finale. Variation 5.

429

Ex. 430. Op. 67, Finale. Variation 6.

430

25. Variation 7 (in $\frac{6}{8}$, " doppio movimento ") has been much commented upon on account of its introducing a scrap of the first subject of the opening movement, the principal rhythmical attributes of which are however entirely absent. It is claimed that, by this means, unity is given to the entire work; and there can, of course, be no objection to so amiable an interpretation of the expedient. But it is doubtful after all whether Brahms is really honoured by elevating what was evidently a mere after-thought to such importance; for it implies that even with this serious intention he could do no more. In such an event we should not only expect to find much more, but there is a feature in this variation which we should then expect *not* to find; and that is that the third bar of the second section is made to repre-sent a full bar of the theme, whereas according to its standard relation to that theme it is the equivalent of only a half-bar. The effect is disturbing even to the listener—that is, if he carries

the theme in mind. To the analyst it must not only appear worse, but also in marked contrast to the precision which has been everywhere else observed.

Ex. 431. Op. 67, Finale. Variation 7.

431

26. Variation 8 reverts to B flat minor and is based upon the figure represented by the scrap of first subject used for Variation 7. Its principal interest however is in its cadence, which for the first section is in D flat—that of the second being interrupted as a join to Coda.*

Ex. 432. Op. 67, Finale. Variation 8.

432

27. Interruption of the Cadence is immediately followed by union of the same first-subject passage with the present theme in augmentation—this forming the leading trait of the entire Coda. Mention should however be made of its extraordinary

Ex. 433. Op. 67, Finale. Coda.

433

* It has been remarked of this variation that in it the leading note of the key never occurs, its absence contributing to the beauty of the cadences—just as omission of the third in the final chords adds to the effect of the interruption for Coda.

rhythm, which, especially for Brahms, is of the most erratic character. The theme has prepared us to expect some freedom in this respect, it is true, but scarcely so much as we actually find. The summary is admittedly only a tentative dissection, but it will at least serve to indicate the peculiar rhythmical difficulty of this department.

RHYTHMICAL TABLE.

Ex. 434. Op. 67, Finale.

PORTION	RHYTHM	BARS
Theme and Variations 1 to 6	2 × 4 2 × 6	20 each including repeats
Variations 7* and 8	the same doubled	40 each including repeats
Coda	1 2 × 4 + 3 4 × 3 + 2 4 × 2 2 × 4 3 × 2 + 1 4 × 2 + 3 2 × 7 1	75

28. Epitome.

(a) Theme, Ex. 424. Var. 1 to 8, Ex. 425-432. Coda, Ex. 433.

(b) Key, B flat major for Theme, Var. 1 to 4,† 7, and Coda after the first 11 bars. B flat minor for Var. 5 and 8, and first 11 bars of Coda. G flat major for Var. 6.

(c) Time, $\frac{2}{4}$ for Theme, Var. 1 to 6 and Coda; $\frac{6}{8}$ for Var. 7 and 8.

(d) Length, 227 bars, as printed; the number in performance being 295.

Ex. 435. Op. 67, Finale, outline.

THEME	VAR. 1 TO 6	VAR. 7, 8	CODA
20	120	80	75

* Var. 7 is one bar short for the reason mentioned in par. 25.

† Var. 4 is really in B flat minor.

(C) ANALYTIC.

INCLUDING CLASSIFICATION OF WORKS, INDEX TO MUSIC
EXAMPLES, RHYTHMICAL TABLES, ETC.

I. CLASSIFICATION OF THE CHAMBER AND ORCHESTRAL WORKS IN GRADUATED ORDER AS TO MEANS.

1. FOR TWO INSTRUMENTS:—
   Op. 38. Sonata for Violoncello and Piano.
   Op. 78. Sonata for Violin and Piano.
   Op. 99. Sonata for Violoncello and Piano.
   Op. 100. Sonata for Violin and Piano.
   Op. 108. Sonata for Violin and Piano.
   Op. 120, No. 1. Sonata for Clarinet (or Viola) and Piano.
   Op. 120, No. 2. Sonata for Clarinet (or Viola) and Piano.

2. FOR THREE INSTRUMENTS:—
   Op. 8. Trio for Piano, Violin and Violoncello.
   Op. 40. Trio for Piano, Violin and Horn.
   Op. 87. Trio for Piano, Violin and Violoncello.
   Op. 101. Trio for Piano, Violin and Violoncello.
   Op. 114. Trio for Piano, Clarinet (or Viola) and Violoncello.

3. FOR FOUR INSTRUMENTS:—
   Op. 25. Quartet for Piano, Violin, Viola and 'Cello.
   Op. 26. Quartet for Piano, Violin, Viola and 'Cello.
   Op. 51, No. 1. Quartet for two Violins, Viola and 'Cello.
   Op. 51, No. 2. Quartet for two Violins, Viola and 'Cello.
   Op. 60. Quartet for Piano, Violin, Viola and 'Cello.
   Op. 67. Quartet for two Violins, Viola and 'Cello.

4. FOR FIVE INSTRUMENTS:—
   Op. 34. Quintet for Piano, two Violins, Viola and 'Cello.
   Op. 88. Quintet for two Violins, two Violas and 'Cello.
   Op. 111. Quintet for two Violins, two Violas and 'Cello.
   Op. 115. Quintet for Clarinet (or Viola), two Violins, Viola and 'Cello.

5. FOR SIX INSTRUMENTS:—
   Op. 18. Sextet for two Violins, two Violas and two 'Cellos.
   Op. 36. Sextet for two Violins, two Violas and two 'Cellos.

6. FOR SOLO INSTRUMENT (OR INSTRUMENTS), WITH ORCHESTRAL ACCOMPANIMENT:—
   Op. 77. Concerto for Violin with Orchestra.
   Op. 102. Concerto for Violin and Violoncello, with Orchestra.

7. FOR ORCHESTRA:—
   Op. 11. Serenade in D.
   Op. 16. Serenade in A.
   Op. 56a. Variations on a Haydn Theme.
   Op. 68. First Symphony in C minor.
   Op. 73. Second Symphony in D.
   Op. 80. Academic Festival Overture.
   Op. 81. Tragic Overture.
   Op. 90. Third Symphony in F.
   Op. 98. Fourth Symphony in E minor.

Note.—The Hungarian Dances, No. 1, in G minor, No. 3, in F, and No. 10, in F, were also orchestrally arranged by the composer.

II. INDEX TO MUSIC EXAMPLES.

MUSIC EXAMPLES. 299

SCHERZO.

Ex. 193, First subject, 149.
Ex. 194, Second subject, 149.
Ex. 195, Third subject, 150.
Ex. 197, Trio subject, 150.
Ex. 198, Intermediate motive, 151.
Ex. 199, Outline, 151.

FINALE.

Ex. 200, Introduction, 153.
Ex. 202, First subject (a), 154.
Ex. 203, First subject (b), 155.
Ex. 205, Second subject, 155.
Ex. 206, Third subject, 156.
Ex. 207, Intermediate motive, 156.
Ex. 209, Subjects of Allegro and Presto compared, 157.
Ex. 211, Final cadence, 158.
Ex. 212, Outline, 158.

Op. 36. SEXTET.

ALLEGRO NON TROPPO.

Ex. 213, Semitonic rise and fall, 161.
Ex. 214, Illustration of same by first subject, 161.
Ex. 216, Semitonic depression, 163.
Ex. 217, First intermediate motive, 163.
Ex. 218, Semitonic wave in augmentation, with repeated notes, 163.
Ex. 219, Second subject, 164.
Ex. 220, Second intermediate motive, 164.
Ex. 221, Bridge, 164.
Ex. 222, Canon, 165.
Ex. 223, Depression of subdominant, 166.
Ex. 224, Cadence, 166.
Ex. 225, Outline, 167.

SCHERZO.

Ex. 226. Subject, 167.
Ex. 228, Contrapuntal basis of Fughetta, 168.
Ex. 229, Continuation of subject, 169.
Ex. 230, Evolution of Fughetta-subject, 169.

Ex 231, Composite episodial motive, 169.
Ex 232, Affinity with coming movement, 170.
Ex 233, Trio subject, 170.
Ex. 234. Contrapuntal bridge-passage, 170.
Ex. 235, Trio, intermediate motive, 171.
Ex. 236, Outline, 171.

POCO ADAGIO.

Ex. 238, Theme, 172.
Ex. 239, General motive, 172.
Ex. 240, First variation, 173.
Ex. 241, Second variation, 173.
Ex. 242, Third variation, 174.
Ex. 243, Fourth variation, 174.
Ex. 244, Fifth variation, 175.
Ex. 245, Outline, 175.

POCO ALLEGRO.

Ex. 246, Introductory motive, 176.
Ex. 247, First subject, 177.
Ex. 248, Second subject, 177.
Ex. 249, Durchführung and Coda motive, 177.
Ex. 251, Outline, 178.

Op. 38. 'CELLO SONATA.

ALLEGRO NON TROPPO.

Ex. 252, First subject, 179.
Ex. 253, Second subject, 179.
Ex. 254, Third subject, 179.
Ex. 257, Outline, 181.

ALLEGRO QUASI MENUETTO.

Ex. 258, First section (subject), 181.
Ex. 259, Trio (subject), 181.
Ex. 262, Outline, 182.

ALLEGRO.

Ex. 263, First subject, 183.
Ex. 264, Second subject, 183.
Ex. 265, Third subject, 183.
Ex. 267, Outline, 184.

Op. 40. HORN TRIO.

ANDANTE.

Ex. 268, Beethoven, Op. 54, 186.
Ex. 269, Form-diagram, 187.
Ex. 270, Form-diagram, 187.